Jacob,

ALWAYS CHASE EXCELLENCE!
OTHERS ARE WATCHING AND WILL FOLLOW YOU

Peth Hetz

Jacob,

ALWAYS CHASE EXCELLENCE!
Others Are Watching And Will Follow You

VARSITY
SEVEN

AN AMERICAN RIFT VALLEY

VARSITY SEVEN

AN AMERICAN RIFT VALLEY

Peter Hawkins

STARR
PRESS

Spokane, Washington

Cover and interior layout design by Hannah Ungricht Design

ISBN 978-0-578-20332-4

Printed in the United States of America

For Tom

Contents

Foreword

With this book you do not have to like running, Spokane, or know anything about either of them to appreciate the stories within these pages. By the end of reading it you will likely find yourself wanting to find a way to participate in your own distance running scene. You may want to move to Spokane after reading this, or you may say to yourself, *Why not take this work as a blueprint to my small town, my small area, and make this thing big where I live?* Whatever you choose to do, do it the best you can and let the results come as they will.

There are no instant results. For me, that idea came home when I waited at the Tacoma Public Library to see the newspaper that came two or three days late. I had to take the city bus to read the *Spokesman-Review* and look at all the pictures of Rick Riley, Gerry Lindgren, and the rest of the people they inspired. These men were all in all the time because their coaches, Tracy Walters and Herm Caviness, were also all in. And anyone who could taste of what they were saying, or doing, anyone that could see it for themselves felt determined to dream and work as well.

The great Spokane sports writers of the time, Bob Payne and Kevin Taylor, wrote pieces that stuck to you. Their words worked like an elixir; distilled in dreams and brewed in belief. They knew what they had in Lindgren, Riley, and the rest that followed. And anyone who read about them or saw them was inspired. This includes Prefontaine.

Pre was inspired by Lindgren and Riley. There is a border between Oregon and Washington but it is all the Northwest. These may have been men on different teams but they came from an area of the world he knew. They all inspired and fed off of each other. The Spokane legacy took off much like these runners and is still near the front of the pack nationwide.

The beauty of this book is that Peter Hawkins has crafted an accurate and detail rich story. All who are within these pages have been amazed at how this book rings so true to the tenor of the time. Just as Spokane seems to be a city locked in time, like *The Wonder Years*, so too are these vignettes snapshots into an era. And Peter has done what he has seen other athletes and coaches do in Spokane, he has made this accessible to everyone.

It's nothing in the water that makes Spokane a perennial power in high school distance running. It's in the history of coaches and athletes passing the baton to the next generation. They start into this running with Junior Bloomsday, or their own elementary school running program, and they just don't ever stop. Everyone pushes each other to reach new heights. These structures of success are unique to Spokane but they can be adopted anywhere.

Tracy Walters was pushed by Herm Caviness' brother Jim and then Tracy pushed Gerry. Gerry inspired Rick, and then Herm and Tony Dolphin at Ferris pushed Rick in the workouts they outlined. In running, as in life, you need to be pushed by the efforts of excellence that you see around you. Other coaches that kept the running moving in Spokane through the decades were Len Long at North Central, Dwayne Hartman at Mead, Max Jensen at Ferris. No one was going to let you take it; you had to earn every step.

These types of people are found in special pockets around the country and throughout time. This book is about those that shape our lives and inspire us to be the best we can be. It is about someone like Dan Watson in Tacoma, Dellinger in Eugene, or Joe Newton in Chicago. These men had a vision and gave glimpses of it to their athletes. As much as this book is about Spokane, the reality is that the setting of the future of running can be placed anywhere. So long as there are athletes and coaches willing to challenge themselves to new heights. As long as there are teachers, counselors, administrators, janitors, and bus drivers that catch the vision of running this dream can continue. As long as there are parents who trust the process and the coaches then this running dream can continue for years untold.

Pat Tyson
December 2017

x

Introduction:
Spokane, An American Rift Valley

The strongest city for distance running in the world is located in Kenya's Rift Valley, near the western border of Kenya in the village of Iten. This small town with just over 42,000 people in it lays claim to 25 individual world champions and four Olympic medalists.

The grandfather of Kenyan distance running is not a native Kenyan, but rather an Irishman by the name of Brother Colm O'Connell. He came as a missionary to Iten's St. Patrick's High School in 1976 to teach Geography. What was initially scheduled to be a three month stay focused on teaching ended up being a forty year coaching odyssey. A running revolution has since taken place.

The name Iten is a corruption of the words *Hill Ten* and was named by explorer Joseph Thomsen who visited the area in 1883. He gave the name in reference to the number of hills he had conquered in order to reach the area. Iten sits at just under 8,000 feet in altitude. The thin air, coupled with the hard working attitudes of local farm children and a missionary zeal, have helped transform this otherwise unknown, sleepy farming community into the greatest training ground for distance running in the world. Brother O'Connell continues to preach the same message to his athletes: "This is not a training camp, this is a learning camp." To that end he has coached, and the results have followed.

Spokane, Washington shares similarities with Iten, Kenya.

The largest population in Washington State is found on its western side where a majority of its 7.2 million residents live. Spokane, situated on the eastern side of the state, holds claim to just over 210,000 people, and the distance runners from this community come from only ten high schools: Mead, Ferris, University, Central Valley, Gonzaga Prep, Rogers, Shadle Park, North Central, Mount Spokane, and Lewis & Clark. Yet these schools have perpetually won. Over 60% of the state championship boys teams in cross country since the first recorded state championship in 1959 have come from Spokane. There is even the impressive run of Spokane boasting the best boys team in the state in either 4A or 3A division since 1988: Spokane has produced almost 30 straight seasons of championship teams, to say nothing of the individual champions that have poured out of these same schools year in and year out.

Spokane is named after the Indian tribe that settled in the area before explorers, trappers, and businessmen eventually pushed them out. The name Spokane means, *Children of the Sun*. The altitude in Spokane is not as high as Iten. However, Spokane is a geographical gift for distance running. The various hills, mountains, and trails surrounding the area make it a unique training ground for athletes at any of the high schools. Running through the thoughts and hearts of kids growing up in Spokane is the belief that they can climb any hill and run with anyone. It's a belief that is ingrained in the culture of the town. The league in which these 10 teams compete is called The Greater Spokane League (GSL), but it may as well be nicknamed the Greater Shadow League based upon the light and example that athletes and coaches have aspired to achieve.

There are nearly 15,000 boys cross country teams in the United States. The GSL makes up 10 of those teams. Five of the teams in the GSL, half the league, have competed for the National Championship at Nike Cross Nationals since the inaugural race in 2004. Spokane has sent multiple boys teams various years to this event and has competed at all but two championship races. Spokane has been represented at this event just over 85 percent of the time. There have been multiple podium appearances by various teams in the GSL and a National Title.

Another statistical measure of Spokane's running strength is seen in the Foot Locker National Cross Country Championship. This race is made up of individual All-Star teams representing various regions of the country. Since the first Foot Locker National Championship in 1979, Spokane has sent runners, male or female, 24 out of 38 years. That is just over 63 percent of the time one city has been represented on a national level.

High school cross country has over 266,000 male participants and 226,000 female participants nationwide. Spokane prep runners are a statistical outlier in every respect. Often the question is asked, how does this town end up producing consistent winners? This book is an attempt to answer that question.

Spokane is pound for pound one of the strongest areas for raising competitive boys cross country teams on the west coast and the nation. The GSL is only as good as its coaches. And like Brother O'Connell, the aim in Spokane distance running is to help the athletes learn, not just train. This book will look at what each coach, athlete, and family has learned from the miles and trials on the road. The volunteers, athletes, coaches and families collectively make Spokane a Rift Valley of American Distance Running.

This book is divided into two parts. Part one shows several vignettes of the coaches and athletes that started and sustained Spokane's running legacy. These people set the pace, tone, and expectations that everyone since them have been racing to catch. Part two delves primarily into the journey of one family, the Hawkins, and their attempts to run during a period of time when the GSL distance running scene was at its finest. Obviously there are more coaches and athletes than the ones outlined in this work. There are individuals, teams, or families that won state titles that could rightfully claim their story within these pages. But this work looks into stories of the human race, not just a catalog of top times and teams.

Navigating the cross country scene and understanding the uniqueness of Spokane's first runners, helps put everything in perspective.

Part One: The Hounds and the Hares

Since the reign of Queen Elizabeth I in the 1500s, there has been a game commonly referred to as the Hounds and the Hares. The game is reminiscent of hunting practices. The game revolves around one individual being the Hare that is being chased while everyone else acts as the Hounds seeking out the elusive Hare. Once that runner is caught by the group, the one that caught the Hare takes his place and is again chased by the remaining Hounds. This game was the precursor to modern cross country running.

2

Tracy Walters: From Wimpy to Tuffy

Tracy Walters is one of Spokane's first great distance runners. Little did he know of the footprint he would leave on this running community. The only real running Tracy participated in as a kid came with a fishing pole in hand and eyes set off towards a distant riverbank coming into view. He was a kid growing up in the Depression, but life for him seemed anything but depressed.

Born on December 23, 1930 in Seattle, Washington, Tracy and his parents moved to 1705 N. Hamilton in Spokane when he was just a few months old. Tracy's father worked in the forest service. During their summers Tracy, his parents, and his younger sister would make their way to Priest Lake where they would spend the summer. There was no electricity, and Tracy did not need electricity when there was the whole wide world to breathe in and experience.

Besides a love of fishing, Tracy gained a love of athletics because his father signed him up for the YMCA. When he wasn't running to the rivers he was trying to navigate himself through the sea of people at athletic events, even when he wasn't participating in them.

Gonzaga University once had a football team. Before being a Cinderella story in the NCAA Basketball Tournament, Gonzaga's football team was known as the Notre Dame of the west. One of their players and future NFL hall of famer, Tony Canadeo, stood on the sidelines. Tony would go on to have an outstanding career with the Green Bay Packers, being coached by Curly Lambeau. Tracy enjoyed watching Tony and all the football players in Spokane as they ran ragged around the football field.

Tracy was anxious to meet this rising star. The only problem he faced was the fact that it was the Great Depression and he had no money. Seizing an opportunity, Tracy would wait until he saw a family heading into the stadium. He would quickly step in front of the family and say to the ticket collector at the front, while hooking a thumb over his shoulder, "Dad has the tickets."

After Tracy had a step on the ticket collector he would race inside. Often security would run after Tracy, catch him, and then throw him over the fence.

There was not anything malicious about Tracy's intent to get into the game; he just wanted to see the show and be able to hear that roar of the crowd.

Tracy did not care that he had been tossed over the fence, because days prior he had gone to the restroom that bordered the outside world. When it was unoccupied days previous Tracy had made sure to loosen a few of the boards leading inside. Sure enough, Tracy slid back through and saw the game. Tracy wasn't alone in his mischievous endeavors for many of his school friends also snuck in following Tracy's lead.

Tracy's father graduated from Washington State University with a degree in horticulture. A love and respect for plants grew within Tracy. He understood at an early age the law of the harvest; of reaping what was sown. Had this principle been lost in its literal application he had it reinforced spiritually as he attended church to listen to his mother sing.

Tracy's mother had an outstanding voice. She sang at the First Presbyterian Church in Spokane. Tracy sat in the rafters looking down and listening to his mother sing, feeling a great swelling pride in her abilities. Tracy's strong voice no doubt springs from his mother. Accompanied by the strong singing voice came a message of conservative principles.

"If we can give people something to work for and call their own Tracy, we will rule the day," Tracy's mother told him.

Small decisions cultivated the character of Tracy. Playtime was had in abundance and his energy could be doled out at the YMCA, on his way to fishing, and imitating the latest touchdown run by his football hero amongst other neighborhood friends. He saw the growth of plants, the growth of his faith, and the growth of his role models in front of him. The only question Tracy had was whether his body would grow as high as his hopes.

Childhood has a means of refining or revealing the nature of each person. Amidst all the positivity Tracy kept within himself he still had run ins with those that would try to bring him down. As a five year old, Tracy remembers being taunted due to the fact that he was a Presbyterian by his Catholic friends who said that he would not go to heaven. In his grade school days those moments were typically followed by hot tears running down Tracy's cheeks. The tears then brought other jeers and taunts from those that should have been his friends. They called into question his toughness. But Tracy endured, the moments passed, and a question of toughness actually brought forth a desire to show it.

Tracy attended North Central High School in Spokane, Washington immediately following the end of World War II. Playing sports and enjoying in physical exercise was a diversion, not a discipline and definitely not a pay-day expectation.

And yet Tracy enjoyed all the athletics, even if distance running was not his first love, or his first thought. In fact, running was the last option, the least suspected route that would change the trajectory of his life.

Tracy played basketball on North Central's state championship team of 1948, where North Central beat Bremerton in a 42-37 shootout. Prior to Tracy's senior year the team had not won the state championship in basketball since 1930. Fresh off the state victory, Tracy went into his art class with his letterman's jacket. He stood taller than his five-foot-eleven-and-a-half-inch frame carried him.

Sitting in the art class was a beautiful brunette haired girl named Lita who looked at Tracy and took note of his letterman's jacket.

"Where did you get that?" she asked.

Tracy, looking around to make sure that Lita's comments weren't directed at somebody else, turned back to her.

"I am on the basketball team," he said while adjusting his jacket.

"No you're not." Lita said.

"I played every game" Tracy said. His face started to turn the color red matching the jacket he wore.

"No you didn't" Lita said.

Tracy squirmed in his jacket.

"I know all the guys on the basketball team, including the manager, and I don't remember you." Lita said.

Like the kid that had been caught and tossed out of the game, Tracy proved resilient. He may have been small but he most certainly was on the team and he would dig his heels in with this girl.

Tracy was hurt, but there must have been more chemistry than the initial conversation between the two. Little did he know at the time that this conversation with his classmate would turn into a loving relationship with his future wife. She knew how to level with him then and she would level with him in the future when far off dreams truly were calling for him.

Tracy would add more pins to his letterman's jacket as he participated in multiple sports: football, basketball, and baseball. Finally, in his senior year he decided to turn out for track.

Curly Barns was the track coach at the time. Tracy thought he would run the 100 and 220 yard races, figuring he was pretty fast. He thought, if he had to, the most he would run would be the 440 yard dash. As the season began he realized there were other guys that were faster than him in the 100 and the 220. Relegated to the 440, Tracy owned the event and became the best athlete at that distance.

During a spring vacation period Coach Barns developed an intersquad competition. He had every athlete on the team compete in all the events. Tracy started in the 100 and got beat by two guys on the team. Then he went over to the pole vault and was decent but nothing stellar. In the 220 Tracy was beat by one guy. After that he went to the high jump where he felt pretty good until those specializing in the event soared well beyond his best. By the time he made it to the 440 Tracy was tired but resolute. He won the event edging out those that were near him.

Next came the 880 yard race. He had seen others participate in the event but Tracy had never tried it himself. The race began and Tracy ended up beating everyone by a larger margin than he had won in the 440. After this he clocked a 4:50 on his first attempt at a mile.

The first attempt at the mile was a tiring experience. His lungs burned and legs ached, but there was a joy that came from testing his own toughness. The time was not as impressive as the character it revealed. Tracy could run into difficulty and hang there longer than others on his team were willing to go.

And with that resiliency, Tracy kept showing up to practice. He practiced what was more important than the workouts themselves, he practiced a mentality. Reinforced in his ears rang the message and mantra from his mother, "If you give someone something to work for and call their own you can rule the day." He he was owning his time on the track.

Encouraged by Coach Barnes to run the mile race, Tracy kept toeing the line late in the season and kept beating everyone he raced against. He ran on pure guts and determination; it was the same approach he took to everything he did athletically. He approached the mile like he approached the basketball team: with an internal belief that he would give his all and win.

Tracy continued to race the mile, the 880 and the 440 during his senior season. He thought he might have a future as a distance runner due to his winning record. When the city championship came, Tracy won the mile running 4:48. Off he went to compete at the state championship. He met his first defeat at that distance but lowered his personal best to 4:33. Tracy finished fourth at the state meet, missing out on any awards because they only gave them to the top three athletes.

Tracy's best time in high school was 4:33. During spring break he had run 4:50 with no training except for sprints he had done for the 440 yard dash. Tracy, by just showing up and giving his best, had become the best on the team. By the time he ran his 4:33 he was the best in the city. With only a few weeks worth of training Tracy had dropped his personal best by 17 seconds and was one spot away from standing on the podium at state.

Tracy attended Eastern Washington University in Cheney which sits just twenty minutes southwest of Spokane. He figured he would turn out for the basketball team because he had been, after all, part of his state championship team. The coach of the basketball team and the coach of the track team at Eastern was the same man: W.B. (Red) Reese. He informed Tracy after tryouts that he would not make the team. However, the coach liked his enthusiasm and wanted to keep him on as a team manager. Eventually Tracy saw that if he were to compete at anything in college athletics it would be distance running.

Coach Reese was a very caring and loving man. He was trying to fulfill the obligations of running two programs at full speed. On the track team Coach Reese was the lone figure trying to coordinate workouts between all of the various disciplines. Tracy took note of Coach Reese's ability to simplify, instruct, and care for his athletes.

Practice began with Coach Reese giving individual instructions to the various athletes and then he would turn to his distance runners.

"Run three laps and then take a shower," he said.

Obedient, Tracy took to those three laps with everything he had.

The next day brought with it Coach Reese yet again giving instructions to the sprinters, the hurdlers, the throwers, and the jumpers and then, finally, the distance runners.

"Run three laps and then take a shower," he said again.

This was collegiate athletics of the late 1940s.

Even with the limited practice and a lack of understanding as to the why's and how's of distance running, Tracy continued to improve.

He gave everything to what he did.

By Tracy's junior year his time had lowered in the mile to 4:21, cutting off 12 more seconds from his personal best.

Tracy was invited to the Nationals race (NAIA) in 1950. Tracy did no real training leading up to this or any race he participated in. He would sprint from goal post to goal post on the track and run just over a total of half a mile before calling it a day.

Tracy stepped on the track, knowing as he always did that he would give everything he had. Running in the race that day Tracy lowered his personal best to 4:17. He finally had someone to chase after in a race. One of those people that Tracy chased was Javier Montez, who won the race. Tracy took fourth place, again missing the podium, but this time not on a state level but rather a national level. His own exploits would always be just off of the podium and out of the picture.

© EWU Hall of Fame

Javier Montez would eventually run on the 1952 USA Olympic team in Helsinki, Finland.

Unlike Tracy, Javier knew the what's, why's, and how's of training. After their race, Javier approached this unknown Tracy Walters from little known Eastern Washington and asked him about his own training methods, with the hope to glean some new technique. Tracy did not know how to respond. Foregoing the silence, Javier jumped in.

"I like to do ladders," Javier said.

Tracy had no clue what Javier was talking about. He stood silent as he continued.

"I like to do intervals like Zatopek, doing intervals to exhaustion and then trying to run a little bit further." Javier said.

Again, Tracy was drawing a blank stare.

"I also like to do hill repeats," Javier continued and then asked, "What do you like to do?"

Tracy did not know what to say, but he decided in that moment that if he ever did coach, he would do the homework that Javier had done and learn how to answer all the what's, how's, and why's of running. Little did Tracy know that the world of distance running was about to take a momentous step forward.

Tracy did as well as he could with what coaching, talents, and opportunities he had. The experience at Nationals gave him a glimpse into a world he had not known. He planned to return to the National's race in his senior year with newfound excitement towards training but due to a sprained ankle he suffered in his gym class he was unable to return.

As fate would have it, Tracy's senior year in college would be the start of his coaching career; due to an unexpected staff vacancy. Tracy stood as both coach and athlete his senior year and led the Eastern Washington track team to an undefeated season and conference championship.

Tracy liked coaching, the athletes liked Tracy, and winning was fun. Tracy became a coach from then on.

The coaching worked out nicely as Tracy had been married for three years already and had children. The running took second place to his family and the ability to provide for them; this decision would be the pattern he followed throughout his life, despite the enormous success that was before him.

Tracy Walters started his teaching career at Endicott High School in Endicott, Washington in the fall of 1951. The town had a population of just 397 people. Endicott was somewhere between farmland and nowhere, and on the backstretch of forgotten.

Endicott was founded by a Wimpy, or at least someone married to one.

Major Robert H. Wimpy served for the Union army during the American Civil War. The only problem with his allegiances to the north was the fact that he lived in the south; Arkansas to be exact. The rebel forces eventually arrived at the Wimpy home and ransacked all of their food, stock, and anything they could get their hands on. Wimpy took his family and headed north to Fayetteville, Arkansas and then eventually Springfield, Missouri. The war ended with Major Wimpy fighting on the winning side, but after the war he decided he did not want to return back into what was once enemy territory.

The Wimpy family took what belongings they had and joined a wagon train heading west, looking for new hopes and opportunities. With sixty other wagons they walked west from Leavenworth, Kansas and ended up in Helena, Montana. They decided to leave the wagon train at that point and head to the

Clearwater district of northern Idaho. Once there they established a boarding house for the miners in Orofino, Idaho. The call for gold in northern Idaho had sent many sprawling towards the area.

Jenny Wimpy was the daughter of Major Wimpy and ended up marrying Henry Dayton Smith in 1875. Henry and Jenny would be the first settlers of Endicott, Washington. Henry hoped that by creating the town it would eventually be a major metropolis that could compete with the likes of Spokane for population. In order to do so he knew they needed a railway line. Endicott eventually earned a railway line but the main depots were in Spokane and Colfax. Colfax, Washington sits nearly twenty miles east of Endicott.

The first round of settlers that came to Endicott were German and Russian immigrants who sought out similar topography. The rolling hills and the cultivation of wheat were not foreign to these people who had raised rye and sunflowers in their native lands.

Tracy went to Endicott with his wife and three children. Despite all his local success in running the better paying job was not available in Spokane. Tracy was lured to Endicott, Washington. The remote location brought with it an increase in pay as a means of incentivizing teachers to stay. He took on all the opportunities at the school that he could find to help support his wife and three children.

Wallowing and shrinking were not in Tracy's makeup. He did not bemoan the deck dealt him; he doubled down on the opportunity. Tracy became the football coach, the baseball coach, the volleyball coach, and the producer of the senior class play. Where others would have only seen the people and the place as something small, Tracy saw the big heart hidden behind all those oversized letterman's jackets. He knew how to speak to the hearts of his students. He tried to stoke inside them what he had felt inside himself.

Tracy knew that young people are filled with hushed dreams. Tracy saw in those about him his younger self. He saw others itching to put on a uniform and play for their team. He saw the minds of his students caught up in visions of a team basketball championship. The whisper of these thrills were not shown on the surface or vocalized. These students sat before Tracy as farm boys and girls alike. They wanted to dream and needed someone to dream with them. Tracy had dreamt and stood just off the podium in fourth place not once, but twice in his life and was thrilled at the opportunity to let others stand on the podium. Tracy never played small to the people around him because he had never played small to himself.

Prior to showing up in Endicott it is no wonder that the school had not won a football game. The town has numbered streets and the highest number on them is four. That is not a sign of hope for any outsider looking in. Endicott, Washington could just as well of had a sign in front saying: *Endicott, Where Dreams go to Die*.

The saving grace of those first settlers of Endicott was the fact that these were people of faith who knew how to endure difficulty. Fourth street may have been the highest numbered street but there were three churches packed into this town. These were people of faith, or work, and who had a vision of what could be with effort and grace. Farmers know their fields, they know that seeds will grow, and they know the law of the harvest. The lessons Tracy's parents instilled in him prepared Tracy for these people.

Expectations are powerful, but reinforced expectations are formidable. The trouble lay in helping those first few students to breathe life into dreams that lay beyond the rolling hills of Endicott. It was hard mustering faith within those that had only known defeat. Tracy needed to help them see that the future held everything.

Everyone beat Endicott Tracy's first year-everyone. However, the second year brought with it new hopes and new talent. Faith in the coach and his system came because the team finally had a football field to play on. Tracy leaned once more on his mother's mantra, "If we can give people something to work for and call their own Tracy, we will rule the day."

During his summer break and with no extra pay coming in Tracy built his team a football field. Previous to Tracy the team had no football field, they had no confidence, and they had no real wins to speak of.

And so in the heat of the day as crops were growing all around this small farming community, Tracy was out sowing his field of dreams. With stakes and string he measured out 10 yards for one end zone and kept going 100 more yards until he came to the next goal line, measuring out another end zone. Then it came time to get the width right: 53 and 1/3 yards across. As a youth he had snuck into a stadium to see a field bursting with life, and now he tried to bring to life a field that had not existed.

While working and measuring his field, Tracy thought over how to measure the desire of his athletes. He thought over how to help them gain the confidence they would need to burst tackles, to read defenses, and to come together as a team. Before they would ever hit the field, Tracy saw his team moving about it.

After the field was sown and started to grow, it came time to make the goal posts with the crossbar being 10 feet off the ground. While rummaging through the old high school gym looking for materials, Tracy discovered an old shot put and javelin. He realized that the school had once had a track team, and in an instant he determined that they would yet again have a track team. Tracy would breathe life into the programs.

Tracy would make a football field, just as he would help string together the props needed for the senior play.

He just needed time and effort and the results would come.

The ability to hush fear and fan the flame of faith proved as valuable in making a football team as it did with the drama department. He coordinated the scenes and blocked out the movements of actors just as well as he put together blocking schemes on his grassy field. And just like the football team, the school play had everyone right on cue and in uniform. Tracy worked behind the scenes to make sure everything was spotless.

When Tracy helped others enunciate and emphasize the words in each scene, he remembered that body language and facial expressions said as much as any word ever spoken. His coaching toolkit was being built on stage and amidst teenagers. He found his own voice and knew how to play to an audience.

The second year in Endicott would not be a repeat of the first. Tracy's team had a field to call their own and confidence to match it. They started to win. Tracy's vision became the student's vision, and after each and every practice, the team started to make it all a reality. Those farm boys had someone who helped them take the mystery out of success. He gave them a program to believe in and he spoke to their hearts.

Taking notice of the small town victories was a man by the name of Carl "Tuffy" Ellingsen. Tuffy was an administrator up at Rogers High School in Tracy's native Spokane. Tuffy came to Tracy in 1954 and asked if he would be interested in taking over as the Cross Country and Track Coach at Rogers High School, knowing that Tracy had been a great runner himself.

Tuffy was a good man for Rogers and Tuffy might just be the name that has always been associated with Rogers High School. Another pseudonym for the area is Dog Town and it's not because these were show dogs. Rogers has been an area of stagnant growth and poverty since the time before Tracy was showing up to coach and it has continued to fight against stereotypes and poverty long after his departure.

Rogers had many homes at the time that had nothing but dirt floors. Lacking any foundation these homes were standing, but were not fit to last long. Instead of tracing out football fields, Tracy would have to be the foundation that young men could build upon. Tuffy himself was one such cornerstone in the Hillyard community.

Tuffy got his nickname at a young age. He was a boy acquainted with hardship. His mother had died when he was only four years old. He was raised by his brothers and father. His father's work consisted of fishing and paving roads as a means for providing for his kids. Tuffy helped his father mix the cement. At only 95 pounds, Tuffy kept pace with his father and could lift the 100 pound bags needed to mix the cement.

This work ethic and toughness were matched on the wrestling mat where as a freshman in high school Tuffy became the Tacoma city champion, pinning his competitor in only six seconds. Tuffy continued to wrestle in high school and played football as well. He caught the attention of the coaches at Washington State University where he went on to play football and wrestle. He was an instrumental part of Washington State's Rose Bowl team in 1931. As a triple threat halfback Tuffy orchestrated everything on the field. Unfortunately the dream season of 1930 ended when they faced off and lost to the Alabama Crimson Tide on January 1, 1931. Tuffy went undefeated in wrestling his senior season at WSU competing in the 175 pound division. He lettered in basketball, baseball, wrestling, and football.

After college Tuffy was drafted by the St. Louis Browns in baseball and the Detroit Lions in football. Tuffy decided to place his own athletic endeavors aside and instead took up coaching. He ended up at Rogers High School where he taught, coached, or acted as athletic director for 33 years from 1938-1971.

In an area stereotyped as tough, thuggish, and difficult came a man who defied stereotype. He had each of his three sons eventually leading the Rogers football team as quarterback. Tuffy himself helped coach Rogers to five city championships in thirteen seasons as coach. Tuffy's sons excelled in football and in the classroom. They would all follow their father's footsteps and go on to Washington State University. One became an orthodontist and the others were ophthalmologists. The sons must have caught something of their father's ability to correct vision.

Tracy Walters, far right, with his first cross country team in the fall of 1956.

Tuffy had the vision to see what Tracy had to offer and wanted to find another cornerstone to bring in and defy stereotype. Tuffy sought out Tracy and told him that Rogers had done alright in cross country in the past. What he really meant by this was that a few individuals had taken up the sport. Cross country running was a relatively new sport of high school athletics and Rogers had never won a cross country meet.

15

Tracy left the town founded by a Wimpy and went on his journey back to home and was welcomed by a Tuffy. Such was the story of Tracy's life.

As Tracy stood in the halls talking with Tuffy about the cross country team it finally came out that they had never won anything. *Maybe that's true,* Tracy thought as Tuffy told him this, but with resolve he said to himself, *We will win a cross country meet.* Tuffy knew he had hired the right man. Tracy knew full well the challenge before him, having attended North Central only years before. Whereas at Endicott there were endless rolling hills, Rogers brought with it cramped quarters on confined city plots.

Tracy sent out a bulletin to all of the 2,000 students at Rogers inviting them to come to an informational meeting. Three students showed up on time and Tracy found himself sitting and stalling the start time. Time went by and still no one else arrived. Eventually Tracy realized that this was it.

I can't even field a cross country team, Tracy thought. But he redoubled his efforts and made a more personal approach. He went classroom to classroom pulling out students trying to give them a glimpse of what they could be if they were willing to show up and work. After this second combing of the school he was finally able to field one varsity squad and one junior varsity squad. He had a team of 14 out of a school of 2,000. Tracy could have gotten more than 14 to turn out in Endicott, where the town was less than 400. Tracy knew, however, that inside each of the 14 was a desire to run and to succeed, and he could work with that.

That first season at Rogers played out much like Tracy's first season at Endicott. Races were run and the defeats kept coming. Tracy's team of champions and vision of the future was met with the reality that they lost every single race. The team needed some traction; it was like they were running on ice.

In the fall of 1957, which was the start of Tracy's second year back in Spokane, Shadle Park High School opened up its doors as the newest high school in town. The new school brought with it a new approach and new attitudes, as well as the desire of those in the area to attend it. The school was named after Eugene Shadle, a prominent local businessman who had worked alongside J. Comstock. Together these two had supplied Spokane with their retail goods and resources.

Exactly 2.3 miles west from Rogers sits Shadle Park High School. The major road between the two schools running north and south is aptly titled Division Street.

Rogers was divided from the new part of town and all the success that came with it. Shadle Park would be the school that everyone wanted to attend, with the new amenities and new expectations. Saddled with the old expectations, the old problems, and the old familiar failed results sat Rogers High School.

The distance of the average high school cross country race at the time was 2.3 miles. The state standard was spread out on that spectrum between Shadle Park and Rogers. The state standard for excellence at that time was Shadle Park High School. The very first ever Washington State Cross Country Championship meet was held in 1959. The first Washington State Cross Country team champions were from Shadle Park High School.

The students at Rogers had to only look down the street and see all that they were not.

If it wasn't Shadle Park that Rogers was fighting against then the next closest school was Gonzaga Prep. This private school would take second place at the second state meet in 1960, edging out Shadle Park which would take third. Gonzaga Prep had the fastest individual runner in the state, Paul Schlicke, on their team. Gonzaga Prep sat just under a mile south of Rogers High School and they were afforded privileges that money could buy.

New schools were cropping up. Gonzaga Prep, which had started in 1887 as a feeder school for Gonzaga University, had recently moved to their present location in 1954. The new school again attracted the attention of those that could afford it. North Central had been around since 1908, Lewis & Clark since 1912.

Rogers High School was built and opened its doors during the bottom of the Great Depression in 1932. Hillyard High School, which had previously serviced the area, had caught fire and was in disrepair. As a means of creating something new, Rogers High School would replace the crumbling Hillyard High School. It was named in honor of John Rogers, the third Governor of the state of Washington who is most famously known for his *Barefoot Schoolboy Act*. Sadly, the name of the act and the status of Rogers High School in Spokane continued to be linked together. If the students were not barefoot, some were without floors.

The law's purpose was to allow all children to receive equal education no matter the financial status of the area. The tax proposed was originally a six dollar amount on any child that was of age in a district, thus a child from a rural area with, conceivably no shoes, could still obtain the same quality education as someone in the city.

Fighting expectations, fighting poverty, and fighting against the newer and richer schools around him, Tracy kept true to the tenor of his speech. *We will be winners.* He did not focus time and attention on what they were not, he focused on what the students and athletes could be with a little more work. He infused belief by speaking and listening to his athletes. Tracy, always known as a great speaker, also became a great listener. Carefully calculating the feedback of his athletes, Tracy modified workouts to balance their needs for recovery. He had done his homework on the sport and believed the results were only a matter of time.

Often Tracy would start practice by explaining the workout he had planned for the day. He would explain the distances and times he expected the athletes to hit as well as his reasoning for the workout. After explaining he would then ask his own athletes if they thought his workout could be improved or if they had an idea for a workout they thought was better than the one he proposed. He did not build a track or a cross country course for his athletes, but he did give them ownership in the affairs of the team. Once more he relied on the words of his mother, "If we can give people something to work for and call their own Tracy, we will rule the day."

Tracy then listened as his athletes searched inside themselves and shared ideas of what they thought would be a better workout. In this process Tracy showed the athletes that it was not his team but their team. Their voice was just as important as his own. Due to this approach his athletes felt an ownership and an accountability over their work. The results soon followed.

In Tracy's second year coaching the cross country team, Rogers won their first meet. It was the only meet they would win that year, but by the time the third year rolled around Rogers hadn't lost a meet leading up to the state meet. Rogers had the two best runners in the city and they would likely be a pair of the best runners in the state. Unfortunately tragedy struck during a practice session meant for fun. While playing ultimate frisbee, Tracy's two top runners both sprained their ankles. The team did not win state that year.

But in 1962, Rogers had an opportunity to win it all. While driving to the meet there was a traffic accident on the highway. The state championship trophy had been won by Lewis & Clark High School the year previous, but they were not returning to the meet and had asked the Rogers team to take it back to state. The state title is a travelling trophy with the names of the teams on it and the team that won it the previous year holding the trophy for a year. Lewis & Clark either did not have the funding or they did not think they could win the trophy and so they did not send a team.

In the car wreck full of Rogers runners the trophy hit up against a runner by the name of Gerry Lindgren. The next day Gerry ran well, winning the race. The rest of the team, however, was still shaken up by the events of the previous day and so Rogers finished third at the state meet. Going from three people originally showing up, to third in the state was a satisfying experience.

A year later, in 1963, Gerry would again win the individual title and smash the course record around Green Lake and the Rogers team would finally win the state meet.

One unique aspect of those first state championship races at Green Lake is the fact that there were only two markings on the course: a start and a finish line. Once the gun fired each athlete had to navigate around the lake, running the shortest path they could find. When measured, the fastest route came out to 2.3 miles.

As Tracy stood on the sideline at the finish he heard one spectator say as Gerry ran by, "He cut the course."

Tracy rolled his eyes and thought to himself, *How do you cut the course running around a lake?*

In 1964, with no Gerry Lindgren on the team, Rogers finished second at the state meet. They adjusted and worked hard and in 1965 they would be state champions once more. Those were Tracy's teams while at Rogers. The *Barefoot Schoolboy Act* school had proven that they could beat anybody and anything, including the expectations heaped upon them.

Tracy Walters knew how to talk to anyone. He helped all his athletes see the value they had and how they could contribute to the team.

Left to right, Gerry Lindgren, Billy Mills, Mohammed Gammoudi, and Ron Clarke competing in the 10,000 meter final at the Tokyo Olympics in 1964.

Gerry Lindgren: Hillyard's Finest

From Bemis Elementary School, to Shaw Middle School, and then Rogers High School, Gerry Lindgren went through like any other kid lost in the crowd of Spokane Public Schools. He was shy, small, pale, and looked like a stiff breeze could knock him over. Coming to and from school with his crooked haircut and crooked smile, Gerry tried to straighten out the facts of life before him. He was a product of Hillyard, an environment known by all who live in Spokane.

As one Superior Court Judge said during a sentencing of a man found guilty in a shooting in Hillyard, "There are only three things that come through about Hillyard. One is that everybody drinks or is drunk. [Second] Everybody fights or is about to … and the third thing is that everybody is armed."

Hillyard became, in the eyes of some in the Spokane community, the wrong side of the railroad tracks to be on as the city expanded. The new name of the school, inspired by the pity of those in poverty, stuck as a stereotype of those growing up in Hillyard and attending Rogers High School. The perception, as unfair as it is, has been reinforced since the time of the railway and the naming of the school. This perception persists to this very day.

This heritage has surrounded Hillyard seemingly forever. This is what Gerry Lindgren inherited throughout his public education in Hillyard.

Hillyard's neighborhood brought with it kids from tough family situations, including Gerry's. Each day Gerry was confronted by bullying, name calling, physical abuse, intimidation, and punishments. This gauntlet of stress and suffering were the crucible of his early education. These suffocating circumstances were thought of as normal for young Gerry who knew no differently.

As such Gerry's mantra in education, at home or at school, consisted of fighting back and surviving. He would have to battle with his own doubts and fears. Gerry had to deal with an abusive and alcoholic father in his early years who towered over everyone in the family. Though these abusive moments may have been forgotten by his drunk father, they were not forgotten by young Gerry who had to face these sobering situations. Fortunately Gerry's parent's separated from one another so that the only abuse Gerry had to face was at school.

Growing up in the 1950s of Hillyard with a small size and squeaky voice, Gerry found himself bullied almost everywhere he went. Years of school following the same pattern of abuse did not instill confidence in him.

The tune of Gerry's original dreams followed the jingle of football on TV. Seeing the rise of the National Football League Gerry thought it would be nice to participate in organized and controlled violence. The only problem besides Gerry being small, skinny, and uncoordinated was the fact that he did not see the middle school coach's scheme to blindside his dream.

At an after school practice a play was drawn up for Gerry to make a tackle on defense. Unsure of where he was supposed to go, Gerry went towards the ball carrier but was leveled by a large boy who bowled over Gerry.

I feel like I got hit clear into next week, Gerry thought.

The football coach only learned Gerry's name so he could quickly help him see that football was not for him. After getting up from the hit Gerry realized that he did not have a future career in football.

Wintertime brought with it the next sport in the school year: basketball. However, being short again did not help Gerry's case. What added to his consternation was that unlike football, that demanded only running with a ball, Gerry would be expected to dribble and pass a ball to another player. Confusion ensued when scripted plays were introduced. Everything was complicated by the fact that Gerry lacked coordination.

Gerry was left off the team roster.

As spring came along, baseball was his next chance to succeed. Instead of dribbling a ball he was expected to take a bat to it. Gerry would swing away at the approaching pitches, but he would connect with nothing but air. Suffocating in self-consciousness and unable to connect with anything or anyone, Gerry sat in the dugout frustrated. He could not coordinate his body to do what his eyes were seeing. Besides the ignorance and ambivalence of coaches too concerned on winning, Gerry received the attention of teammates only insofar as they could sneer or make a joke of his efforts.

Sports had yielded nothing for him. It became time to think about a job and the future. After school Gerry landed a job delivering 60 papers in the area surrounding his home. After school he would roll up his papers and run them to the houses on his usual route.

As Gerry ran alone on his route he circled in his mind the lonely realities: he was not coordinated and did not feel wanted by his coaches or teammates.

Unbeknownst to Gerry his middle school track coach Don Hughes had noticed the fight that he had. When Tracy talked to Don Hughes to ask if there were any athletes he should try to get to turn out for cross country, the coach made mention of the boy near the back of the pack that had a lot of fight. Tracy developed a great relationship with Don and loved his enthusiasm and shared belief that any kid could accomplish great things with just a little structure and encouragement.

After finishing up his after school paper route Gerry went over to try and find this new coach and last stop for opportunity: Tracy Walters at Rogers High School.

Gerry ran the .7 miles up to Rogers and met Tracy Walters for the first time, but practice had just ended. Tracy told Gerry when and where to show up for the start of next years practice.

Gerry had watched from the sidelines as Jim Juul and Barry Robinson, who ran for Tracy, had rounded the track in the mile and tried to lower their own personal bests to under 4:30. Robinson would run up against the first individual state cross country champion in Washington State history who was a runner from Mead High School, Frank Knott.

Rooted on the sideline Gerry saw Juul and Robinson, on the same team, running against each other and pushing each other to the limits. Trading the lead these two fought for the winning position down lane one.

It was a simple sport.

But running demanded excellence in areas that other sports would never know; running was relentless.

No time outs.

No rest.

No waiting for a new play to be drawn out.

No overtime.

Running would forever be played out in real time demanding best efforts from the very beginning to the very end. Running required endurance. The goal was not to eliminate pain, but rather to embrace it.

Seeing Robinson and Juul's success, Gerry decided he would join his newfound heroes and try to run with them. If the cross country team had not found success, the track team at Rogers was rolling in the late 50s as Tracy Walters helped inspire the team and the school to greatness. During Tracy's ten years as track coach the team only lost four league meets. The team that season had gone undefeated in league matches and would end up taking second at state.

But the first part of the season did not go well for Gerry and he even thought of quitting, unbeknownst to Tracy. He felt like another forgotten athlete. Sitting in his World History class Gerry saw that his teacher had stopped instructing as Coach Tracy Walters had opened the door to the room and asked if he could have a moment with Gerry Lindgren. After exiting the classroom the coach and athlete sat next to some lockers.

Tracy was looking at someone who needed some encouragement. He saw an inner monologue at work and realized some outer dialogue might help.

Gerry knew abuse, he knew the fist that came towards him, he knew the hurtful word and the laughter aimed at him. When kindness appeared and came from a real place Gerry truly appreciated it.

According to Gerry the conversation by the lockers went as follows:

"You know, you have something special that perhaps nobody else has on this team" Tracy started. "Do you know what that is?" Tracy asked.

Gerry looked at Tracy, his coach. Gerry expected the same pass around routine he had heard from previous coaches. Those coaches had always spoke about how maybe there was another sport or another position on someone else's team out there. He was waiting for the words that would knock him down and take his wind from him.

"Gerry," Tracy said, "You have the ability to inspire those around you."

Gerry realized this coach knew his name, and he was approaching him as he had never been approached by anyone in his life.

"When all the other athletes storm off in practice, bigger and stronger as they are, they don't have much to give to the team.

© Spokesman-Review

But that's where you come in." Tracy said. "When you go out, small as you are, it's different. You have the ability to show those guys what it's really like to give it your all."

It was ok to be weak.

It was ok to be small.

It was ok to be slow.

It was all ok, so long as Gerry remembered to put his best efforts first; for as long as he could. The effort, not the physical attribute, was what mattered.

"Gerry, who knows what you could be. You are an inspiring runner. The best thing you can do in life is not winning but helping other people. Leave the world a better place than you found it."

All of Gerry's previous coaches had only pointed out what Gerry lacked and equated it with a weakness. Tracy spoke about what makes anyone weak: their inability to sacrifice everything. Gerry's vulnerability became his vitality.

The two parted ways, with Gerry heading home to that house he would rather not be in. He walked inside his house with wonderful words echoing inside of him and protecting him. Through the fog of former frustrations he heard the clear truth that his mundane movements could move an entire team to excellence. Burning with a desire to step on the track once more, Gerry waited for the hours and minutes to pass.

The next day at practice brought with it an interval workout and a young, small, slow Gerry, eager to be just what he was and a little bit more. After the warmup it came time to crank up the speed.

At Tracy's command the team started their first interval. Gerry took off like he was running through a fire and bolted to the front. Everyone would have to run through the wildfire like pace he set in order to try and chase him down.

Gerry fought to hold the lead as long as he could. He would eventually be passed by the older, taller, and stronger athletes.

The interval ended.

Gerry's heart was racing, pounding, and bounding inside his chest. His legs and lungs had taken a beating. There were only a few more seconds before the next interval of speed.

Off they went on the next lap.

Again, Gerry shot to the front trying to hold the lead just a bit longer this time. Like before, the other athletes came up to pass Gerry. Sensing their movements, he threw in another surge.

Once again Gerry was finally passed and finished up the interval. The aching of his arms, legs, and lungs continued but paled in comparison to the aching he had to stand tall in the eyes of his coach. He wanted another chance to try and run for the lead.

Interval after interval proceeded in the same manner. Interval after interval and practice after practice, those catching this rabbit had a harder time doing so. The initial lead he held became larger and lasted longer than the previous practice.

Gerry fought against his home and his environment by using pain as a point of reference. More pain over longer periods of time eventually equated to winning races and fast times. In a sport and atmosphere where sustained abuse was not only needed but encouraged, Gerry thrived. The consequences of standing up to pain and having an outlet for it unlocked a whole new world for Gerry. Running within the bounds of the practices that Tracy created, Gerry ran amok; thrashing his body, his mind and his heart. And after every interval he toed the line again, waiting for another opportunity to go longer, harder, and faster than before.

Finally, this small boy was not being caught by anyone on the team.

This would be the style of running that Gerry adopted for his entire running career. From the moment the gun fired he shot to the front, pushed the pace, and held on for dear life. All five foot five inches and one-hundred and fifteen pounds of this dark haired, scrunch faced, and crooked smiled kid came into and out of curves. World class athletes step farther into the hurt and stay there longer. The reward for punishing oneself in a grueling workout was more punishment in future workouts. This was a language that Gerry could not only speak but he was fluent in. Gerry outworked everyone around him. He continually tested the limits of his mind and heart. He charged into a world of pain that others were unwilling to go to and then he went beyond it. Nicknamed the Spokane Sparrow, Gerry was a bird bursting from the cages that had kept him bound.

The Paper Chase

The old game of the Hounds and the Hares had gone through another iteration as history progressed and it became known as the Paper Chase. The Hare would occasionally drop bits of paper along the trail so that those chasing could know where the Hare had been.

Gerry Lindgren, who started his running career by delivering papers, would someday end up in them.

Track and Field News-regarded as the Bible of track records and information on the sport-was looking to promote meets in the 1960s and wanted to have the best high school runners in the country compete in a two mile indoor race. They had invited select individuals to compete in the Holiday Invitational at the Cow Palace in San Francisco, California. As part of the field of national caliber athletes they had Jim Ryun and Ralph Gomez. These two were expected to be battling it out for the win in the two mile race. Jim Ryun eventually became the first high school athlete to break four minutes in the mile and he became the world record holder in the event. Ralph Gomez was an up and coming star of his own right, boasting some of the best times in California.

Paul Schlicke, a Spokane native who had won a pair of individual state titles while he ran at Gonzaga Prep in 1960, had graduated and was attending Stanford University where he competed and lowered his mile PR to 4:02.3. Paul talked to the meet promoters of *Track and Field News* and mentioned that there was a boy from his home town that had run 9:17.00 on a grass two mile course during the fall of 1963. This information eventually made its way to Cordner Nelson and his brother Bert Nelson who were the founders of *Track and Field News*. They knew if the information was true, Gerry could be near a new national high school two mile indoor record. The current record was sitting at 9:23 for indoors.

A letter was sent to Tracy Walters asking if the rumors were true regarding Gerry's speed and whether Gerry would be interested in competing. A phone number was listed for them to call and confirm or deny the times.

Gerry had come a long way already in his running journey. Gone were the early thoughts of nearly quitting the sport as a sophomore. In the winter of 1963 Gerry was coming off his second straight Washington State individual title in cross country, where he set the course record.

Before making the call Tracy had to speak with his athlete.

"How fast do you think you can go in this indoor two mile Gerry?" Tracy asked.

"I really don't know, I think...I think I could go nine minutes." Gerry said.

Slapping his hands together, Tracy then smiled. "Let's call them up!" he said.

The promoters at *Track and Field News* told Tracy that Gerry could be in the race provided they could drive themselves down. The race was slated to be run on December 27, 1963, just two days after Christmas.

Tracy, Gerry, Lita and the kids got into the Walters' station wagon and drove the near 900 miles to San Francisco, California. They left Spokane cresting the hill up Interstate 90 hoping to avoid snow, black ice, and the winter weather that are known to plague Spokane for months at a time. Slowly routing their way through the interstates they kept that 50mph clip all the way to California. Tracy kept driving, with multiple stops for gas and bathroom breaks that stretched the 18 hour road trip into a 24 hour experience.

Gerry readied himself to run in front of a real crowd of over 12,000 people. The cramped car ride had hardly been conducive towards creating a top time.

The crowd was much larger than the few dozen spectators that showed up for races in Spokane. If there was one consolation for Gerry, it was that the eyes of everyone were on the two headliners: Ryun and Gomez.

Ryun was growing into his six foot two inch frame while Lindgren was already maxed out with his five foot five inch height. Ryun appeared like Goliath, and everyone knew it. Unbeknownst to anyone but Tracy Walters and his wife Lita, there was a David in their midst.

© AP Photo

Standing beside Jim Ryun was his high school coach Bob Timmons. Tracy went up and talked with Bob and they compared coaching techniques with one another. Tracy had not forgotten the lesson he learned from his own running days with Javier Montaz asking him about training ideas. Both coaches would swap ideas from each other and keep in contact thereafter as good friends.

Eventually it came time for the meet to start and the athletes prepared for the various indoor events. After sprints of various distances it was time for the distance event of the evening and all the runners approached the track.

The starting marshal called these young preps to their marks, asking them to take their sweats off. All eyes were fixed on Ryun and Gomez. The commands came.

"To your marks!"

Silence.

Bang!

Gerry jumped to the lead while a jostling occurred behind him. Amidst the casualties of the start was Jim Ryun tripping and falling to the ground. The eyes of everyone were split between Gerry shooting out to the lead, and Jim Ryun trying to get back up. It was as if a knockout blow had been landed with the firing of the gun; the only difference being that this knockout punch still had 21.5 laps to go till it could be said to have landed. Ryun would quickly get to his feet and continue to fight his way forward, but even had he not fallen he would be hard pressed to catch Gerry.

The track was a 160 yard wood surface with banked curves. 11 laps equaled a mile.

Just as Gerry would hit a curve he would accelerate and just as quickly he would round the corner and be shot out into a straightaway. Once more he would hit a curve and be shot out. A rhythm was being established. *Banked curve, then shoot out in the straightaway, then into the banked curve, see my coach, then into the straightaway, banked curve, shoot out, straightaway, banked curve, coach, shoot out, straightaway.* Gerry went around those banked curves and into the straits like a metronome.

Gerry treated this race as if it was his last. For inspiration he looked from himself, to his coach and to what he had before him: an opportunity.

The first 440 yards came and went with Gerry holding the lead, clocking a 59.7 second blistering pace. He went through the 880 yard mark slowing only slightly to 2:07. The second half of the first mile again was slower than the first. His first mile was 4:26.5. Yet, for anyone watching the race, it appeared to be anything but a slow pace. It seemed that Gerry was pulling away with every stride. Before the first mile was up he was already beginning to lap people.

People in the stands expected to see Ryun at the front. They were stuck staring at this unknown short and small kid that seemed to have been sprinting from the gun. Some spectators in the stands started to make bets as to when they thought this nameless runner would die out. He seemed more of a nuisance than someone to take seriously, because they had never seen someone take out the race at such a break neck speed.

Sitting and listening to these people sat Lita with her kids. She knew how to place a word when she needed to towards her high school sweetheart and she knew how to place one now to strangers.

"I'll have you know he always races like this," she said. "And no one is going to catch him." She finished. Those beside her were suddenly silenced. The only other words uttered out of her section were the many cheers Lita and the kids gave for their local boy.

The race announcer finally brought into perspective what was happening before their very eyes. "Ladies and Gentlemen Gerry Lindgren who is in the lead is well under the national high school two mile record. Let's cheer him on!" The crowd that had been in disbelief turned their doubts away and got behind the dark haired boy setting the blistering pace.

Gerry frightened by the shouts thought someone was behind him and charging to pass and so he continued to push ever harder. Through the first mile and a half he went, clocking 6:44. He had only slowed to 4:29 pace per mile.

The laps continued to tick away. Gerry kept lapping those that had fallen off pace. Swinging towards lane two he would dart out and then back into lane one. His eyes were ever up and on the next curve, the next person to pass, the next straightaway. Gerry was unrelenting in his pace and kept lapping the other competitors.

The field marshal finally rang the bell signaling the last lap of the race. The crowd was on their feet. Gerry kept charging, passing people as if they were standing still. Off in the distance, Gerry saw the frame of a tall figure coming closer with every stride. *One more banked curve, one more glance at coach, one more straightaway.* Gerry kept charging and lapped Jim Ryun just before hitting the finishing tape.

Applause thundered down on the track.

"9:00 minutes even!" The announcer shouted.

Gerry broke the indoor two mile record by 23 seconds and broke the outdoor record which sat at 9:09 all in the same race.

To break an outdoor record on an indoor track was doubly impressive. The difficulty in indoor running is the shortened track; more laps equals more curves. Momentum is lost and inefficient in indoor running. It would be like hitting a homerun off a pitcher 30 feet 3 inches away as opposed to the regulatory 60 feet 6 inches. The reaction time and precision had to be nearly perfect.

Gerry was entering into a new world of competition and he had knocked the ball well out of the park.

Left to right, Gerry Lindgren and Gaston Roelents

After this explosion on the track, offers for Gerry to race began to pour in from all over. Meanwhile, Gerry, Tracy, Lita and the kids got back into the station wagon and began the 50mph trip back towards Spokane, recovering the 900 plus miles back to obscurity and out of the limelight.

The car ride brought with it welcomed rest, but that rest was short lived. The next big test for this unknown youth came quickly.

Nearly a month later on January 18, 1964 Gerry was back in California, now in Los Angeles running another indoor two mile race. This time he would be going against Gaston Roelents of Belgium, who was the current world record holder in the steeplechase.

The high school competitors had been dropped by the wayside; Gerry was now competing against the best in the world.

Once more, Gerry tried to shake out his legs, and remember his strategy that had worked so well for him before.

Once more the field marshal called the participants to the starting line, only this time Gerry was the only high school athlete running against collegians and professionals. The field was faster and deeper.

"Runners to your marks!"

The pause.

Bang!

Gerry again shot out to the front. Those who had been at the Cow Palace a month prior saw yet again this scrunchy faced, dark haired, pasty white kid jump to the front with legs churning through the lanes like milk into butter. Lap after lap they went with the pace kept honest.

Gerry took the world class field through the first mile in 4:21, faster than the pace he had done just a month prior. Like his previous races Gerry was trying to deliver the knockout punch on every lap. The pace was fast and he kept driving into the lead. However, Gerry wasn't the only one that knew how to throw a punch. Gaston Roelents waited till the last possible moment to throw in his surge as he passed by Gerry into the last lap.

The bell was ringing. All five foot nine inches and 148 pounds of the man Gaston Roelents swept by the kid in front of him like a counterpunch. The thicker, taller, stronger Roelents showed his world record physique as he drove into the lead. Gerry tried to respond. The crowd got behind the boy and cheered him down the backstretch, chasing, fighting, and trying to hold on to the foreign figure flashing towards the homestretch.

Gaston Rolenents finished first in 8:41.4.

Holding on, the high school senior, finished second place to a world record holder, running 8:46.0.

Gerry Lindgren was rewriting the record books. He had improved his personal record as well as high school indoor two mile record by 14 seconds.

To put a 14 second personal record (PR) in perspective would require looking to another distance record: the mile. The first sub four minute mile was

Gerry Lindgren leading Gaston Roelents

© Track & Field News

run by Roger Bannister in 1954, when he clocked 3:59.4. Going back in time to when the mile world record was 14 seconds slower one is in a very different world. John Paul Jones of the United States held the world record at 4:14.4 back in 1913. It took the world's best 41 years to make up 14 seconds worth of time.

Gerry had beaten the high school two mile world record not once, but twice. His second time carried with it a PR of over 14 seconds. All total he had smashed the previous high school indoor two mile record by 37 seconds.

Gerry accomplished all of this in a one month span. Gerry was in the process of etching his face on the Mt. Rushmore of American high school distance running.

Once more race organizers hounded Tracy and Gerry, asking for more races, more opportunities for this boy to compete against men. Always Gerry returned back to the cold, the dark, and the lonely roads of Spokane.

From limelight to twilight, Gerry went. From cheers to silence.

And yet the calls kept coming in at the Walters' house. Tracy managed the workouts, the races, and the opportunities. Tracy continued to keep the workouts, encouragement, and routines in order. It was the great capacity to prepare and train that had yielded all their results so far.

A month later, on February 15, 1964, Gerry was back down in California for another race. This time he was competing against Ron Clarke, who was the world record holder in the six mile and 10,000 meter races.

The race started off in typical Gerry fashion. Never mind that he was running against another world record holder. Never mind that Clarke was 11 years older than him, seven inches taller than him, or 40 pounds stronger. Gerry warmed up like he had done for the past three years when he competed against the best athletes Spokane had to offer. He took off his sweats, strode out, and waited for the field marshal to direct them to the start line.

The gun was raised like before.

Silence ensued.

Bang!

Gerry instinctively jumped to the front. He did not know how to do otherwise. The pace would be quicker, the competition better than even Gaston

Roelents, and so the pace had to be honest. The lights were brighter and the pressure greater, but Gerry simply focused on putting one foot in front of the other and tried to stay ahead of everyone in the race. He could at least inspire those that were watching.

Gerry led the first mile going through in 4:19.7. Again it was a faster first mile than he had ever run in a race. Gerry was leading the world record holder and had yet to graduate. Gerry, as a senior in high school, was still a month shy of turning 18.

It seemed no matter the initial pace of the race Gerry could hold on. The same scene seemed to be playing out in California as the crowd welcomed this short, pale boy who moved with a dire focus and force of will.

Gerry continued to lead until there was 500 yards left in the race. Could he beat the world record holder?

Clarke jumped into the lead with just over 500 yards to go and would win in 8:37.0. Gerry finished second running 8:40.0. Again Gerry had improved and shown that he could run with the very best in the world. The indoor two mile high school record had been lowered 43 seconds from the start of the indoor season.

Only one week later Gerry would make a cross country trip to New York where he would have a second crack at running against Ron Clarke. On February 22, 1964 Gerry competed at the National AAU Indoor Track & Field Championships at Madison Square Garden. Both Ron and Gerry were slated to run the three mile race.

Gerry again would try to take the lead and hold it but Ron Clarke would take control and run 13:18.4. Gerry placed third overall running 13:37.8.

Gerry was averaging 4:32 miles, back to back, to back. He could hold a 68 second quarter mile split for 12 consecutive quarter miles. In other words, he could hold 24 consecutive 200 meter splits at 34 seconds. If anyone wanted to trot out to their local track and cover 100 meter in 17 seconds, they could see for themselves just how quickly he ran. Gerry kept that pace 50 times in a row.

Finally the indoor season was over and Gerry headed back to Spokane. Working his way through his classes at Rogers High School, he studied, learned, and wondered how far he could push himself with the time remaining in the

Gerry Lindgren far right, at the start of his 4:10.5 city record in the mile

outdoor season. After school hours brought continued training. League meets didn't hold much competition and yet Gerry would run fast times clocking 8:56 at a dual meet against Central Valley. That 8:56 time was a national outdoor two mile record, beating the previous mark by 14 seconds.

Running against other high schoolers carried with it little competition in comparison to what he had faced during the winter. However, there would be aches, pains, and the natural flare ups that came from pushing his body to the absolute limits.

Gerry's notoriety did not go unnoticed by the local populous. As Gerry's final high school races dwindled away the crowds began amassing. Everyone wanted to see or hear about this boy wonder.

In a day and age when broadcast television only had three channels and there was no such thing as 24 hour programing, Gerry's mile race at the Washington State track meet easily out competed other interests for air time.

At the race Gerry would run 4:06.0 and in the process set the national high school mile record. Jim Ryun would eventually beat Gerry's record a year later and also become the first high school runner under four minutes in the mile. What Gerry had accomplished in the longer distances, Jim Ryun was about to do in the shorter distances; these two high school athletes were the new legends of the sport. Gerry's state mile race record would stand for almost forty years until Carl Moe from Auburn Riverside beat it by one tenth of a second. However, Carl

Moe had the advantage of running on a synthetic surface while Gerry ran his races all on either dirt or cinder tracks.

Even if you give Gerry only a modest .5 of a second per lap, he would have run 4:04.00. If you gave Gerry a lenient second per lap he would have run near 4:02, almost reaching the four minute barrier as a newly turned 18 year old.

One week after graduating from high school Gerry went off to run his first 5,000 meter race on the track at the Compton Invitational. Gerry went through the first mile in 4:20, two miles in 8:53, and finished the race in fourth place running 13:44.0. Gerry's time was the 13th fastest time at that distance in the history of the sport. This young boy was starting to set the distance world on fire. The winner of the race was Bob Schul who would go on to win in 13:38.0. Eventually Bob Schul would go on and become the only American to ever win the 5,000 meter race in the Olympics, which he won in the 1964 Tokyo games.

In his second week after graduating high school, Gerry raced his first 10,000 meter race in Corvallis, Oregon where he would win the race and run 29:37.6. Gerry's pace in the race averaged right at 4:46 per mile. Most national caliber high school athletes today are lucky to run around that pace for half the distance; Gerry could keep form for almost any distance. The time he ran put him under the Olympic qualifying standard of 29:40.0. As a newly graduated senior, Gerry proved he was Olympic material and had yet to step foot into a college classroom.

One month after graduating from high school Gerry ran in New Jersey against Bob Schul again. Bob again won, but Gerry finished second place and assured himself a spot on the USA national team that faced off against the Soviets in late July of 1964. Gerry went from representing Rogers High School to now representing the United States of America.

Before Lake Placid

The race against the Soviets was held at the Los Angeles Coliseum where over 50,000 Americans showed up to cheer on their nation's team. The Americans were not expected to win, let alone place, in the 10,000 meter. The USSR vs USA dual meet started in 1958 and the Soviets had won every contest. Five straight years team USA had lost.

Left to right, Gerry Lindgren,
Leonid Ivanov, and Nikolay Dutov

In 1957 the Soviets had sent Sputnik into space; it appeared that the United States was losing the space race as well as literal races against the Soviets. They were a political and physical force.

Representing the USSR was Leonid Ivanov, who in 1963 had the third fastest time in the world at 28:48.6. Gerry not only had to face off against Ivanov but he had to face off against his teammate Nikolay Dutov, who in 1964 had the seventh fastest 10,000 meter time in the world. Both of these competitors were in their mid twenties and had the strength of men. They had run times of nearly a minute faster than Gerry. Against high school athletes Gerry looked immortal; the Soviets could make Gerry really look like he was in high school.

Two days prior to the race, Gerry had gone for a training run along the beach. Tracy drove ahead only a few miles and waited for Gerry to run by. Unfortunately there was a mistake made; neither coach nor athlete saw each other and Gerry just kept running.

After hours had passed, Tracy called the Police and found they had picked up Gerry who had gone missing and run almost 17 miles. Cold, dehydrated and a little frightened Gerry had to prepare for the 10,000 meter race in just a day and half's time.

The longest race at Gerry's state meet in Washington was the mile race, with only four laps around the track. He had run two mile races throughout the season but it was not a state adopted distance till 1965. Gerry was being asked to race six times farther than his usual race. And he was being asked to do so against literally the world's best on the biggest stage in the United States at that time. The race organizers were either asking for the moon, or sending a sacrifice towards the Soviets who had no doubts that likely they would win the event and the meet once more. Their confidence was exhibited by their coach who remarked that "it is a mistake to send a boy against our giants."

Adding to the recipe for disaster was the fact that the 10,000 meter race was run in very warm conditions, over 90 degree heat. The odds were stacked heavily against him. Gerry should have been beat many times before he ever stepped foot on that track. Hits of possible doubt and despair came from every side, but they never landed a punch.

Gerry put on his race spikes, his new singlet and shorts, and started to warm up. There were only two thoughts running through Gerry's mind at the time: the game plan and the telegram.

The game plan Gerry had devised and worked on with his coach Tracy Walters for a few weeks.

The idea had come a few weeks prior to the July 4, 1964 race. During a 400 meter interval workout on the dirt track at Rogers, Gerry thought of his upcoming race against the Soviets. Between the intervals Gerry proposed an idea to his coach.

"Hey coach, I got an idea. I think I could pull this one off" Gerry said.

Tracy, ever encouraging his athletes to take ownership over their own training and running experiences merely opened up and acted as sound board to his athlete.

"What's your idea?" Tracy asked.

"How about I feign like I'm really tired with the Russians." Gerry said.

"Ok and then what?" Tracy asked.

"Well you know how they like to throw in surges on alternating laps," Gerry said.

Tracy had taken his lessons from when he had run against Javier Montaz and transmitted them to his young athlete. It was important to know what the other athletes did, and Gerry, as well as Tracy, had done their homework on the Soviet athletes. In the longer races the Soviet runners Ivanov and Dutov would take turns increasing the intensity of the pace and alternating hard laps with relative easy laps as a means of breaking up the race and breaking the form and confidence of other athletes. It broke the stride and rhythm of their competition, forcing them to change their cadence to fit the pace they demanded and set.

"Yeah," Tracy said.

"Well, I was just thinking, when they go to an easy lap between one of their hard laps part way through the race I could let them pass me and I can start breathing hard, but then when they don't see me coming how about I do my own fast lap?" Gerry said.

"Gerry that's brilliant!" Tracy said.

"My guts will probably end up all over the track but who cares? Nobody expects me to beat Ivanov or Dutov," Gerry said.

The practice continued with a blueprint in place. Over and over again they simulated what they hoped to accomplish in California. Gerry would run a 70 second lap followed by a 60 second lap, then jog for a little recovery, then he would run a 70 second lap followed by a 60 second lap. Rest. Then Gerry would run a 60 second lap followed by a 70 second lap and then run another 60 second lap.

This sequence was practiced over and over again.

The other thought in Gerry's mind was with regards to a telegram he had received just prior to warming up for his 10,000 meter race. In the telegram he saw the names of various people and organizations from Spokane that sent

their well wishes; Spokane as a town said they stood behind their boy.

Gerry felt a burning sense of pride from those he knew back home. He did not want to let those he cared about down. As he went into the stadium and warmed up he saw the eyes of 50,519 Americans that he also knew were behind him.

Gerry walked to the start at the command of the starting marshal.

The gun was raised.

Bang!

50,519 Americans cheered as the longest race of the day got underway. Gerry did not bolt to the front as he always had but sat just off of the Soviet leaders who set the pace. The pace was still fast, even if Gerry was not setting it in the front.

Gerry was sitting behind the Soviet runners through the first three miles. Shortly after the first three miles, Ivanov made a move to push the pace starting into the typical routine of placing a hard lap and then a recovery lap to try and break up the field. Gerry kept with him and bore a grimace on his face. The boy from Spokane was running with the hopes of America.

Coming around the home stretch Gerry decided it was his time to put in a hard lap of his own and take the lead.

A picture was taken when Gerry finally decided to make his move and Ivanov's look of disbelief is caught on his face. A world leader passed and beat by an unknown. Ivanov was breathless twice; once by his own effort and twice by surprise. The only people that were not breathless were the 50,000 fans who came to life as Gerry took over the lead.

Everyone in the stands stood and started to cheer.

On the track and during the heat of the Cold War was a young man pushing the pace and opening the lead on two of the world's best runners. There would be an arms race, there would be a race to the moon, but at this time there was a literal race being run on the track and America had sent their David to fight the USSR's two Goliath's.

Again the cheers of the crowd crashed upon the track and Gerry, being frightened that one of the Soviets would pass, continued to charge. He could hear the crunch of shoes behind him and he dared not look back. The cheers would come and he would push the pace and then the cheers would come again and he would try to throw in another surge. Still he heard the crunch of spikes behind him; could he hold on?

Before the race Gerry had coordinated with Sam Bell, one of the USA coaches at the meet, to set up a system whereby he could find out how much distance there was between himself and the Soviet runners. Gerry using hand motions asked how much distance he had. Sam Bell indicated that Gerry had 100 yards and that it was growing. Gerry continued on in disbelief thinking that somehow there was a miscommunication with their hand signals.

Gerry kept throwing surge after surge not daring to look behind him but he still heard the crunch of spikes right on his heels. Down the final homestretch Gerry went giving everything he had.

Crossing the finish line Gerry won the race 29:17.6, beating Ivanov and Dutov. Gerry looked behind him and saw no one even on the home stretch; the footsteps he had heard were his own. Ivanov and Dutov would finish second and third respectively in 29:38, and 30:51.

As one sportswriter put it, "The kid who looks like your paperboy owns Los Angeles." Gerry Lindgren, the boy who had gone from delivering the papers was now front page news. Gerry's efforts coupled with others in varying events led the USA to win its first dual meet on the track against the Soviets.

Before there was ever a Miracle on Ice there was a Miracle on the Track. United States President John F. Kennedy's brother, Bobby Kennedy, was in attendance and was reportedly brought to tears in seeing the effort of this kid from small town USA fight and demonstrate the American spirit amongst the world's best. For a brief moment everyone in attendance was touched by what they had witnessed for 25 laps on the track. Although Gerry was small he stood larger than life in everyone's eyes for that moment.

After the race, Gerry was invited with some of the other athletes to a special awards ceremony. At the event, Bert Nelson, founder of *Track and Field News*, asked Gerry, "What were you thinking while you were lining up for your race?"

Gerry, with his squeaky voice said, "Well Mr. Nelson, I looked down at the end of the coliseum and saw the Soviet flag, the symbol of totalitarianism on the one hand and then I saw our American flag with democracy and all our faults, and I thought, maybe this is more than a race. Maybe this a race for men's lives. Mr. Nelson I had to try my best." The somber crowd in attendance were brought to tears as they saw this small boy speaking from his heart.

Bert Nelson then asked a follow-up question, "Let's talk about the race itself, what were you thinking during the race. It has been so hot with the smog - did that affect you?"

"Oh no," Gerry said. "You have to realize for half of each lap I was in the shade running behind those runners." Gerry said, indicating his small size. The room that had been brought to tears was now laughing. "In fact," Gerry continued, "I thought it was raining out there because I kept so close to them that the sweat coming off them was hitting me." This was Gerry acting as only he could.

A few weeks after Gerry's miracle in the City of Angels, he was invited to race down in Kingston, Jamaica. On August 13, 1964 Gerry ran his fastest mile ever in 4:01.5 and finished third in the race, again on a dirt track. Had the surface been synthetic it is likely that the first high school athlete to break four minutes in the mile would have been Gerry Lindgren and not Jim Ryun. As an afterthought, two days after his mile best Gerry ran the three mile race in Kingston and won in 13:17.0 (4:25 pace).

It seemed that every race Gerry entered he improved; no matter the distance. He made sure the pace was sweet and that everyone running would earn their place.

The next time Gerry ran the 10,000 meter race was was at the Olympic trials on September 12, 1964. He again lowered his 10,000 meter PR to 29:02.0 (4:40 pace) and won the race easily by more than 45 yards over second place Billy Mills.

The best American 10,000 meter distance runner in the United States at the time was a newly graduated high school senior who had yet to attend his freshman classes at Washington State University. Gerry was not only the best American runner entering the 10,000 meter race in Tokyo, but he was also one of the favorites to win it all.

Gerry had eaten up miles during his training. He had chased down every individual he could and was improving with every race. There seemed no limit to his future and his success. The world had never seen success in distance running at such a tender age and it would not see it again for nearly four and a half decades; this was a seemingly once in a century moment. Gerry was writing the record books at almost every turn for high school distances.

This obscure boy quickly become known the world over by those who were students of the sport. However, Gerry would be eclipsed in Tokyo by another unknown who would give the Olympics one of it's most iconic moments in distance running history.

Competitive distance running is a sport built for the small town with all its lonely roads. Three of the greatest young rising stars of American distance running in the 1960s were Jim Ryun from Wichita, Kansas, Gerry Lindgren from Spokane, Washington, and Billy Mills from the Pine Ridge Indian Reservation in South Dakota. Ryun's hometown was the 51st most populous city in the 1960 census, with a population of just over 254,000 people. Lindgren's Spokane was only the 68th most populous city in the country with just over 181,000 people. Mills, another Olympic hopeful, came from Pine Ridge Indian Reservation in South Dakota where the population was just over 1,200 people. The elevation of the reservation was higher than the amount of people living in it.

Area codes alone are not any indicator of an inverse relationship to running greatness; however, area codes accompanied by attributes of excellence may be that magic paring. Being able to run over land with varied backgrounds of nature enable the long distance runner. Locked inside the concrete jungles of big cities runners are kept at bay yielding to the stop and go traffic of city streets. It is no wonder therefore that these country boys with the open air chased limitless horizons in their respective and isolated parts of the country.

Mills had finished eight seconds back of Gerry in the Olympic trials. He had performed marvelously well, but was not expected to be in the realm of Olympic medals because in order to do so he would have to run nearly a minute faster than he had ever run before.

Gerry appeared poised to medal, if not win the Olympic gold.

Late in the fall of 1964, Tracy Walters sat inside the sleeping quarters of his most famous athlete who sat nursing a swollen ankle. Tracy had his own hopes sidelined by an ankle injury his senior year of college. In Tokyo, Japan inside the Olympic Village, Tracy sat with Gerry.

Tracy kept staring at Gerry and kept shaking his head.

Gerry kept sitting there with his eighteen year old worry-ridden face. Over and over again Tracy's mind kept lapping through the events of the day. Gerry had come back from a training run in the Niche Gardens where he sprained his ankle. The doctors and trainers in the room had all looked at Gerry's leg and they all came to the same conclusion: he had torn a tendon in his foot.

The swelling in the foot was obvious. Also swelling were the somber truths confronting all present in the room. The doctors and trainers, moments prior, had each advised that Gerry not compete in the race the following day.

Then the doctors and trainers finally left the room.

Tracy looked at his young athlete before him. Gerry sat there, all five feet, five and a half inches and 115 pounds; hardly the appearance of an Olympic favorite in the 10,000 meter race.

A squeaky voice from within the boy finally spoke out.

"I want to at least step on the track and try to run in front of those tens of thousands of people," Gerry said. Tracy had learned to ignore the squeaky noise and focus instead on the content of the message. This small young man before him had a toughness he had witnessed on a daily basis. He was the embodiment of his coaching experience: going from wimpy to tuffy.

Tracy saw the kid that ran like a man and tried to find the words to speak to him.

"You know maybe there will be a miracle Gerry," Tracy said.

This boy, who had been passed over by his classmates, teachers and even family, had shocked the distance running world with his ability to endure pain. It was now painful for Tracy to try and confront the reality that this dream may have run its course.

Tracy continued his line of thought, thinking out loud.

"Let's look at the competition that can win this thing," Tracy said.

Maybe there was something they had missed, something that was still left for them to do.

"There is Clarke and Gammoudi, Dutov and Ivanov," Tracy said, listing the athletes off on his fingers. "Have I missed anybody?" Tracy asked.

"Yes," Gerry said.

Standing silently in that same room of the Olympic Village stood Gerry's roommate and teammate who had silently listened to the conversation. Gerry finally looked from his ankle to his roommate.

"Billy Mills. He could win," Gerry said.

Tracy, realized instantly the irony of the moment. There stood Billy Mills, an athlete representing team USA who also harbored Olympic dreams and had no injury, whom he had just passed over. Tracy had never wanted to be passed over himself and quickly said, "You're right." Being passed over was a lesson he had fought to learn throughout his life.

With Gerry's ankle bandaged as best it could be, he made his way to the track and tried to warm up and run against the world's best. The race started and Gerry was competitive for the first two miles, but he essentially was running on only one good leg. The race would end with him finishing ninth overall as Billy Mills, America's least suspected champion ever, won the 10,000 meter in dramatic fashion. Mills would pass Mohammed Gammoudi who finished second and Ron Clarke, the world record holder, who finished third in the race. Ivanov from the USSR would finish fifth.

That day in the room in the Olympic village had passed. Tracy's words about there being a miracle were prophetic, but they involved Billy Mills and not Gerry Lindgren. As such, history has now overlooked the boy that may have been champion and his coach. However, it was not overlooked by Billy.

After the race, readily recognized as one of the greatest upsets in Olympic history, Billy stood, still sweaty before Tracy Walters and Gerry Lindgren. They were outside of the view of cameras and away from the public.

Tracy ruffled the hair of Gerry.

"Well ninth in the world isn't too bad for a high school kid." Tracy said.

Tracy then went over to Billy, took him up in his arms and spun him around.

"Billy that is the most amazing example of athleticism I have ever seen in my entire life." Tracy said.

Billy not skipping a beat looked at both Tracy and Gerry before speaking.

"Coach I proved one thing," Billy said, "I'm the second best runner in the world."

He stood there, the Olympic record holder and champion, praising the coach and the boy hurting before him. Billy extended a hand of kindness and represented more than the medal he would receive. He stood there a true champion.

Gerry and Billy would compete against each other when they were both healthy. Their most famous race came in 1965 as they competed at the AAU National championship in San Diego. They ran in the six mile race where Billy was aiming to take down Ron Clarke's world record.

The race started with Billy leading from the beginning. The pair of them went through the laps keeping a steady pace. Through the first mile in 4:29, then the second mile at 9:04 (4:35), the third, 13:40 (4:36). Gerry attempted to take the lead at various points throughout the race but each time Billy responded with the confidence of someone who had won a gold medal. Through the fourth mile in 18:16 (4:36) they went on with neither of them succumbing to the pace or each other. The fifth mile was 22:50 (4:34). For the last mile they would have to run sub 4:27 if they wanted to beat the world record.

The 15,320 people in attendance realized that the record was within reach. The pace increased for the last two laps as they both made one last push to the finish. As they came to the end, Billy dove for the tape looking like he was on the wings of eagles, while Gerry was locked next to him in lane two. Their last lap was under 58 seconds as they both pressed through the tape.

Both were recorded with the same time of 27:11.6 and both went under Ron Clarke's world record by more than six seconds.

Gerry had run and beaten some of the world's best and he had just barely graduated from high school. The future held everything for Gerry and all who watched him knew it too.

© Easterner 1954

Left to right, Herm Caviness with his brothers Ernie and Jim

Herm Caviness: Spokane's First Hound

If Tracy Walters is the first great distance runner and first great coach, the Hare that set the pace for others to chase after, then Herm Caviness would be one of the first coaching Hounds trying to chase down the scent of success that Tracy left in his wake. If Spokane's running legacy had its first stride with Tracy, then it's second stride keeping balance must be with Herm Caviness on the other side.

Born in Henrietta, Oklahoma in 1934, Herm was the fourth and last of the sons born to his parents. His father was an oil rig worker. Due to a decline of oil rig construction following the crash of the stock market in 1929, Herm's father heard of construction work needed at the Grand Coulee Dam. In 1935 Herm's father went to see whether he could land sustainable work and then, in 1936 he sent word back home for the rest of his family to join him. Depression era decisions brought with it Depression era choices that were based out of necessity.

The family moved up to the unknown desert-like area. They arrived in a place that looked like the one they had left; the only real difference was that their father had work. As such, food was more substantial and served at predictable intervals than had been the case in Oklahoma.

Herm, as the youngest of four brothers, tried to keep pace with the adventures and exploits of his older siblings. His older brothers would go out trekking through the hills and fishing in the streams while trailing close behind was young Herm. He always had his eyes on what his older brothers Ernie, Ray, and Jim were doing.

After school if they were not involved with some sort of sport or self created game, they would be out in the hills, running about or fishing and bringing home food for the family's dinner. Herm grew up amidst poverty, but he and his family were not poor in values.

Herm did what all younger brothers do: he copied what his older brothers had done. As the older brothers got into athletics, so too would the younger ones follow suit and so baseball, basketball and football were commonplace.

Like with Tracy, track again was not the first choice for sports. However, Herm's experience with running was shaded by his circumstances. Tracy was the oldest child and only had a younger sister as a sibling. Herm had brothers to compete against, and sibling rivalry is strong in any generation. Once one of the brothers got into track, the rest soon followed and each kept track of their respective times and places.

Herm was at a disadvantage to succeed athletically against his brothers because he was only 13 when he entered high school. He was 16 when he graduated from high school and 20 by the time he finished college.

In the current day and age it is not uncommon for parents to hold children back so as to give them an advantage athletically. Often seniors graduating high school are 19 years old. Herm, in today's culture, would have been placed as one of the older children in a sixth grade class at the age of 13. As it was, Herm was in high school and he carried with him all the strength that his 97 pound frame could muster. He competed against the local farm boys who were not only older but stronger.

Herm was a product of the Depression era. It was a time of doing the best with what you had and not giving excuses, but solutions, to problems. His problem was how to compete with guys bigger and stronger than him. The solution was simple: continue to train and try his best. Herm's best allowed him the opportunity to follow his brothers up to Eastern Washington University. His older brothers were on the track team and so Herm followed suit, having run a 4:57 mile. Herm graduated high school four years prior to Roger Bannister breaking the four minute mile.

It is hard to believe there was a time when it was actually believed that running under four minutes in the mile was deemed impossible. The power of expectations may have kept people from running under the four minute barrier. Herm's introduction to the sport ended with him understanding the power of expectations.

It's important to recognize the moment in which athletes sink their teeth into the sport. For Herm Caviness, it was seeing his brother Jim run one race, a mile, that changed his life forever.

It was a hot spring day in the late 1940s in Omak, Washington. Inside of the town boasting no more than 5,000 residents a high school track meet was underway.

The track was an oval and full of dirt, not the nice tracks that are commonly found around the country today. The dirt was not some smooth composite but was filled with the small pebbles and rocks that could be found bursting through the surface. The moment of truth had come as Herm watched his older brother Jim race the mile against Ben Sadler, another local talent from a neighboring town.

Around the dirt track these two went sending dust into the air with their every stride. It quickly became apparent that it would be a two-man race, decided by boys who didn't have the sophisticated equipment or training methods of today. They ran for the pride and bragging rights of being the best. And yet this race would be decided as any race is, by one wanting it more and lasting longer in his efforts to achieve it than the other.

It would be a battle of wills.

They volleyed for the lead trading places throughout the course of every lap. These were two boys accustomed to winning races around their respective local towns and had finally met their equal. Each boy was accustomed to running from the front and winning by a large margin; however, that would not be the case for either of them that day.

Lungs past burning and legs past aching, these boys reached the bell lap, left to fight it out over yet another four hundred and forty yards. Usually Jim or Ben would be padding their lead, but much to the consternation of each other, neither would submit. Hot and sticky like the day, these two could not separate from one another. With legs churning, and excited shouts from all around these two boys traded the lead yet again down the backstretch. Neither would relent more than inches to the other.

Standing on the sideline Herm yelled, cheered, and hoped his brother could bring it home as he had done previously. Ben took a slight lead. Jim pulled it back to even and they continued this way on the back corner with 220 yards to go. Ben again made a strong move hoping to take the lead for good with 150 yards to go but grabbed only a slight lead.

Rooted on the sideline Herm began to doubt but continued to cheer. There was still time left, still time to believe his brother could respond.

And down the home stretch Jim did respond, pulling even.

The race would be decided in the last one hundred yards.

Ben and Jim kept their focus on the finish line while trying to separate, trying to break each other.

Back and forth these two went, finding gears they did not know they had all while the real estate in lane one shrank before them. In a betting game of wills these two were now leaving everything on the table and calling all bluffs; they were throwing down their cards.

Jim was able to keep form to the tape and lunge with one last effort at the line, winning the race in four minutes and twenty-seven seconds. Training had not taken either of them to that time, but a will to win had dragged both of them through that experience. Their legs, lungs, and arms were left in a nightmare of oxygen debt.

And yet this was only part of the conversion Herm had to running, the real experience happened over half an hour later.

The meet had ended and the team was getting ready to get on the bus and leave Omak for home. Herm's coach counted and realized that they were one man short; Jim had not gotten on the bus. The coach simply told Herm to go find his brother and to get him back quick.

Herm left the bus, saw that the dust had finally settled on that old dirt track, and wound his way through the field house only to hear a shower going in the men's locker room. Rounding a corner and saying his brother's name, Herm found his brother in the shower.

Jim was stooped over with his head directly under the showerhead, completely exhausted. Herm could tell his brother had given everything he had. Jim eventually turned off the shower, dressed and got to the bus with his brother, but that image and moment stuck with Herm. He resolved in that moment that if he ever were to coach someday he would make sure to prepare his athletes so that they could withstand the demands of the sport.

Herm saw that both Jim and Ben expected to win. Their expectations grew out of what they had experienced and had reinforced: they were winners. Their times that day improved but not because they were focused on improvement. Their times were secondary to their ultimate goal, winning. Herm knew that if he were to coach someday that he would need to couple high expectations for his athletes and the requisite work to lead them to new heights.

As it would turn out, Jim ran against Tracy Walters in high school and beat him at the state meet. That would be the last time that he ever beat Tracy, but the two would go off to run at Eastern Washington University together.

Herm had seen Tracy and knew of his success in Spokane and at Eastern. Herm himself would compete at Eastern and run under the same coach, Red Reese. The workouts Herm endured were only slightly tougher than the ones Tracy endured. Instead of three laps and the showers it was at most six laps and then the showers.

Unlike Tracy, who was from Spokane but initially did not teach in it, Herm who was not originally from Spokane, found work at Hamblen Elementary. He worked at Hamblen until there came the opportunity to work at a new high school being built on the South Hill of Spokane.

While the name of Rogers High School has become synonymous with poorest in the state, Ferris High School was named after one of Spokane's most successful businessman Joel E. Ferris. Born in Carthage, Illinois in 1874, Ferris eventually headed west where he started his undergraduate education at Carthage College in California. He returned to the University of Illinois to finish his undergraduate degree in 1895, the same year that Roger's *Barefoot Schoolboy Act* was passed into law. After graduation, Ferris worked as a law clerk and bank clerk before eventually ending up in Spokane, Washington in 1908, the same year as North Central High School's grand opening.

Ferris worked as a banker. His successes in creating and maintaining smart loans did not go without notice. In 1913 Ferris established an investment banking firm in town known as Ferris & Hardgrove. On the eve of the creation of Rogers High School in 1931, Ferris became president of the Spokane & Eastern Trust Company. As one school would be touted as a pity to poverty, the other became instantly associated with business and money; the self-made man who was fulfilling the American Dream.

Ferris' prosperous name followed him about as he was sought out to serve on boards for Whitman College, Washington State University, the Hutton Settlement, and St. Luke's Hospital. Being the Renaissance man that he was, Ferris studied history. His interest turned into a passion as he wrote parts of the history of the Pacific Northwest while serving as President of the Eastern Washington State Historical Society. He even wrote academic articles on James J. Hill and his involvement in Spokane. Upon Ferris' death in 1960 his entire library on Pacific Northwest Americana was donated to the Eastern Washington State Historical Society. Little did he know that a high school opening its doors in 1963 would bare his name.

Herm Caviness would be Ferris High School's first track coach. A boy whose father and family had known much of hunger, scrimping, and saving, would be instantly cast into a school and reputation of money. Stereotypes of rich and poor are dangerous when used on either extreme.

Spokane expanded outward in all directions from its initial creation in the late 1800s. The southern part of the city rises steeply in what is commonly called the *South Hill.* The boom of post World War II brought with it baby boomer children reaching high school age in the late 50s and early 60s. New high schools were constructed to keep pace with rising number of school children. These new schools in growing neighborhoods attracted those wanting more.

Herm also wanted more for those in the Spokane community. He saw Tracy's rise as a coach and Gerry's prominence in the local paper. He also competed against Tracy's teams in track. Instead of envying success he tried to compete against it.

Tracy Walters took a kid from Spokane to the Olympics. Herm Caviness would try and take the Olympics to the kids of Spokane.

Herm called it *The Spokane Summer Games*. The first Spokane Summer Games took place in 1966 and continued up until 1973. Gerry would compete in the games, so too would runners like Rick Riley and Don Kardong. Before Bloomsday ever existed, there was Herm Caviness hosting and creating a local event of various races to encourage anyone to get out and compete. In conjunction with the Spokane Summer Games was also the Spokane Road Race. There were few road races being run in the city of Spokane, let alone the country at this time. Herm stood at the forefront, helping all in the community to expect more out of themselves.

The three most powerful tools in Herm's coaching toolkit consist of the most unlikely material: a stapler, construction paper, and an ink pen. It was not shoes, it was not workouts, nor impassioned speeches, equipment, or attire of any kind. His greatest tools were used for psychological sharpening.

Early on, Herm recognized that everyone wants to see their improvement, they want recognition, and they want to be part of the group. As such, Herm had a whole wall in the gym at Ferris High School dedicated to the PR and All Time lists. Athletes and students alike could see where everyone stacked up on these lists.

Immediately following a race, Herm would go about marking and comparing times and distances for that season. If an athlete improved, he would take out his ink pen, mark it down on a piece of construction paper, and then make sure he had staples ready for use in his stapler the following day. Once practice started, Herm would go over the previous meets performances and announce to all his athletes the times, distances, and marks that improved. Each individual athlete would then stand, receive a hearty applause from their teammates, and then take their PR and place it accordingly on the wall.

After the brief announcements and recognition, the athletes would then know it was time to get back to work. Those that had improved found greater incentive to work harder. Those athletes that had failed to achieve what they wanted also redoubled efforts. The targets for improvement were in plain view of everyone. Those wanting some recognition tried to make it on the top 10 for the season; others had more alluring goals of making the top 10 all time list for the school. Although Ferris was a young school, they already had a system set up for success.

At the end of each season the athletes would collect their season best's and take them home where they could pin them up in their rooms and have added motivation to train in the offseason.

Some people just need someone to help them believe.

Left to right, Randy James, Herm Caviness, and Jerry Morton in the fall of 1969

Herm had the ability to make his athletes live up to the title of his own coaching book *The Win Makers*. Rick Riley, Randy James, Tim Riley, Doug Beckman, Britt Brewer, and Jon Knight all won individual titles in either cross country or track under Herm's coaching. He had the ability to not only capture the mind of his athletes but their hearts as well. Perhaps his greatest success as a coach came not from any of his individual title winners, but rather from an athlete least suspected to succeed.

Herm acted as the head track coach at Ferris High School from its opening in the fall of 1963 till his son Chris' graduation in the spring of 1982.

Tim Hatton competed on Herm Caviness' cross country team in the early 1980s. He bought his first pair of running shoes, Nike waffle trainers, from Rick

Riley. Tim grew up amidst a home life that was less than desired. Running was an escape. Tim's freshman year he was a second away from being the freshman city champion. With added hopes that he could do well in running Tim tried out for his sophomore year and was on the varsity squad. He was able to run at the state meet in 1978 where he placed 65th overall with a time of 16:45 for three miles. The team took fourth at state that year. Unfortunately for Tim, he was unable to compete at the state meet his junior year due to a back injury he had suffered. He had been in a car accident earlier that season and was still recovering from it. He was unable to practice and perform as he knew he could.

During the 1979 season Herm gave his athletes a plaque made out Ferris' team colors, red and white, which stated the goal in white lettering: State Champions.

Herm believed that his athletes could win the state title and wanted them to look at the plaque each day as a reminder of what they could accomplish.

Herm made sure to have individual conferences with his athletes where he discussed their goals and gave each of them the "State Champions" plaque to hang in their house. For the 1980 season Herm added another plaque to the mix when he met with each of his athletes. This one, also made up in Ferris colors, stated simply "You Can Be Great." As important as the miles, workouts, and the rest were, it was not as important as the focus and feelings behind it.

Tim had both of his plaques hanging in his locker of the gym where he changed for practice each day. He stared at those before and after every workout. Life outside of school may have been terrible for Tim but he could place all of that away while he practiced each day with his teammates. They alone would share the roads and trails of the South Hill with a common belief stirring within them. Staring at the plaques before and after practice Tim began to feel something change inside himself. He felt that he truly was great and state was within his grasp. He had heard those words but now he felt them. His senior year he knew would be his last opportunity to succeed.

As a senior Tim stood five-feet seven inches tall and weighed a hundred and twenty four pounds. During the off season he delivered two paper routes, cut and stacked wood, and mowed lawns and performed other odd jobs as a means of making money. For a time Tim worked with Herm's son

Chris Caviness. The two teamed up and created their own business called, C&H Yard Care Service. The "C" stood for Caviness and the "H" for Hatton.

Despite being unable to practice as much as he would like, Tim believed he could be great. He was trying to provide money for his unstable family. Throughout the course of the season Tim ran as the seventh man on the team. In cross country the top five runners on a varsity squad are counted for points based upon their overall finish. The team with the lowest points win. Tim was on Ferris' team but he was not scoring points. This did not deter Tim.

The day before the state meet in 1980 was filled with rain. The team previewed the Evergreen High School course, ate dinner together, and then went back to their motel which was near the Space Needle in Seattle. Most of the athletes on the team were nervous for the last meet of the season. Some even kept the window shades to their rooms peeled back so that they could at least have a view of the Space Needle to distract them for the night. Tim could not sleep seeing the Space Needle all lit up and decided to sleep on the floor between the beds in the room. He taped on the wall above him his two plaques, "State Champions" and "You Can Be Great." Tim had looked at his signs and went through a mental visualization of the race one last time. He knew he could do it; he just needed the opportunity to go out and execute.

Tim Hatton, far right; Jon Knight, 3rd from right

The next morning came with a light rain still falling. Herm gave last minute instructions to his athletes reminding them of where they needed to be at each mile and section of the race. He also had vegetable oil on hand and told his athletes to rub it on their arms and legs as a means of repelling the water and keeping their bodies warm.

Tim stood at the starting line with six other Ferris athletes who had all beaten him all season.

The gun was raised.

They all crouched down.

The gun was fired.

They all sprang into action.

Tim Hatton ran with confidence. As the race progressed Tim passed Ferris' sixth and fifth runners. Through mile two of the race Tim continued to pass competitors as well as teammates. To his teammates he said, "Come on, let's go! Go with me!"

Tim continued his surge and passed Ferris' fourth, third, and second place team runners. As he made his way towards the track near the finish of the Evergreen course, Tim was able to see Jon Knight, Ferris' number one runner. Towards the finish Tim continued his charge.

Tim finished fifth overall at the state meet clocking 15:35 for three miles. Tim was Ferris' second runner in and was only eight seconds back of Jon Knight, who had finished second overall. The individual winner was Jim Coombes of North Central High School. Tim went from not scoring points for his team to being on the podium as an individual. Ferris won the state team title in 1980.

After the race Herm ran up to Tim.

"Tim, that was one of the greatest races I've ever seen. How did you do that?" Herm said.

"Coach, I never forgot that I wanted to be a state champion." Tim said.

Herm thought back to the plaques he had seen hanging in motel earlier. It reaffirmed the fact that the messages molded in the mind and heart of athletes are the strongest motivators.

Besides being a great motivator and technician of the sport, Herm Caviness is a great human being. Shortly after the state championship victory in the fall of 1980, Tim's parents divorced and Tim was left floating around from house to house. Tim struggled to find work and provide for himself amidst all the drama that unfolded at home. As a consequence of this Tim had to work three jobs.

Before school started Tim was at Ferris High School working in their green rooms to keep the plants alive and well. Working in an early release program at school, Tim left to go to his second job with the Spokane Pruning Service until five at night. After his second job he went to his third job at Aunt Verna's Restaurant on Trent Avenue where he washed dishes till closing at ten or eleven at night. Tim worked Father's Day and Mother's Day at Aunt Verna's Restaurant instead of spending time with his family. Each day this tiresome routine continued. After work he drove home, did what homework he could and then readied himself for the next school day. Tim had no time for track his senior year of high school. Since his last race in cross country he was trying to navigate the realities of the adult world. He had to pay bills and make it from one month to the next.

As Tim tried to figure out the direction of his life he eventually stayed with the Caviness family for a few months. Herm became the father figure that Tim never really had. Herm encouraged Tim to join the Airforce which he eventually did. While Tim was stationed away from home, his wife delivered their first child, a boy. Herm's wife, Jeraldine Caviness, was there by Tim's wife's side in the delivery. Tim's first child was named by his wife; she chose the name Chris Allan Hatton. One of Herm's son's names is also Chris Allen with just a different spelling of the middle names.

Tim's kids grew up calling Jeraldine, Mama C and Herm, Coach.

Herm saw that the human body needed to be worked, but he realized the greatest movements always sprung from the mind. Tracy's and Gerry's success allowed for Herm's dreams to gain traction. What initially made Tracy great was not the lack of competition in Spokane, but the fact that the state champs were at Shadle Park just down the road. Competition made Tracy better just as it made Herm better. Tracy's success at Rogers caused everyone to elevate their game if they wanted to compete, and Herm wanted to compete. Tim Hatton was one of the last athletes Herm influenced as a head coach, but Herm is often remembered for the first athlete he made into a win maker - Rick Riley.

Left to right; Jack Bacheler; Steve Prefontaine (tucked behind Bacheler);
Rick Riley; Gerry Lindgren (tucked behind Riley); Frank Shorter

© Track & Field News

Rick Riley: Running in the Shadows

The Amateur Athletic Union's (AAU) National Track and Field Championship occurred on June 26, 1970 in Bakersfield, California. With a lap to go on the track in a hot, under the lights, three mile race it was still anyone's race.

Gerry Lindgren had shot to the lead trying to make a break for victory, much like he had done against the Soviets years previous. Six years had passed since his magical run to the Olympics in Tokyo. The Olympics in Mexico City had come and gone and Gerry had not been part of the team, yet he was still an indomitable force. He was nicknamed the Spokane Sparrow and everyone knew this bird could fly. 11 individual NCAA Championship title victories in cross country and track testified of Gerry's ability to win.

Charging and trying to chase down Gerry was Steve Prefontaine, whose only NCAA Championship in cross country he had not won came by way of Gerry Lindgren. In that race as a freshman Prefontaine had finished third in the country; just 13 seconds back from Gerry's victory. After exiting high school Pre was put on the cover of *Sports Illustrated* with the caption reading "America's Distance Prodigy." He had set the national high school two mile record of 8:41.5. Prefontaine was the future of distance running, but at the time of this race he was still two years away from his shot at Munich and the Olympic dreams he had harbored in his heart since childhood.

Following after Pre and passing both of them as they headed into the turn was Frank Shorter, a man who had only won one NCAA Championship in the 10,000 meter in track in 1969. Frank was on the rise and only two years away from an Olympic gold medal in the marathon at the Munich Olympics. He was six years away from a silver medal in the Olympic marathon in Montreal, a medal that should have been gold but was cheated from him by Waldemar Cierpinski of East Germany, who used performance enhancing drugs.

Jack Bacheler, the tallest runner in the field, towering over everyone with his six foot seven inch frame, was in a position to pass his training partner Frank Shorter, and prove that he was more than just someone to key off of. After all, Jack Bacheler had run in the Mexico City Olympics and was the only American to qualify for the 5,000 meter final at that Olympics. The only problem with that final in Mexico City was that Bacheler never raced in it due to the unlikely and unlucky fate of contracting dysentery on the day of the final race.

Perhaps the least likely person to win would have been Rick Riley. Sandwiched in the same town as Gerry Lindgren and having his national two mile high school record taken from him by Prefontaine, Rick has been the forgotten runner of his generation. His greatest races had come in high school and just shortly afterward as he represented team USA in international competitions just weeks after graduating high school. Injuries, setbacks, and seconds in the shadows of others had derailed promising hopes.

And so as they ran through the sweltering heat and down the backstretch of the championship race, the kid who was once nicknamed the Ferris Flyer looked as if he had laced up with Herme's winged sandals for spikes. Rick came screaming and soaring around the curve into the homestretch, out of obscurity and the shadows of those who came before and after. Rick Riley was making his charge toward the tape. If Rick's legs were the engine, his desire was the fuel.

Rick passed by Prefontaine, a future Olympian (72).

Rick flew by Bacheler, a former Olympian (68) and future Olympian (72).

Rick zipped past Lindgren, a former Olympian (64) and hometown hero, now teammate.

Rick was closing like a freight train on Frank Shorter a future Olympic champion (72 and 76) but ran out of real estate while peeling off his 54 second last lap. Frank Shorter won the race running 13:24.2 and Rick was second at 13:24.4. Had his charge started sooner or the race been longer, Rick Riley would have been the champion. As is so often the case, timing is everything.

And as unfair as it is to run by three Olympians and be lost to the memory of distance running in this country, Rick was lost because he did not beat that fourth Olympian, Frank Shorter. The late sixties and early seventies were the Golden Age of distance running in America.

Rick would beat past and future Olympians, but never be an Olympian. Such is the harsh reality of this cruel sport. Time meets twists of fate on the track and success is only remembered on certain dates due to certain times. The stars must align for those hungry for success.

After passing through the finishing tape and looking back at those he beat, it would be hard for Rick, young as he was, to recognize how far he had come when the elusive prize had disappeared in literally the blink of an eye.

With laces undone, sweat soaked through his body, Rick quietly exited the track and made his way towards his old pair of trainers, towards the cool open road of the evening, and to the past he was still trying to catch up with.

It was all right there in front of him, and yet it was still just out of reach.

Rick was sitting shotgun in his Dad's 1964 silver GTO during one cold January night in 1964 and listened to the static between radio stations. The car sat parked and overlooking the dirt track of Hart Field on the South Hill of Spokane. Rick's father fidgeted with the dials and tried to find the station relaying the race from San Francisco. Rick, only a sophomore in high school, looked out on the dark and empty track before him. As the announcer's voice came through the static during those late winter months, so too appeared ghosts and visions of Ron Clarke, Gaston Roelents, Jim Ryun and others running about on the Hart Field track.

Rick waited to hear that familiar voice of Tracy Walters coming on to announce Gerry's race for all those tuning in from Spokane. Rick listened to the races of Gerry running and improving from lap to lap and race to race. Tracy, excitable as he was, would use his voice to bring to life the race to all those who could not see it.

Sitting in the dark cold muscle car alongside his father, Rick's dreams played out through the foggy windows and on the silent track before him. Hearing of a five foot five and one hundred and fifteen pound boy with a never say die attitude and approach to running sounded familiar to Rick. Those words and ideas seemed to echo inside of him. The size and weight seemed to be eerily similar to Rick who stood only one inch taller than Gerry. Both showed they were more than what they appeared to be. The air was cool inside that muscle car yet burning within Rick were visions of what could be.

Rick watched Gerry run in person at the state meet in 1964. Rick sat in the wooden bleachers along with 8,000 other spectators who had shown up to see the state's finest. Lost in the sea of the crowd, Rick watched as Gerry ran his 4:06.0 mile race. Hearing the announcer state that Gerry Lindgren had just set the national mile high school record and then seeing the size of his hero brought home the reality that Rick could see himself running just as fast.

He is so small, Rick thought to himself as he sat in the stands at the state meet.

Sitting in the shade of the stands a seed had been planted in young Rick's heart. While crouched amidst the masses chattering about the record they had just witnessed, Rick sat in silent contemplation. He formulated the goal of how good he wanted to be.

If he can do that I can do that- I want to do this.

Rick had determined right then and there what he wanted. Days, weeks, months, and years would be spent living up to that resolution he made.

While Gerry was finishing up his senior year and capturing the hearts, minds, and imaginations of what was possible, Rick was finishing up his sophomore year at the newly constructed Ferris High School, where he would be part of the first graduating class.

Fortuitous circumstances, outside of the range and scope of Rick's own choosing brought him and his family to Spokane. Rick was born March 5, 1948 in the tiny town of Curlew, Washington, where he was raised for the first 13 years of his life. The population was just over a hundred people.

Curlew sits just south of the Canadian border. During the 1950s there was an air force station that was really nothing at all, but it was connected to the DEW line (Distant Early Warning). During the Cold War, the United States had set up radar stations around the Arctic Circle, another in what was referred to as the Mid-Canadian Line, and then finally the lowest and most outer ring along the 49th parallel called the Tree Line. Curlew, Washington had a station setup as a means of defense and Rick Riley's father was stationed there.

Rick's father, a World War II veteran, came home from the war and worked for the government as a painter. His post was originally in Curlew, Washington but by the early 1960s several of the stations were deactivated and so the Riley's relocated to Spokane, Washington. The Riley's ended up settling on the South Hill near 32nd and Division Street. Rick's father would end up working at Fairchild Air Force Base in their paint shop until his retirement.

The family first settled on the northside of Spokane and one can only wonder what may have happened had the family stayed there instead of moving towards the South Hill.

Originally, Rick was planning on attending Lewis & Clark High School, but he had some friends that were going to attend the new Ferris High School and the allure of being the first graduating class at the new school was just too much.

The new school was staffed with its first coaches, Herm Caviness in track and Tony Dolphin in cross country.

Rick's earliest attempts at distance running came on the Hart Field Track. While attending Sacajawea Middle School, Rick had turned out for track and ran the 100 yard dash. This was what he considered his warm up race. His third

place showing in the 880 yard dash at the All City meet his ninth grade year showed he had ample foot speed. He had never run cross country.

During the summer before Rick's first year of high school as a 10th grader at the newly constructed Joel E. Ferris High School, Rick spent his time at his grandparents house up in Curlew, Washington bucking hay.

Rick's work started early and lasted late into the day as he helped out on the farm. After the long, strenuous work was completed, Rick would go out for a four mile jog to relax and end the day. These

© Exeter Yearbook, Spokane Public Schools

Rick Riley competing for Ferris in 1964

simple runs with gradually increasing speed were his only training.

High school at the time consisted of only 10th, 11th, and 12th grade. With the new school opening, Rick showed up with all the other 10th graders; there were no 11th or 12th graders at the school. When Rick transitioned into 11th grade, they started to have two grades attending the high school.

Rick decided to turn out for cross country in 10th grade with no one having recruited him to turn out. This was entirely Rick's decision and it proved to be a good one; one that he stuck with and developed with each passing year.

The biggest jump for Rick came between the summer of his sophomore and junior year. Just after the season had concluded and Rick had won the city championship, he went off to run at a junior Olympics event on the western side of the state unbeknownst to his coach Herm Caviness. Rick entered his age group mile, having only run a 4:36 as a sophomore that season. In the race he would lower his PR to 4:25 and placed second in his age group. Not feeling tired and actually rather encouraged from the results, Rick decided to enter into the open mile a mere two hours later where he ran and took second again, lowering his mile PR to 4:23. The winner of the race was none other than Kenny Moore, who would go on to run at the University of Oregon, becoming an Olympian, and accomplished author.

Rick did not know who Kenny Moore was at the time. He did not know that he should be afraid to run against other athletes ahead of him. He did not know that he was supposed to be afraid of anyone in a race. He knew he was a hundred yard dash, warm up kid, who tried to run from the front and hold on to the very end. This unassuming approach aided Rick to reach beyond whatever barriers could have been placed on himself.

Rick began to see that increased effort off of the track led to a direct correlation with results on the track. During Rick's junior season he did not lose to anyone the entire cross country season. The state meet of 1964 arrived and Rick toed the line at Green Lake assuming he would continue the brief but already stellar legacy of those runners and teams from Spokane who had gone before.

The gun was raised and fired and Rick ran to the lead.

He was met by another runner also sticking to the front and never fading.

Around the lake these two went, but they could not shake one another. No matter how hard Rick pushed, this no name kid beside him responded.

The finish finally came into sight and still there was no separation. Rick made one last effort, but the boy to his right continued to the tape opening the slightest of leads. They would finish in this order and it would be the first loss of Rick's junior season. The winner was none other than Roscoe Divine, the 18th American to ever break the four minute mile, a future University of Oregon distance runner who ran under Bill Bowerman and alongside Kenny Moore.

Again, Rick had never heard of Roscoe; he did not know what the future held for him and all that he would accomplish. At the time, all he knew was that he had been outkicked by someone and that perfect season or Lindgren like mark had been taken from him.

Rick could hold fast to the consolation that Gerry had lost too before he became Gerry Lindgren the high school running god. Gerry had lost in his sophomore season at the state meet as well, taking second place. Yet, Rick was a year older taking second.

Another offseason of work awaited Rick and with it a renewed sense of urgency. During track, Rick again improved. At state, Rick would opt for the newly added two mile race. In a time when only one event was focused on, Roscoe ran the mile winning in 4:12.2 and Rick won the two mile in 9:11.2.

Following the state meet, Herm found another race for Rick to run in down in California at the United States of America Track & Field (USATF) junior national three mile race. Rick had never raced three miles in his life. Cross country races at the time were typically 2.3 miles in the state of Washington. The longest race in track was two miles. At this meet in California Rick would run 14:08 and take sixth overall. Rick was the highest placing high school finisher and was running against collegiate aged and collegiate quality competition.

Standing on the sideline and orchestrating the confidence building before these races was Herm. He outlined the splits he wanted Rick to run during the race. Practices simulated what races would feel like. Herm took Rick as close to the race like experience as could in practice. All of this was accomplished on a grass track on the backside of Ferris High School.

Rick could take comfort in the fact that Roscoe was a senior and therefore

Rick's senior year he would have no one left to challenge him except himself and the clock.

Much has been made of the myth of Gerry Lindgren's training. His own claims are of running in the realm of 25-35 miles a day, averaging somewhere in the vicinity of 175-245 miles a week. His own coach, Tracy Walters, believes the number of miles was likely no higher than the 120 mile range. Yet, Gerry could be right, if his midnight runs are true then the added mileage could be tabulated, but still, Gerry was human and needed rest and recovery like everyone else.

What is not disputed is the amount of work that Rick Riley did. His running journal would be copied by coaches and shown to athletes. The pace and demands of success had become ingrained in Rick. It all became second nature to him. Averaging from 25 to 30 miles a week as a ninth grader upwards toward 65 to 70 miles a week as a sophomore, then 80 to 85 miles as a junior, Rick had seen a pattern. Hard work yielded results. Finally, for an entire calendar year during Rick's senior season he averaged 92 miles a week.

It bears repeating that for an entire calendar year Rick Riley ran an average of 92 miles a week.

The highest mileage he ever had was 130 miles in one week. Many of his weeks were at 100 miles. The shoes came and went quickly as he wore them out before he wore himself out. And the shoes were not that good at the time anyway. To accumulate such mileage, Rick made sure to run twice a day and his morning runs, which as a junior had hovered around three miles now doubled and became six miles. Each week also contained at least one run that ranged anywhere from 18 to 22 miles. Sometimes there would be two runs of that distance.

Another way of looking at these numbers is to view the total miles he put in each year. For his freshman year, Rick logged 1,300 miles. As a sophomore he ran 3,380 miles, more than double his freshman year. As a junior Rick ran 4,160 miles. Finally as a senior he logged 4,784 miles. In Rick's high school running career he ran a total of 13,624 miles. That is twice the circumference of the moon and just over half the circumference of the earth. It was no moon shot for Rick Riley to believe he could compete with someone like Gerry Lindgren. When Rick eventually travelled and competed internationally representing team USA, his running could have literally covered the distance to get him there. Running was a means of seeing the world in very real ways.

Herm would get creative in the ways in which he would challenge his athletes and Rick seemed the perfect person to test the limits on. Heading out south of Ferris High School runs the Palouse Highway. Herm would tell his athletes to run as fast as they could for an hour. They would synchronize their watches and then be sent on their way down the winding highway. The rolling hills of the Palouse Highway look like something out of Dr. Seuss' *Oh the Places You'll Go!* children's book. Instead of the bright colors striped across the hills there are wheat fields.

Rick covered 11.6 miles in 1 hour rising and falling on those rolling hills that twisted and turned about. He averaged 5:10 pace for an hour. Most high school kids cannot average that pace for two miles on a flat surface, let alone 11.6 in a row over steep inclines and declines.

The most intervals Rick ever did in high school was 25 X 440 yards. His toughest workouts consisted of longer intervals such as 6 X 1 mile repeats or 5 X 1.5 miles, or 3 X 2 miles. He became acquainted with distances, but he also became acquainted with pace as he survived and thrived on the workload. Rick's legs survived the workouts due to the grass track he ran on. The school had decided to burn out the lanes for the track.

The workouts Rick ran varied. During the summer, living close to Hart Field, Rick would run anything from 100, 220, 330 or 440 yards as intervals. Variety was ever present, but there was always the consistency of effort.

Rick ran as much as some people drive in a year. The distance across the United States is 2,802 miles. Rick could have ran across the United States, then turned around and ran back.

Rick Riley was Forrest Gump before Forrest Gump.

Washington as a state is only 360 miles long; Rick could have ran back and forth across it 13 times. At least once a month Rick was crossing the state with the number of miles he was running. If there was ever going to be a state champion, Rick Riley would have been it because he covered it extensively. If there were to be an All-American Runner, Rick would be it having spanned the country twice his senior year.

What possessed Rick?

The opportunity to achieve.

For as fast as Gerry ran, his records were not all included as high school records recognized by the governing body of the sport at that time. This was due to the fact that Gerry's times were clocked at competitions that had athletes not in high school. Since that time, record keeping has changed so that the fastest time is the key factor, not the competition it was run against.

The nation's fastest two mile recognized at the time was owned by Mike Ryan of Wilcox High School in Santa Clara, California. He had run an 8:57.8 in 1965. Rick, knowing that he was near that mark with enough work, wanted to zero in on owning the record.

Rick wanted this so badly he made sure that the first and last thing he saw each day was a message taped to the bunk bed slat directly above him which read *8:48.00 - 2 Mile National Record.*

The mileage was an indication of confidence. When the mileage dropped for Rick, the results were slower times. As the mileage increased, the confidence, the pace, and the strength all increased. Blisters came and went but Rick's feet calloused and his confidence likewise toughened. He could run with anyone and he could beat anyone.

The only question was whether he had enough time left in high school to train for this ultimate goal.

Meet after meet in the season began to tick away and although Rick was hovering around nine minutes, he needed to have a breakthrough.

April 22, 1966 was a Friday. On the South Hill of Spokane several athletes and teams came together to Hart Field to race. Just two years previous Gerry had set the city mile record on that same dirt track running 4:10.5.

This was the same track that Riley had run intervals on at varying distances during his summers. It was the same dirt track that he had gazed out on while sitting in his father's silver mustang and listening to Tracy Walters announce Gerry's races. Rick only had four more chances to make runs at Gerry's records.

At the meet, Rick was entered in the mile. In his previous races he had taken out the pace fast, going out as quick as 57 seconds for his first lap.

The gun was raised and the race started.

The wind was present that day but not overbearing. Rick ran from within himself and did not go out at a suicidal pace. He was focused, determined, and resolute to run fast. After the race started it became clear to anyone watching that Rick was running by himself. The first three laps went by and finally Rick threw everything he had into this last lap.

Around the curve he went and down that old dirt backstretch he

© Spokesman-Review

sprinted. He had one more curve to go, one more bend, and then a straightaway that he charged through all the way to the finish.

4:08.5

The new city mile record was Rick's.

He had peeled off a 58.5 second final lap and took down Gerry's city mark by two seconds. In this instance, Rick had surpassed the ghost of Gerry Lindgren. When Rick's 4:08.5 mile is converted to a 1,600 meter time it equates to 4:06.9. It is still the fastest time for interleague Spokane only competition ever run. Other Spokane athletes would run faster times, but just not in league meet competition. With just under a month to go before the state meet Rick set his eyes on another mark.

On May 26, 1966 the state championship was held in Pullman, Washington on Washington State University's track. Rick's senior year track season was the culmination of years, hours, and days spent running and chasing the ghost, the dream, the vision that Gerry had set. Gerry competed at Washington State University and decided to show up to watch the race and cheer Rick on from the infield.

Gerry Lindgren cheers as Rick Riley runs in state meet two mile in 1966

In distance running there is never anyone that ever boos an athlete as they run. Most sports carry with them fans that will boo, belittle, or demean another athlete. In track and field and distance running there is too much respect for each athlete to ever cause anyone to try and discourage those competing. The sacrifice they offer when they toe the line before the start is always a consecration of the self and their will to give everything.

And so Gerry stood planted on the infield of the track, with his new letterman's jacket on, clapping and cheering loudly for the boy from his hometown who was warming up and readying himself for a run at greatness. Gerry wanted Rick to succeed; there was no ego in the way of sportsmanship.

Rick warmed up with his red and white Ferris uniform, knowing it would be the last time he would wear his high school singlet. He heard the cheers and the encouragement from Gerry and others in attendance. Gerry had rewritten Rogers High School's record book as well as the nation's; Rick had been writing Ferris' pages since his first days at school. This would be the end of its first chapter.

The call came for the athletes to remove their sweats and make their way to the starting line. With spikes crunching on the old dirt track, Rick made his way to the starting line as the obvious favorite.

Rick had enjoyed winning a state title in the two mile during his junior year. He had enjoyed winning his only cross country title his senior year. He wanted more than the track title, he wanted the national two mile record.

Lining up on the track with the other athletes, Rick lined up the thoughts, the routines, the habits, the numbers, and racing logs he had dedicated for the past year.

"To your marks!" came the command from the starting marshal.

Rick toed the line.

Bang!

Rick bolted to the lead, silent and focused. There were people cheering in the stands but Rick muted them out as he made his way into the straightaways and out of the curves. On a warm, late spring day, Rick had to stay cool and run within himself.

He had to take something he had seen before, thought over and heard, and then transform it into his own experience. All the work, effort, and focus were being aligned as he tied one lap into another, into another.

Through the first mile Rick went, under the national two mile record pace. Onward he went into the suffocating world of the unknown. Legs kept steady, while arms pumped evenly and Rick's eyes stayed up and focused.

The bell lap finally rang.

One last push.

The dream that he forged inside his imagination now burned itself out in reality through his legs. For the last time Rick ran down the backstretch. Gerry's amazing times under nine minutes had come in pursuing professional runners

like Ron Clark, Gaston Rolents, and Bob Schul. Rick had no one in front of him to chase; he was both hound and hare in that instant.

Into the last curve he went with all he had left and shot out onto the homestretch. He took his final effort all the way to the tape where he finally threw up his arms in victory.

Exhaustion had been overrun by endurance and a will to win.

The official time was finally announced.

8:48.13.

© Spokesman-Review

Herm Caviness with camera; Tony Dolphin shaking hands

Rick Riley was the new officially recognized national two mile champion. Gerry was there cheering on an exceptional talent and future teammate.

After a cool down, Rick stepped atop the medal podium. Surveying the cheering crowd, he couldn't help but see in his mind's eye the bed slat above his bed flashing before his eyes and the number written there. And he couldn't help but ask the nagging question at the back of his mind.

Why didn't I write a lower number?

The day after graduating from high school, Rick would be on the track with his future teammate, roommate, and childhood idol in the Compton Relays three mile race in California. Gerry would win the race and tie an American record 13:38.0. Rick took fourth in the race finishing with a 58 second last lap running 14:00.2. Rick was the first high school athlete to cross the finish line and held the second fastest time for a prep at that distance behind Gerry. The future held everything for Rick, including higher expectations and greater goals. Rick saw a future full of more workouts. But sometimes more work does not equate with better results.

Injury: Latin, for Not Right or Lawful

The work that Rick put in during his high school years, outlined by Coach Dolphin and Coach Caviness, gave him confidence. When the lap times they wanted him to hit on Ferris' grass track were shouted out, Rick ran through right on pace. Then when it came time to step onto a sterner surface such as a cinder or dirt track, Rick could go through on pace or just faster than pace and feel the confidence that he was exceeding expectations.

Shortly after graduation from high school, Gerry had gone on to Olympic success as an eighteen year old. Shortly after Rick graduated from high school on June 11, 1966, he was down at a meet in San Diego, California running the mile inside of Balboa Stadium. Featured in the race was Tim Danielson of Chula Vista High School who ended up becoming the second high school athlete to break four minutes in the mile, clocking 3:59.4. Rick ran in the very same race and finished dead last with a time of 4:04. The time was amazing, but the place was not something Rick had ever experienced before.

As much as Gerry had revolutionized high school distance running, there were others shortly thereafter that were also rewriting the rules and expectations on what could be accomplished. A 4:04 mile in high school is outstanding; it's just that when someone else break's four, it is not recognized as the outstanding mark that it is. This race in Balboa Stadium foreshadowed Rick's future with running in college and beyond.

College brought with it a change of coach: Jack Mooberry. A product of coaching at Rogers High School himself, Jack had jumped at the opportunity to coach at Washington State University in 1945. College also brought a change of location and an update in the surface. WSU renovated their track with a synthetic surface just after Rick's national two mile performance. Rick trained on and attacked these hard surfaces with the same zeal he had on the grass. However, the grass had been more forgiving to Rick's legs and ankles. The synthetic surface was unforgiving.

The sanity of distance running comes from consistency. Eliminate consistency from the minutiae of putting one foot in front of the other and the sport becomes maddening.

College running is different than high school running.

It is said that high school quarterbacks can throw a football into a 10 foot window; meaning that as long as the ball is within a 10 foot space, it's likely the defender may miss and the receiver will catch the ball. In college football that window shrinks to anywhere between 3 and 5 feet. Defenders are better. Finally professional football players have a single square foot window to throw into and they must do so with pinpoint accuracy.

Running in high school you can have the best runner in a race winning by 20 to 30 seconds in cross country. In college, that same athlete will be surrounded by 20 to 30 guys throughout an entire cross country race on the national level. In collegiate and professional distance running, the winning times also shrink by a significant margin.

Rick was running in the steps of Gerry who had made the voyage down to Pullman, but as Gerry ran away to NCAA Championship after NCAA Championship, Rick fought to stay healthy. The dreams of distance running that had started all while he listened and conjured the spirits of the nation's best in his Dad's muscle car had now turned to nightmares.

Rick had set a national two mile record in high school; a record that would only last for three years. In 1969 a kid by the name of Steve Prefontaine would lower the time by almost seven seconds.

The problem Rick faced was knowing himself.

Rick knew what training he had done in high school. He knew all the miles he had tallied and how that compared with his weekly average. He knew the pace he needed to hit on the track. He knew all the competition he was facing in college. There were no more close calls running against the unknown Roscoe

Rick Riley and Steve Prefontaine compete in the three mile dual meet at Hayward Field in 1970

Divine's and Kenny Moore's of the world. He knew these men and others like them. He competed against them in PAC 8 meets routinely. Rick knew what it took to run a national caliber time.

What Rick had not been acquainted with in high school was long term injury and setback. Running had been relegated to the dirt roads and the grass track. But workouts with Gerry at the helm and on synthetic surfaces left their marks on Rick's legs and on his mind.

Rick had caught the running bug late in his sophomore year of high school and within two years time he was the nation's best prep athlete. In college he did not need to convince himself that he wanted to run fast, he just needed to convince himself that he had done enough in practice. When time seemed to shrink before him in high school Rick relied upon the miles, the routines, and results that came from training on long grass and racing on dirt tracks.

In college the training was not on a grass track and the races were on hard surfaces. The realities he was running against were likewise harder. He could not just run away from anyone by running through the first mile in 4:20. That pace could crush high school spirits, but collegiate athletes all know that pace and lived it. How does an athlete that has anchored himself with hard work differentiate himself amongst athletes that are all as hungry and hard working? Not to mention the fact that Rick was roommates with Gerry Lindgren, who won national title after national title like he was ticking off laps on a three mile race.

Rick went back to the staples of a little hard work being good and a lot of hard work being better. Unfortunately Rick was like most athletes who are not afraid to push their body to the limits. Rest needed to have its day, or else the result would be an overcompensation of tomorrow's gain for today's effort.

Season after season, the start would hold promise. After a good workout the thoughts of an athlete race towards judgment calls where they act like they are their own coach. It becomes easy for an athlete to justify going a little bit faster a little bit sooner in the next interval workout so that they can be that much further ahead by the end of the season.

Instead of recognizing the need for rest, the athlete looks for instant results.

These thoughts and others similar to it lingered in Rick's mind. Sure enough, the next workout would come and the added strain to shave off a second or two would spell ruin. The mind demanded what the body was not ready to give and it demanded it for a longer and faster period of time. Only rest and recovery were needed in order to properly achieve the long lasting results.

Injuries started for Rick in this manner. Illnesses also accompanied injury because the body was being pushed to the limits. At such a high level of intensity, the body becomes fragile and susceptible to coughs, colds, and the elements. Pushing the body to the limits is an invitation for illness.

Too much too quickly is the pattern.

The body then surrenders and brings to a halt the activities it had not been prepared to endure. Then there is the balancing act of ice baths, massages, and strengthening or stretching exercises that ask some broken part of the body to pretend it's not broken. Time is needed to fix the injury but once more, when the time of a season is passing and pressure is mounting to perform, time is the last thing an athlete wants to surrender. Instead of asking less, he asks more. After all, it's a simple thing, as simple as putting one foot in front of the other and alternating that motion, hundreds and thousands of times over.

The problem of injury only compounded itself when Rick would have to explain to other athletes or people in the press why he was not racing at the time. He had to acknowledge that the season was not going as planned. He had to confront the fact that the Rick everyone had known and heaped great expectations upon exiting high school was currently unable to perform.

Multiple times Rick would have to explain how he had come to this situation and multiple times those asking would again offer their expectation at the end of the conversation.

People offered Rick their sympathy and well wishes for a speedy recovery.

As if it was a simple as flipping a switch.

Makeshift movements to manage the problem led to long term systemic issues. Eventually all running would have to be drastically altered or completely eliminated and he would have to start from square one.

What should have been sacrificed for a day or a week would ultimately sacrifice the season. Rick was running on hard surfaces and against hard realities; everyone was getting better and in college, you run away from no one.

The rising tide of distance runners that Gerry had inspired were not all from Spokane, although many of the men making up the varsity squad from Washington State University were from Spokane. Five of Washington State's runners from their 1969 team were from two schools in Spokane: Rogers and Ferris. The runners from Rogers were Gerry Lindgren and Jim Isitt. The runners from Ferris were Rick Riley, Tom Robinson, and Wayne Ristau. This Washington State University team placed fourth at the National Championship race.

Jack Mooberry did not have to travel far for his recruiting visits. Just over seventy miles north of Pullman, Washington sits Spokane. Jack could field one of the premiere cross country teams in the entire country by simply visiting two high schools an hour away.

Even when Rick was healthy, he would go through the first mile of a race in 4:17 and look around to see a handful of guys right there with him. He had gone out on pace; the problem was there were three or four other guys right on pace too.

Rick did not run at the 1967 NCAA Cross Country Championship race where Gerry won.

By the spring of 1968, Rick was healthy enough to run in the NCAA Championship 10,000 meter final. However, Rick had his Gerry like moment where he turned his ankle in the week leading up to the race. Rick ran on it, not knowing when he would have the opportunity to race at a championship level again.

© Chinook Yearbook, WSU Manuscripts, Archives, & Special Collections

Tom Robinson, far left; Jim Isitt, third from left; Wayne Ristua, middle; Rick Riley, third from right; Gerry Lindgren, far right

After 25 laps of painful effort Rick finished in eighth place clocking 30:30. Gerry won the race, almost a lap ahead finishing in 29:41. Rick knew that barring injury the results could have been different. He sat on the sidelines and watched Gerry win the 5,000 meter race as well, clocking 13:57.

Two years had been spent training, running, and competing to stay healthy so that a race could not only be run, but won. The confidence and joy of running came from seeing the fruits of running; when those fruits were denied, it was hard to continue onward.

After his sophomore year of college, Rick went back to Curlew, Washington for the summer. He once more worked the hay bales that

Rick Riley, far left, Gerry Lindgren, far right, competing in a dual meet against University of Washington

© Chinook Yearbook, WSU Manuscripts, Archives, & Special Collections

had made him strong in his youth. In this dark hour Rick considered quitting for the first time in his life.

By the time of Rick's junior year of college he had not beaten his 8:48 PR for two miles. Two years of torturous effort had seemingly yielded nothing.

Rick's junior year brought with it another cross country season injured and no one from Washington State ran in the NCAA Cross Country Championship race. But with his tonsils removed and a balance finally struck in his training, Rick's times started to drop.

On a cold day in March with a slight wind, Rick circled these thoughts of doubt, of self pity, and wonder once more as he circled the track warming up for yet another race. Finally on this cold spring day Rick held to the pace and beat his 8:48 two mile time. He felt he was back to being the runner he knew he always could be. By the end of his junior track season Rick was healthy and confident. He competed in the six mile final at the NCAA Championships. He placed second overall, running 29:23. Frank Shorter won the race.

Entering Rick's senior year, he finally competed at an NCAA Championship

Steve Prefontaine, left; Gerry Lindgren, right - finishing PAC 8 Cross Country Championship 1969

© Charles Dyer

race in cross country. He finished 19th overall, running 30:02, he was only a minute and three seconds behind his teammate, Gerry who won the race in 28:59.

Gerry had grown up in dogtown, and Rick had learned through his collegiate experience that it was a dogfight every time he stepped on the track. It was the Golden Age of competitive distance running. No athlete was trying to save themselves for a bigger race. It was expected that everyone run from the front, run a fast tempo, run at a death's pace, and see who was living after it was all over.

The PAC 8 Cross Country Championship race held on November 15, 1969 has been labeled the greatest footrace ever. The race occurred on the Stanford University golf course. This one race was indicative of Rick Riley's collegiate experience. Gerry and Pre took off on the six mile course at a suicidal pace. In this race Prefontaine and Gerry gave no ground between the two of them for the entirety of the six mile race.

Gerry ran as a 5th year senior having redshirted in 1968 with hopes of joining the Olympic team in Mexico City, and Pre had graduated high school only to land himself a cover photo on the front of *Sports Illustrated* with promises of being America's Distance Prodigy. It was a battle between the old guard and the new talent with neither yielding a step to one another.

Pre and Gerry took the rest of the field through the first mile in 4:18. Chasing these athletes that ran like they were going through fire was Rick Riley. He was trying to keep pace and survive. The closest runner to him was Steve Savage of Oregon. Behind Rick was Roscoe Divine of Oregon and Don Kardong of Stanford. They all went out too fast, they all went out a too hard, but they had no other option. They were chasing greatness and courting their own disaster all at the same time.

Gerry and Pre ran to the finish line unable to separate from one another. Their arms and elbows were at each others sides as they blitzed their way to the finish. Originally the two were said to have tied. After the photo finish it was determined that Gerry had crossed before Pre, but they were both awarded the same finishing time of 28:32.4. The other competitors in the race were nowhere to be seen in the final finishing shot of Gerry and Pre because they were all still nearly 30 seconds back. They were all trying to recover from oxygen debt, deal with the lactic acid pulsing through their legs, and try to beat the guy that was running beside them on the fairways. They were all readying for their finishing kick, or whatever was left of it.

Rick was one such competitor racing to the finish with everything he had.

Steve Savage of Oregon finished third in 28:58 and Rick Riley was fourth in 29:02. Don Kardong was farther back with some of his Stanford teammates finishing in 29:41. After the race Rick knew without a shadow of a doubt that this was the toughest cross country race he ever ran.

Rick's senior year of track he qualified for the six mile final in the NCAA Championships again but he would finish sixth, running 28:44. The three mile winner that day was Steve Prefontaine running 13:22, and the mile winner was Marty Liquori running 3:59.9. Rick Riley's college career, injury filled and frustration full, ended. There was one race, though, that gave a glimpse of what Rick Riley could have been when placed in the right event with no injury.

PAC 8 Championships: Channeling Bannister

Earlier in the 1970 spring track season, Rick had faced off against Roscoe Divine, who had given Rick one of only three losses in high school cross country. Roscoe had beaten Rick at the state championship race in 1964. When they had entered the finishing shoot, Rick was within arm's length of a state championship he knew could have been his. Roscoe went on to run at the University of Oregon under Bill Bowerman. Roscoe was a year older than Rick.

In college they had met on the course a few times, and in Rick's senior year (Roscoe's last year due to a redshirt season) they faced off in the mile twice. In their previous meeting Rick pushed the pace early in the race. He wanted to separate, but Roscoe merely sat on Rick's shoulder and passed him in the final straightaway, winning in 4:01.8 compared to Rick's 4:02.8. The arm's length distance was still there.

Rick had finally beaten Roscoe in the NCAA Cross Country Championships in 1969 where Rick had finished 19th overall and 10 seconds faster than Roscoe.

But it seemed that Roscoe had Rick's number each time they raced.

Heading into the PAC 8 Championships on May 16, 1970 Coach Mooberry had Rick set to run the mile race against Roscoe. He told Rick to sit back and try to outkick Roscoe, instead of doing all the work and letting Roscoe pass by him at the finish.

© Spokesman-Review

With the gun raised and the runners crouched and ready to run Rick decided to heed his coach's advice and go out slower.

The gun fired.

There was a runner from California that took the lead. Through the first lap they went, Rick going through in a relaxed 63 seconds.

On the second lap Mike Mullins of UCLA took the lead and held it to the halfway point going through 800 meters in 2:02.7. The pace had picked up, but Rick sat just off of the leaders and just behind Roscoe Divine.

As they were finishing up the third lap, Roscoe made a move for the lead. Reacting in that instant, Rick went with Roscoe, but did not see Duncan Macdonald of Stanford making his move as well. Macdonald incidentally pushed his way between Roscoe and Rick, knocking Rick off of his stride and out to lane two. They went through the bell lap hitting 3:03.

Bumped out and back in third, Rick charged down the backstretch sprinting. Running tall, striding smooth, Rick was throwing everything he had onto the track.

This is as fast as I can go. I can't get another ounce of energy out of my body, Rick said to himself.

Full steam ahead, Rick chased the two men charging for home in lanes one and two. Macdonald was in lane two, Roscoe in lane one. As the runners in the lead split between the two lanes, out of the curve came Rick, surging.

Here I come! I'm going to win this! Rick thought. He split between the small gap on either side of Roscoe and Macdonald, who began to fade out to the right of lane two.

Rick threw himself at the tape bent forward as if he were finishing a hundred meter race.

Rick had won.

What added to his surprise was that he had run his last lap in 56 seconds, and broken four minutes in the mile clocking 3:59.2. Rick Riley was the 32nd American to break four minutes in the mile. Roscoe Divine first accomplished the feat as a freshman at the University of Oregon and was the 16th American to do it.

One has to wonder, if Rick had gone to the University of Oregon instead of Washington State, what difference Bill Bowerman could have had. Instead of putting a sub four minute miler in 10k races, the speed Rick demonstrated may have been put to different races and uses. If Rick could peel off a 54 second last lap in a three mile race at the AAU championships in 1970, he certainly could close a much shorter race with incredible speed.

His foot speed was there; in practice he could consistently peel of 24 second 200 meter intervals. In high school he once doubled and ran his 800 meter race in 1:50. Yet in college he never once competed in an 800 meter race.

Sacrifices

Running is a selfish pursuit.

There are teams and athletes that try and sacrifice for the good of the team in cross country, but ultimately, it is a selfish endeavor. Runners, for the most part, look to what they get out of the effort they give.

Gerry's spirit took a beating as a youth, and so physically punishing himself was an escape. For Rick, his spirit had always been indomitable, due to the fact that he could crush his body through a brutal and consistent workload. Now his body was unable to deliver and his spirit was taking all the hits.

Finishing his collegiate career in 1970, Rick began the unenviable position of trying to train for an Olympic summer two years away, with no facilities to train at, or athletes to train with. The very prop that had hurt him in college he needed most after leaving it.

There is a loneliness to long distance running, and Rick was becoming intimately acquainted with it while living in Grandview, Washington. Despite the town's impressive name there seemed to be nothing grand about the 3,605 people that were scattered near and far. Following his graduation and marriage, Rick took a job teaching in this small, isolated farming community near the middle of the state and surrounded by desert.

Graduating with a degree in English, Rick taught elementary school classes. Before school started Rick would get a run in and during his lunchtime he would sneak out for a jog on the grass track behind the school. After classes were done for the day and the students left, Rick would hit the roads out into nowhere, with no one with him and no one watching.

With the exception of his family, the only person aware of his efforts was Herm Caviness, Rick's high school coach.

Rick took consolation in the fact that another famous distance runner had done what he was now attempting: the impossible.

Bill Dellinger competed in the 1956, 1960, and 1964 Olympics. In the 1964 games Dellinger ran the 5,000 meter race. For nearly eight years after graduating from the University of Oregon, Dellinger trained, more or less, on his own.

In particular, Dellinger trained by himself in preparation for his final Olympics in Tokyo. Running along the beaches of Oregon on his own and in isolation, he kept in contact with his college coach. Bill Bowerman, who had architected Dellinger's success, continued to communicate with his athlete sending him workouts through letters. Dellinger ran the workouts on his own, often using time as the measurement against his effort and not distances. At the 1964 Olympics in Tokyo, Dellinger finished third in the 5,000 meter final; his highest placing in an Olympics.

In the isolation and obscurity of Grandview, Washington, Rick continued to train, hoping that the timing would be right for a run in the 1972 Olympics in Munich, Germany.

Time spent training for the Olympics was time spent without his kids. Rick knew he was sacrificing time.

Letters would come like a breath of oxygen. Rick would rip them open to see the workouts Herm had sent. One in particular sticks in his memory to this very day: 30 X 440 yards at race pace, with a 55 yard jog rest between intervals.

True to the task before him, Rick set out to run this workout. Next to the elementary school he worked at teaching English and Social Studies, sat a middle school. A grass track separated the two schools. On this grass track Rick ran all alone.

He followed the weekly workouts and wrote back to his coach the results and how he felt. Then he would wait.

Sure enough another letter with another workout: a six mile tempo run on the grass track.

Dutifully Rick ran a six mile tempo run on the track.

He started his watch and only kept track of the laps. On the final straightaway, as he passed the finish line he stopped his watch, looking at it for the first time. It took exactly 30 minutes

If I can make it through this...If I can do this ... Rick would say to himself.

Running brought everything else in order. His meals, his sleep, everything else took marching orders from his running. Nothing would detract from his ultimate goal.

The mental strength coupled with discipline built and revealed Rick's greatest character trait: endurance. Rick trained himself into the best shape of his life at the age of 24 and there was no one there to see it. He enjoyed the challenge. He enjoyed being outside. He enjoyed all the people and places that the sport had afforded him.

Running had become a lifelong love.

And yet it was not all joyful.

The passion for running did not eliminate heartache, injury, or setback. Satisfaction came from pushing the limits and finding out just exactly where they laid. He knew that at any point it could all come to a screeching halt, as it had for a number of years.

He had bristled alongside and met some of the greatest names and athletes of the sport. He saw on the track Arthur Lydiard, Mihaly Igloi, and Bill Bowerman, the coaches that changed distance running the world over. Whereas others would see the celebrity of these people and their accomplishments on the track, Rick saw their humanity.

On July 25, 1966 Jim Ryun set the world record in the mile at Berkeley running 3:51.3. Rick was on the United States national team and had competed in the 10,000 meter race the day before. Rick was trying to follow the steps of Gerry and moved up to the longer distances. Rick watched as Ryun set the world record in the mile. The accolades of the day went rightly to Ryun. After the meet John Lawson, a teammate of Ryun's from the University of Kansas, and Rick decided to go on a cool down run with Ryun. After they were able to get back to where the athletes were housed for the evening Rick stood just inside of earshot as Ryun got on the payphone and called back home to his parents.

Ryun stood, leaning against the phone booth, speaking softly into the receiver of the phone.

"Yeah, the race went well." Ryun said, rather breathless.

He paused as muffled voices echoed on the other end of the line.

"I ran 3:51.3." Ryun said.

Another pause from Ryun as muffled voices echoed on the other end.

"Yeah, I felt pretty good," Ryun said.

Rick could not believe what he was seeing and hearing. The world record holder was talking into the phone as if it were just another race.

There had also been the time Rick was in Europe with Prefontaine, Shorter, Savage, and others. The pace in practice runs was always sweet. Running at a race in New York Rick went on a training run with Billy Mills. And then there was Gerry Lindgren, teammate and local boy who he ran with and could never escape. While he was with these great runners, both in the time he was with them and every time thereafter, the conversations were always on things other than running. He saw the human side of them.

Frank was Frank, not Frank Shorter, Olympic star. Pre was Pre. Gerry was Gerry.

The unfortunate part of sacrifices, is the uncertainty of them. Not all sacrifices yield rewards.

Rick's late season injury in 1972 lead to successive surgeries on his achilles tendons on both legs. This effectively ended his Olympic dreams and his competitive running career. A life, up until that point, that had revolved around running, seemed to come to a close and there was no last great race to lay claim to because injury had seemingly robbed the sacrifice.

Frustrated and disheartened, but knowing that he gave ultimately everything he could to fulfill his dream, Rick had to hang up his competitive racing spikes. Rick had not realized however, just as he had bristled alongside others and been inspired by their humanity, he too had done the same for many others that followed.

Karel Lismont, left; Don Kardong, middle; Frank Shorter, right

Don Kardong and the Late Bloomers

It was the last weekend in May of 1966. Rick Riley, the Ferris Flier, came screaming home on the Pullman track in 8:48.13, setting the national high school two mile record. Meanwhile Don Kardong was just starting his last lap of the race, unnoticed by all the spectators in attendance.

Don had to merely look over his left shoulder to see the finish and hear the roar of the crowd in attendance.

Don was not lapped but he was not too far off of being lapped either. He had to keep his eyes up and try to finish the race that had already ended for others.

Down the backstretch he went, chasing the time in front of him, not knowing what his story would be. Around the curve he went, trying to give one last push to the finish.

He was welcomed with lukewarm applause as everyone in the stands was still trying to fathom what they had just witnessed on the track. Gerry had run in the Olympics and stood on the infield embracing his future teammate and what appeared to be a future Olympian in Rick.

There was a future Olympian on the track, but it was not the one who won the race with a new national record. It was not the lightweight, sure footed, five and a half foot tall, swift moving workhorse wearing red and white. It was not the young man who stood breathless in front of reporters mugging him for a sound bite after his near perfect performance. It was not the one who had visualized and worked for this moment tirelessly for his entire running career. It was not the confident young man, Rick Riley, standing atop the podium. Nor was it the kid-wonder, Gerry Lindgren, who had competed in the Olympics just two years previous and had stood on the infield that afternoon cheering on Rick.

Rather the future Olympian was the long, lanky kid, who had grown like a weed at six foot three inches tall, who had brown hair, pimples, and a perplexed look of pain on his face as he worked his way down the last hundred meters of the two mile race. It was this fatigued boy in the white and blue singlet of Seattle Prep who looked confused by what he had endured in the race. It was that long-legged fellow who had a poor start and who had remained at the back of the pack from the beginning. It was the kid that did not look like he was fit for the sport, let alone the podium. It was the boy who was struggling down lane one trying to find the air to breathe, the legs to move, and the will to make it one more step towards a ten minute two mile time. Don Kardong did not look like anything of what he would become. He would never win a state title in high school or a national title in college, but he would represent America's best hopes at the Olympics.

Distance races are snapshots into fitness and this picture was only the beginning of what would be an outstanding career for Don. Everyone else at the meet was distracted by the timing of others on that day.

The sixteenth and last place finisher of the two mile race at the state meet in 1966 would go on to represent team USA in Olympic glory. The eventual future of distance running in Spokane did not belong to Gerry or Rick. Perhaps the most impactful figure of distance running in the city of Spokane would not be a native of the town, but rather the gangly guy breathing as hard on his cool down as he did in his race. Don would bloom later in life and he allowed thousands of others to do the same.

Tracy Walters ran out of curiosity. Tracy came from a Ferris-like family only to coach a Rogers-type kid. Herm Caviness ran due to expectations. Herm came from a Rogers-type, blue collar, working family and coached a Ferris-like kid. Gerry Lindgren ran for significance. Rick Riley ran chasing a dream. Don Kardong ran only because he wanted to.

Born December 22, 1948 in Bellevue, Washington, Don had two older brothers he was always chasing. With a father working as a physician and a mother as a homemaker in what was once a sparsely populated part of the state, Don's existence growing up was like any other. His older brothers enjoyed sports and excelled at basketball. Don, seeing his height of six feet three inches as an asset in his freshman year, focused in on basketball as well.

Looking back over his years of running, Don can only guess as to why his PE teacher showed so much interest in him. Perhaps his Physical Education teacher saw stamina instead of shooting ability. During a two mile run test at the beginning of the year the PE teacher, who was also the cross country coach, kept track of the times of those coming through. He knew he needed to get Don to turn out for cross country, but he also knew that Don was motivated by basketball.

The PE teacher spoke with the basketball coach who in turn spoke with Don.

"What are you going to do to be in shape by the time basketball season comes around?" the basketball coach asked.

"I don't know." Don said.

"Why don't you turn out for cross country?" he said.

It was a new varsity sport at Seattle Pre. Don knew he needed to be able to run up and down the court without getting tired.

And with some indirect nudging from his PE teacher Don decided to turn out for cross country.

Seattle Prep may have had an eager coach, but the demands of the program paled in comparison to the workouts and workload that Gerry and Rick carried. Off of seemingly small amounts of mileage (30 to 40 miles a week) throughout his entire high school career, Don's times were impressive.

Timing truly was everything and nothing with Don.

His times on the track and the cross country course were good enough to put him near the top of the state by the end of his junior and senior seasons, but they were not stellar times and therefore meant nothing to college recruiters. What a college coach should have been able to see was Don's potential.

The volume of work was not there, but the intensity of that work never ceased. He made his marks matter with the time he had.

Don's greatest competition would come from himself. With that inward focus he was able to succeed. In order to lower his times on the track Don simply needed more time in practice.

Don's junior year in high school in 1965 had been a time of marked improvement. In cross country he took fifth overall at the state meet running 11:20 on the Green Lake course. He was chasing Rick and all those Spokane runners. Rick won in 10:52, Don Clarke of University High School took third. Right behind Don was another Ferris runner in sixth place named Jack Ishler, and in tenth there was another University runner Cliff Corey. Ferris as a team had taken third at state, Seattle Prep was fourth and University, lacking depth was seventh overall. These Spokane runners seemed to be everywhere, in the upper or lower division, and they seemed to be always near the front.

The results of running lined up in front of Don in the finishing chute, but the methods as to how to gain that success seemed a mystery to him.

Don's senior year he finished second at the state cross country meet running

© Seattle Prep High School Yearbook

a slower time of 11:24. Had Don simply run faster than his junior year time he would have won the race and Seattle Prep would have been sole victors that day for the smallest division schools with student populations under 1,100. Instead, Seattle Prep would tie with Wapato for first place in the team title. A bad case of senioritis sunk in as Don didn't even make it back to state track meet his senior year. He was a talented runner, just not the most focused during his senior year.

He had run decent times in high school with PR's of 4:30 in the mile and 9:24 in the two mile, but he was twenty-eight and a half seconds off of where Gerry had been in the mile and thirty-six seconds off where Rick had been in the two mile. While they were finishing Don would still have half a lap to 300 meters to go.

College coaches were distracted by the times with Don, not the potential he showed. As such, there were no scholarship offers to him.

As Don drove back to Seattle from Pullman after the state meet he wondered whether he would someday be making a return trip back to Pullman to attend Washington State University. The only other school he was considering and planning on applying to was Stanford University.

The warm weather, the allure of California, and admittance to Stanford were all it took for Don to make up his mind.

Stanford had a freshman cross country team that made no cuts; anyone could be on the team so long as they showed up to practice. Don decided he might try out for the team.

On Don's team was another freshman by the name of Duncan Macdonald who would end up being a future Olympian, running PR's of a 3:59.6 in the mile, 8:19 in the two mile, 13:19 for 5,000 meter, and a 28:31 for 10,000 meter. Before Duncan ran any of those times, he was just another guy trying out for the Stanford team, just as Don was a guy turning out for the freshman team. These two were a pair of late bloomers.

Don showed up to practice realizing that collegiate running demanded more. The intensity Don had brought to practice in high school remained the same; so too did the desire and expectation to run near the front of his team. Those running at Stanford were solid runners, competitive by all accounts and Don had to work hard to stay with those in front.

By the end of Don's freshman year at Stanford, his mile time dropped from a 4:30 to a 4:15. Don began to win a fair number of races he entered. His times showed he had entered into a realm of racing he had not known previously. Instead of being several hundred meters back from the leaders, Don was right next to, if not the winner. He was closing the gap on competition and sometimes putting some distance on it.

Intensity plus distance yielded results. Confidence came as a result of the process.

It was not necessarily talent that made a runner, but the ability to come to grips with pain. Don did not run away from pain but ran into it daily, and he became acquainted with what it meant to hurt. He went farther and farther with every run and effort.

During Don's sophomore year he was running on the varsity squad and was the only sophomore to do so. The varsity squad was full of upperclassmen. Duncan Macdonald, this future Olympian to be, was cut from the varsity squad in cross country and did not travel with the team. He too was still developing, but by the spring track season Macdonald was traveling with the varsity.

The University of Oregon and Washington State University were the schools to beat in the PAC 8, as well as the teams to eye for Nationals. Stanford was not on anyone's radar heading into the 1968 NCAA Cross Country Championship race in late November. On a windy Monday morning at Van Cortlandt Park in Bronx, New York Stanford shocked the running world by finishing second overall. Villanova won the championship scoring 78 points, their third straight title, but Stanford gave them all they could handle scoring an even 100. Don would finish fourth for his team and 39th overall running 30:28.

© Charles Dyer

The caliber of distance runners was increasing and so too were the number of athletes participating. The very distance in college cross country had shifted from four miles in 1965 to six miles in 1966. As the shift upward in distance at the college occurred, so too did eventually the distance of high school cross country shift upward. The push toward longer distances brought with it better times and renewed efforts. A wave of great distance runners were in the process of being developed. A championship caliber team could come from anywhere. The northwest did not have a monopoly on distance running in the United States; Stanford could win just as much as Oregon or Washington State.

In the late 1960s the structures of organizing a regional race to qualify for the national title had not been set up. At that time if a coach felt like his team could compete at Nationals and he could convince his athletic director to fund the trip, his team went. Don's junior year did not bring with it a great team success.

During Don's senior year in 1970 he went back individually to Nationals in cross country with a belief that he had a shot to win the race. He had gone from more or less waywardly deciding to walk on the team and try out for collegiate running in 1967, to saying to himself only four years later, *I think I could win this.*

The field of athletes in 1970 would be the largest NCAA Cross Country Championship race ever run. The gun was raised as a line of 307 individuals crouched. Don hunched down with 306 others, who were each on their own running odyssey.

Then the gun fired and a stampede of runners charged forward.

The previous course record was 29:40.1. There would be 82 athletes to run faster than the previous course record that day. The swell of improved distance runners occurred almost instantaneously and from all across the country.

The flat course in Virginia was ideal for Don; with his tall lengthy stride, hills were not to his advantage. Like the game of Hounds and Hares, there was one that shot to the front. Don Kardong was on a fast course amidst the nation's fastest runner: Pre. It took Don nearly four and a half miles to chase down Pre and match his pace.

Pre, sensing that he was not running by himself, which he had become accustomed to at National races, looked over his shoulder to see Don and his Stanford jersey. Then Pre resettled his focus in front of him and threw it into another gear, gaining back the proportionate lead he had held previously.

Pre went on to win the race in 28:00.2. Don finished third in 28:10. Also in the race was Marty Liquori who was the third high school runner ever to break four minutes in the mile. Marty finished ninth. Steve Savage was also in the race and on Oregon's team. Steve would be a future Olympian in 1972 running the steeplechase. Pat Tyson was in the race and was Oregon's sixth and last runner in; he placed 79th overall. Pat's time would have set the new course record, had there not been 78 runners in front of him.

The University of Oregon was originally given the title and believed they had won. Yet, one of Villanova's athletes, Les Nagy, realized upon looking at the results that he was misplaced. He had passed people and fell in the finishing chute of the race, and was misplaced by five spots. Instead of losing by three points they had won by one point. Luckily, there was race footage of the finish to verify that Les Nagy had finished 62nd overall. Oregon lost the title by a single point.

Don Kardong, who had previously finished hundreds of meters back of the nation's best, was able to now look into the eyes of Pre during the closing stages of the race. This was the same Pre who had gone on to take Riley's 8:48.13 two mile national record and run away with it to a lowered time of 8:41.5. Don had essentially closed the gap on the best in the world, surpassing any expectation because there had been no expectations placed upon him.

Don's senior year of track in college would not mirror his senior year of high school. There would be no senioritis or lack of focus; Don was near the best in the country and he knew it.

As the track season neared the championship races, Stanford faced off against Oregon in the PAC 8 Championships. Pre was slated to run the three mile and Don was waiting for him. Don would have somewhat of an advantage by only running and focusing in on the three mile race; Pre was running in his second race, having already won at another distance earlier. Don had fresh legs, Pre's had been burned a bit.

The race started and Pre took the lead as was customary, wanting to make sure it was a good honest pace and honest effort being put forward by everyone. Don was not afraid of the pace. The last time they had met in a championship atmosphere Don had come back and finished only 10 seconds off the man in front of him.

The race continued and the laps continued to be clicked off like a metronome. The pace was quick, the pursuers were dropping off till it was just Pre and Don, in that order, separated by a second or two. Pre made a stronger move to separate with about a lap and a half to go. Don, instinctively responded to the surge and then passed Pre.

Don went from not even being in the discussion of being a distance power

© John Lindstrom

four years previous, to nearly catching the nation's best in cross country that fall, to passing Pre. Don put a few yards of separation on Pre.

Don, the late bloomer was coming into his own in late spring of 1971.

The pace was fast, the track was hot, and Don's feet were burning up. Pre then did what made Pre, Pre: he responded. He found yet another gear and passed Don who was fighting and trying to keep form as they went to the tape. Pre reopened his lead and won yet again.

After the race Don received the highest compliment he would ever receive from Pre who spoke to him as they cooled down.

"Had you kept that pace as you passed me I don't think I would have been able to catch you." Pre said.

Don had made Pre question, if only for a moment, his own abilities.

If there was solace for Don, it was that he had earned and owned every effort to bring himself to this moment. The PAC 8 Championships were over, but redemption could be found at the National Championship race that was hosted in Don's hometown of Seattle that year. Don's running odyssey could be complete, he could beat the mythical beast known as Pre; the man whose name was synonymous with success.

Yet, for all the preparation, for all the work, for all the effort and toil and the storybook ending setup, it would be a nightmare race in Seattle at the National Championships. Don finished eighth out of 11 competitors. He was 28 seconds back from Pre and the leaders; once more he was half a lap back, looking over his left shoulder to see the finish and hear the cries of victory for Pre.

Don ran his worst race at the biggest moment and in front of those who knew him well. He hung his head and wanted to disappear from those who had shown up to cheer. Bitterness, sadness, and anger welled up within him as he walked off the track. He knew he was better than the race he had run. Perhaps, he thought, he had peaked previously at the PAC 8 Championships. In the parlance of other sports when teams drop the ball or lay an egg after a great endeavor, Don had laid an egg. One year previous, at the NCAA Track Championships in the three mile, Don had finished fourth and had been only six seconds back of Pre, who was the winner in the previous year as well.

Don's distance coach at Stanford, Marshall Clark, got a hold of Don who was red faced as he came off the track. Don was red faced not so much from the heat or the effort, but the embarrassment of performing so poorly. Grabbing hold of Don and looking him in the eye, Coach Clark told Don exactly what he needed to hear.

"I know how you feel, but don't let one bad race, even an important one like this, be how you judge your running career," he said.

It took a coach with several seasons in the sport to know how to approach his athlete at this critical time. He did not want Don to let one moment take away his momentum. There was defeat but he was not to be defeated. Other races would be run, there was only one year remaining until the 1972 Olympics in Munich. He was still on the rise.

Don needed to remember how far he had come and who he was rubbing shoulders with in competition. Earlier in his college running he had lined up as the anchor leg of a 4 X 800 meter relay team at a meet in Modesto, California. Standing to his right was Jim Ryun, anchoring for the University of Kansas, and standing to his left was Marty Liquori, anchoring for the University of Villanova. He was running against the best in the country and the world at the time, and Don should have taken solace from the fact that he was still improving. The trajectory of his running career showed he still had everything to run for. Competing against himself, Don was winning each time he stepped out on the track.

Winning is relative.

Pre had just won the 5,000 meter NCAA title in 1971 but the fastest time on that University of Washington track still belonged to Gerry Lindgren who had run 27 seconds faster. Gerry ran that in the cold and the wind, not the warmth and windless day Pre had before him. Had the ghost of Gerry been in the race, Pre would have been in the position of Don.

There is always somebody faster out there.

Munich

There would be more heartache and heartbreak for Don Kardong after he left the track in Seattle; he just didn't know it yet. If he were to reach the highest peaks running had to offer, he still had some of its greatest valleys to delve into.

Wanting to prove he was one of the top competitors in the country, Don entered the 1972 Olympic Trials in both the marathon and the 10,000 meter. Wanting to punch his ticket to Munich, Don had continued to train and had upped his mileage to 140 miles a week, significantly more mileage than he had ever ran before. After graduating he continued to live very cheaply at Stanford and trained with Duncan Macdonald, who was in his last year there.

The absolute dedication and concentration to a singular goal brought with it results. Don made his first USA national team and competed internationally against the Soviets in indoor meets. The increase in mileage, accompanied with a team USA singlet brought Don confidence. The Hare that was running just out of reach was the Olympics.

However, an unexpected case of mononucleosis caused Don to pull back the reins on his training heading into the trials. He had to do his best despite the difficulties that were before him.

Toeing the line of the 10,000 meter final on July 2, 1972, Don Kardong stood just meters away from Gerry Lindgren who was in his last attempt to make the Olympics. The heat was sweltering at 95 degrees and the sweat was pouring out of everyone before the race had started. The 12 athletes at the line had already gone through one preliminary heat. Don had finished sixth and therefore qualified for the final. Gerry had finished fourth, and the winner of their heat was none other than Frank Shorter, who was now the favorite.

The race started and Frank kept the pace honest for the first two miles going through in 4:25.4 and 8:58.5. The quick pace and the heat helped string out the field. Gerry would eventually drop out. Don continued on, but lagging near the back of the chase pack.

The heat was too much. Frank went on to win in 28:35. Don finished sixth in 30:21. Tired and sweaty, having run two races in three days, Don left the track knowing he had one week before he would have his last chance to make the Olympic team. He hoped he hadn't spent useless energy that he would need in his next race.

Lining up for the marathon early on the morning of July 9, 1972 in Eugene, Don still kept alight the hope and the dream that everything might break his way. In spite of the mono, something of those 140 mile weeks had to have stuck to his legs, lungs, and heart.

The gun fired and Frank Shorter and Kenny Moore took off from the field early. In the second pack ran Jack Bacheler, Frank Shorter's training partner at the Florida Athletic Club, followed by Jeff Galloway, Greg Brock, and Don Kardong. Only the top three from each event move on to the Olympics, and in the pack of four only one would advance.

The race continued and the dream started to slip.

Mile after mile came, and mile after mile, the separation that at first was two feet, became five feet, which became thirty, which became a hundred. Don kept giving everything he had, he just did not have enough. With legs zapped he fought on, hoping someone ahead of him might have dropped out.

Kenny Moore and Frank Shorter would tie as they went to the finish, clocking 2:15:58. Jack Bacheler and Jeff Galloway would also be clocked with the same time at the finish but Bacheler out-leaned Galloway and earned the final Olympic spot running 2:20:30. Coming in sixth in the country was Don Kardong, clocking 2:22:42. After 26.2 miles, there was only two minutes and twelve seconds that kept Don from his dream.

Tired and unrecognized by the news media, Don walked away from the finish realizing that his next opportunity to make it to the Olympics was four years away. He had given an Olympic effort, it just did not lead to an Olympic opportunity. Taking sixth twice was an honor, but it did not feel like it at the moment.

Sixth felt as forgotten as sixtieth.

Knowing that he could not hang out in California for another four years, Don decided to re-enter school and get another degree at the University of Washington. For two years he worked on and earned a degree in English with a teaching certificate. School kept his mind busy between the training runs.

During this time, Don also joined Club Northwest. Frank Shorter and his training partners had been part of the Florida Athletic Club. The club system was a way for athletes who had graduated from college to continue to train with other athletes in a similar situation. They could continue to compete against the best while holding on to their amateur status. It was like the professional circuit of running, just without any real sponsorship or payment.

Don's teammates at Club Northwest included Pat Tyson and Rick Riley. This did not mean that they trained with one another, but when meets occurred, they all lined up wearing the Club Northwest singlet. Most of the athletes were self coached, and that included Don.

Training, studying, and living as cheaply as he could, Don went about keeping alive his Olympic dreams. He found a training partner, Jim Johnson, a steeplechase runner, who wanted to lower his times as well. These two would head off for workouts together, and alternate workouts that favored one another's goals. While Don knew he was not a miler, he still wanted to break four. His events were still in the longer races, but for a time he put all his efforts to breaking the mark.

At an all-comers meet in the West-Seattle Stadium, Don paid a fifty cent entry fee all so that he could compete in the mile. Donning his Club Northwest jersey, he went out to try and break four minutes.

Jim Johnson ran as rabbit for the first three laps of the race, leading Don to 3:02. The last lap was Don's alone. On he went, struggling and fighting, while a hundred or so spectators in the stands began to cheer as they saw a man possessed pushing himself around the curve. Those in the stands watched as this long haired, lanky runner was running up against the impossible.

Down the homestretch Don charged, not giving up and not giving in to the lack of oxygen. Through the finish he lunged.

4:01.9.

It was the closest he would ever come to breaking four minutes in the mile. The speed showed, however, that Don's training was effective. He had come a long way since that two mile race at the state meet in Pullman, but he still had a ways to go.

Steve Jones, Stanford's seventh man on their cross country team in the late sixties and early seventies had walked onto the team. Steve was from Spokane and ran at Rogers High School under coach Tracy Walters. Steve even lived with the Walters family for a time. On November 20, 1965, Steve finished fifth at the state meet during his senior year. He finished second for Rogers that day behind Vern Deahl, who took second overall. Rogers would have four of their top five runners in the top nine spots. They won the meet handily with 24 points. Steve had seen the transformation at Rogers and had trained during his sophomore year, watching as Gerry Lindgren was a senior.

On the same day that Steve finished fifth, Don finished fifth in the lower division as he watched Rick Riley take the title.

As teammates at Stanford, Steve and Don became quick friends who shared experiences: both walked onto the team and both were from Washington. Steve spoke highly of his former coach and the athlete Gerry Lindgren, who all distance runners knew at the time.

Over the years, Steve and Don kept in touch and finally Steve suggested that Don come to Spokane to help out with a summer camp called Camp Reed, overseen by Tracy Walters.

Don decided to take the trip.

At the camp led by Tracy, Don would get a nickname from the camp counselors, 'Dingy' Don Kardong. He would also end up getting Tracy as a new coach. Don made the move to Spokane where he found a teaching post and had a former Olympic coach.

Teaching at Loma-Vista Elementary School in Spokane, just north of Shadle Park High School and just down the street from Rogers, Don would start and end his work day by venturing out in the dark to train.

Occasionally the Amateur Athletic Union (AAU) would call Don up and ask him to race. They informed him that they could not get Frank Shorter to run in a race, but they were wondering if he would be willing to run in Rio, Brazil in the 5,000 meter. Don would go. The same was true of his trip to China. He left and then came back to Spokane, back to his sixth grade class, and back to the after school sports he helped out with, only to be exhausted. After the teaching schedule Don would hit the roads, often training in the dark and alone.

Into the darkness he went daily, keeping alight his dreams.

And each day, Don would be back in his classroom, trying to inspire tomorrow's youth. He would have to prepare lesson plans, grade, and be prepared to be evaluated by a principal. The other teachers at the school

© Track & Field News

Don Kardong leading the 5,000m race in the 1976 Olympic trials

did not understand the significance of Don's training or what he was trying to do. He was just the tall skinny teacher, teaching sixth grade at the end of the hall who apparently liked to run for some reason.

Week after week, month after month, the routine continued and so too did the resolve.

Tracy would meet up with Don to watch him go through a workout on the track and he would be there to help Don realize when he had done enough. With great athletes, it becomes necessary for a coach to come in and not so much maneuver big shifts in style, but rather fine tune the athlete before them. Tracy would be there to encourage, and then to help Don see that another interval was not as necessary as some good rest and recovery. Don's ambition was high, but the workload needed to be balanced with rest. Instead of two more intervals at the end, Tracy had the ability to see that two more wouldn't be as beneficial, no matter the time run.

Montreal

Once more, Don made his way down to Eugene, Oregon. This time he went to participate in the 1976 Olympic trials. It was his second and last attempt at achieving his dreams. He was slated to run in the marathon and the 5,000 meter race. Four years had passed, and Don returned to a place that had previously held disappointment.

Thousands of miles, thousands of intervals, thousands of practices had come and gone, thousands upon thousands of calories had been burnt and left remaining was a six foot three inch man burning for one last chance.

Unlike four years previous, the marathon would be raced first and then the track races were run.

Don lined up on Saturday May 22, 1976 against Frank Shorter, the reigning gold medalist, and this new talent, Bill Rodgers, who had won the Boston Marathon in 1975. Don stood, ready to give all that he had for one of three spots. 77 men with similar aspirations, similar workouts, similar scheming and dreaming for the past four years lined up and waited for the gun to fire.

The race began and of the 77 to start the race, only 49 would finish.

Sitting in the stands at Hayward Field was Rick Riley. He listened as the PA announcer gave updates of the race. It was just like when he was first introduced to the sport; when Gerry's ghost had run around the track before his eyes.

Rick had trained with Don occassionally and wanted to see how he would do. Rick's own Olympic dreams had been taken due to injury. He sat before that oval that had given him so much in his life.

The fans at Hayward Field started to get excited and restless, knowing that soon the runners would be entering in the stadium. Shorter had been training under the Florida Athletic Club jersey in the southeast United States, Rodgers was from the northeast. The local fans in Eugene enjoyed seeing greatness but they wanted someone more local to cheer for and call their own.

Entering the stadium came Shorter. Rick had been close enough to touch his jersey once, but now could only view him from the stands.

The crowd applauded and Rick did as well.

Shortly after Shorter entered, Rodgers came on the track greeted with another round of applause.

Shorter and Rodgers would finish in that order running 2:11:51 and 2:11:58 respectively. The question now became: Who will be the third one going to Montreal?

Rick's running experience taught him that everything needed to come together for someone to emerge on the world stage. The coach, the work, the health, the mechanics, the desire, the discipline; it was all needed.

The educated track fans of Eugene waited. From seemingly out of nowhere emerged the tall lanky form of Don.

Rick stood, as did the rest of the fans in Eugene and cheered.

Wearing his Club Northwest jersey and with a grateful crowd cheering him on, Don made his way around the track. Fourth place was a minute behind. Rick shouted for his friend. Don was on his way to Montreal in the marathon.

Don's race plan mirrored the trajectory of his life. He had to run within himself and stayed back the first 10 miles of the race. Don worked his way forward through the field. At mile 15 Don was 12th place. He continued to hold on and improved his position to seventh by mile 20. At mile 21 Don moved into fourth place. In the very late stages of the race, between miles 22 and 23, Don made one last move to separate and finish third in 2:13:54.

The late bloomer was moving on to Montreal.

Weeks would go by before Don would return to Eugene and run in the 5,000 meter heats and final, but a fourth place finish in the event left him focused solely on the marathon. Entering the race in Montreal, Shorter and Rodgers were clearly the American favorites. Lasse Viren of Finland was also a favorite to win. Don was not expected to medal.

67 athletes got ready to race in the final event of the Olympics. Seven would drop out of the race. Off they went, chasing their Olympic dreams. Some of them went running with clean efforts and others ran with the effects of performance enhancing drugs.

The unexpected winner was Waldemar Cierpinski, representing East Germany. Frank Shorter, the reigning champ, finished 50 seconds back in second place. The battle for third was being fought out with Don Kardong and Karel Lismont of Belgium. On the road leading down towards the track Lismont surged pulling away from Don. Around the track they went.

Lismont took third in 2:11:12 and Don finished fourth 2:11:15.

After four years of tireless effort, countless miles, workouts and intervals, and after 26.2 miles of effort, there were three seconds that kept Don from being one of the top three on the medal podium.

Years would go by before documents would uncover the fact that hundreds of athletes representing East Germany were part of a state sponsored and covertly run performance enhancing drug program. Cierpinski's name was one of those known to have cheated. Yet still his medal is held and the standings remain. Don was shut out of his Olympic medal because of another athletes lack of integrity.

Drug cheats had entered the world of sport and they are unfortunately now a permanent staple of all athletic competition. Shorter was cheated out of his second gold medal and Don was cheated out of his bronze. Athletes who have figured out how to game the drug tests are continuing to perform undetected because they are simply one step ahead of the test makers.

Don returned back to Spokane after the Olympics, thinking not so much about the race he had just finished, but about an experience he had in preparation for the Olympics. One road race in the Southeastern United States would forever change Spokane and the Northwest.

Bloomsday

Time helps put in perspective what Don accomplished in Montreal and in subsequent races. Even though he finished fourth overall, he was one spot ahead of Lasse Viren. Running against Lasse Viren, Don has a 3 win and 1 loss record. The only time Don lost to Viren came in 1972 during the summer leading up to the Olympics. That one loss to Viren came at a race in Norway, at 10,000 meters. Don ended up getting lapped by Viren. Don could never beat Pre in any race he ran against him. And Pre could never beat Viren. Such is the unusual and unlucky fate of pitting the world's best against each other in races. The unfortunate reality is that wins and losses are determined with less than a handful of people getting recognized or remembered.

Returning from the Olympics, Don went back to Loma-Vista Elementary school and the lesson plans of his sixth grade class.

Don kept training and racing. He also opened up a running shoe store in Spokane with his friend, Rick Riley. They called the store *The Human Race*.

Don's life changed when he competed at the *Peachtree Road Race* located in Atlanta, Georgia on July 4, 1976. Don ran alongside Bill Rodgers as both used it as the final race to tune up for the marathon in Montreal. Don would win the race, but what amazed him were the number of finishers; over 2,000 local runners showed up to race.

Don had never seen so many people show up for a 10k road race. Heading back to Spokane, a place known for its runners, Don wondered if he could start such a race in Spokane. There had been small fun runs put on by local enthusiasts but the numbers never crept much over a hundred.

After the Olympics, Don was at Spokane's City Hall when both he and the mayor stepped into the elevator at the same time. The mayor recognized this newly adopted local-boy hero.

"You're that guy that ran in the Olympic marathon," Mayor Rodgers said.

"Yes I am," said Don.

"I read what you said in the newspaper about having a big local race. You know I grew up in Boston and they ran the marathon through the town and I think we ought to do something like that here in Spokane," Mayor Rodgers said.

Spokane after all, had finished up hosting a world's fair in 1974 and had revitalized their downtown area to host the event.

Mayor Rodgers wanted to have the race be a marathon, the likes of which to compete against Boston, but Don settled in on a 12k distance that would start and end in downtown. To figure out how to put on such a road race, he talked with Herm Caviness who had run the Spokane Summer Games.

Herm gave Don all the information and suggestions he could, saying to him as they last parted, "The sky's the limit."

Just how big that sky was, no one at the time knew.

The inaugural Bloomsday Race in 1977 brought with it over 1,198 participants, one of which was a friend of Don's, Frank Shorter. Frank showed up and won the race with Don taking third. The number of participants may not seem large now, but in 1977 it was huge. *Peachtree*, the inspiration for Bloomsday, had just over one hundred participants in its first race in 1970. Hitting over a thousand was a huge success from the very beginning.

The second year, Don again phoned his buddy and former teammate Frank. Unfortunately, he couldn't make it. Don hung up and decided to call up another running friend and former teammate, Bill Rodgers. The conversation went well and Bill said he could do it. He made the trip and won the second running of the race with 5,024 competitors.

By the third year of the race the number of participants had already reached 10,070. When the fifth year of the race came around, Don called up his former college teammate and Olympic friend Duncan Macdonald and asked if he would come and race; he did and he won. By the fifth year the race had over 15,546 competitors. Year after year, local runners continued to show up, and year after year the population swelled.

When most people think of the biggest road races in America, they think of the Boston Marathon, the New York Marathon, or the Chicago Marathon. However, in a list of the top ten road races of all time in the United States, the second largest race ever on American soil was run on the streets of downtown Spokane. The largest footrace in America took place on May 18, 1986 at the *Bay to Breakers 12k Race* in San Francisco, California. Ed Eyestone, now coach of Brigham Young University, won the race beating the roughly 110,000 people behind him.

The second largest road race to ever take place on American soil, took place in Spokane on May 5, 1996 where there were 61,298 participants. This town hosted not only the second largest road race in America, it was also the tenth largest road race ever run in the world.

The very name of the race indicates Don's belief that anyone can have their day. Bloomsday is a play on words. Bloom's day is in reference to James' Joyce's classic *Ulysses.* Leopold Bloom is the protagonist and the story revolves around his movements during one day. The story is analogous to the Odyssey taken by Ulysses after the Trojan War. Taking that belief that everyone could have their own odyssey, their own story, Don combined the nickname of Spokane, the Lilac City, with Bloomsday, thus making the official title of the race, The Lilac Bloomsday Run. However, most local Spokane runners simply refer to it as Bloomsday.

Don's race has forever changed Spokane on a large scale. Old and young, male and female, able bodied and otherwise, people have bought into the Bloomsday message. Each spring the masses in Spokane and the surrounding areas are out on the roads training for that 12k race. Four decades have passed and still the race continues. Not all road races attract the masses. Some road races that gained popularity initially eventually died out in Spokane.

Each generation acts as the baton carrier of beliefs and values. Spokane's initial surge in running prominence due to the efforts of Tracy, Herm, Gerry, Rick, and Don could have been nothing more than a passing fad. Spokane's running craze could end with each generation, and yet it has managed to survive.

What Don did on a large scale, a fellow Club Northwest teammate continues to do as he prepares each generation to grip the baton and grab hold of the belief that life can work out for them.

Pat Tyson: Growing Up Never Saying No

Pat Tyson has an incredible track record and yet he has no track to call his own. Both parts of that statement are true. First the track record.

Pat has coached seven individuals to Foot Locker Nationals: Chris Lewis, Greg Kuntz, brothers Matthew and Micah Davis, Skiy Detray, Jesse Fayant, and Evan Garber. His highest placing individual finisher at Nationals was Matthew Davis who was third overall behind Meb Keflezighi and Adam Goucher. Meb Keflezighi would be a silver medalist in the Olympic marathon for the USA during the Athens Olympics and Adam Goucher would be an Olympian representing the USA in the 5,000 meter at the Sydney Olympics. These were the types of blue chip athletes that Tyson had to prepare his teams to compete against and he was able to do so, year after year, and team after team.

In 1986, in Pat Tyson's first year at Mead High School, he pulled an improbable upset at regionals to get his team to state where they finished ninth. In 1987 the team failed to qualify but the individual state cross country champion was Chris Lewis from Mead High School. That would be the only year of Pat's career at Mead that his team was absent from the state meet and it would be the only year that they were not on the podium.

Pat's Mead Panthers won nine straight state 3A Cross Country Boy's team titles from 1989-1996 (3A being the largest classification in the state of Washington at that time). There would be an additional string of three straight state titles from 2000-2002. There were three, second place finishes: 1997, 1998, 2004. There were two third place finishes: 1999 and 2003. All total he won 12 state titles at Mead High School during a coaching stint lasting 19 years. All total he was on the podium with his teams at Mead 17 times. For nearly two decades there was one coach and team to beat: Pat Tyson and the Mead Panthers.

Pat's 1993 squad was arguably one of the best high school teams ever assembled, as they ran a near perfect score of 20 at the state meet (a perfect team score is 15). This team was rightfully ranked #1 in the nation by Harrier magazine. This 1993 team had three future Foot Locker finalists on it.

When Nike Team Nationals had their inaugural race in 2004 (now Nike Cross Nationals), Pat's team was aptly named Tyson's Army and they placed third in the country.

This is Pat's track record. He now coaches at Gonzaga University and is in the process of transforming this college program. As to why Pat has no track to call his own you have to first step back and see what makes Pat, Pat.

Before Pat was a coach and before he was an athlete, he was a kid growing up in the gray rain-filled sky of south Tacoma, Washington. In the city nicknamed *The City of Destiny*, Pat grew up with less hopeful circumstances than the city's slogan indicated. He was the youngest of four brothers who were spread out in age and were even more distant in their relationships with one another. Part of this lack of connection came because of their father's absence from the home. Pat's father was not welcomed there because he womanized. Pat's mother discovered his indiscretions and cut him off from the family.

On a spring day in the late fifties, young seven-year-old Pat was at home when his mother informed him that his father had died of cancer in a hospital in Seattle. People began to show up. Pat moved around in the backyard, trying to play and distract himself from what it all meant. Had he been older and with a car he would have been driving away from the situation, but he was a kid and confined to the world around his neighborhood.

A sad situation could have been sadder still had Pat's mother not set a proper pattern of living for Pat to emulate. It may not have seemed like the future of thousands of people were hanging in the balance at that moment, as this widow was trying to piece together her own life and the lives of her children, but she was in reality affecting the outlook of more than just her youngest child.

Pat's mother was, after all, alone and raising her children without their father in the 1960s. And so with his mother's encouragement and example, Pat continued to dream, work, save, and to prepare for his future. Growing up in a blue collar neighborhood where work, toil, and saving were a part of life would prove ever useful for Pat. He learned to save because his mother was forced to save. Pat may have been without a father but his mother did her best to act for two. He picked up on her cues. During the summers Pat picked blueberries as a means of saving money. Pennies were made to be stretched and pinched. She could not control her circumstances but she did not let her circumstances control her outlook.

Pat learned about effort, sacrifice, and serving from a mother that did not complain. Before he ever learned about the widow's mite from church, Pat saw that sermon lived out daily in his home in south Tacoma. They may not have had much, but what they had he knew his mother had given all to achieve. She did so without demands. She did not force her boys to go to church but they all went to the local Baptist church each Sunday.

Rarely would Pat's mother say no to anything she faced and she taught this perspective to her children. She did not say no to the opportunities, to the hardships, to the realities of life; she owned them with all her might.

When Pat initially wanted to pursue an interest in playing the horn for the school's band in middle school, she supported Pat. She believed in his dreams no matter where they were or what they sounded like inside the cramped quarters of their small house. Pat took to playing and enjoyed it; the poor notes had to be played if rich notes would ever be developed. Fostering that belief changed Pat's life and generations untold. Pat never became a world renowned musician because another love in life stole his ears, eyes, and heart with it's transformative beat and rhythm.

Life on the streets in south Tacoma in the 1960s was challenging. Spread around the city were good families trying to sustain their neighborhoods. However, the neighborhoods were tough. There were those few kids in the area that took to bullying those around them and Pat was on the receiving end of cigarette butts being put out on him. He saw that he had to deal with problems head on.

Using his pleasing personality and his swift early speed, Pat would sneak into neighboring garage dustbins to steal empty glass beer bottles. He would exchange the bottles for money at the recycling plant and then use the proceeds to do one of two things: save some money for later or buy candy to share with neighbor kids. Acting as a Robin Hood of sorts, Pat found he needed to be resourceful when all but hard times surrounded him. His quick speed and sweet offering allowed him to gain one of the most precious commodities in life: friends.

One of Pat's friends invited him to turn out for track and field his first year

© Lincolnian Yearbook, Tacoma Public Schools

of high school. Pat was on the lookout for others like his mother, those that were good people who offered him encouragement. Pat was hungry for acknowledgment of his existence. He wanted to be connected to something good, something positive, something that he could have hope in. Pushing against the obstacles of his environment would only be halfway helpful to Pat; he needed someone pulling for him on the other side to help him out. That someone was none other Lincoln High School's Track and Cross Country Coach Dan Watson.

Dan was a Science teacher and coach who had a passion for all things related to track and field. His scientific mind enjoyed gathering the facts and figures, as well as the tables and charts showing the records, interviews, and workouts contained in the *Track and Field News* magazine. Growing up in Colorado, Dan competed in track and field at Fruita High School, where he won a state championship in the 110 yard dash. His curiosity mixed with his passion for the sport infected the athletes around him.

Dan would be a legendary coach, guiding Lincoln to six Washington State Track and Field Championships during a nine year coaching span (68-70, 72-73, and 76). Pat was part of that first team title at state, where he ran the two mile.

More than a coach, Dan was the father figure that Pat had never had growing up. He provided a place where work and effort would not only be recognized, but rewarded. Dan took an interest in Pat and all his athletes, something that Pat would not soon forget and something which he would emulate himself as a future coach.

All athletes crave acknowledgement; the kind of acknowledgement that rewards hard work with more work. The opportunity of time was both a variable and a constant. Dan helped take the mystery out of success by fostering faith in his athletes and fueling their desires with opportunities to learn.

Dan had *Track and Field News* lying around the clubhouse that his athletes met at each day. He knew the sport and could speak of the current events. He modeled what a fan of the sport should say, think, and feel about it. Dan also took Pat to local meets that housed some of the finest talent. While sitting with Pat at these meets Dan would help him understand the vocabulary, methods, and the meaning behind times and distances. He helped Pat put in context what the numbers meant. It is hard to believe there was a time when Pat knew nothing about distance running, but he was guided and taken under the wing of someone who cared about him and who would explain to him just what it all meant.

And that meant everything to Pat.

A kid from south Tacoma being raised by a single mother knows kindness when he sees it and would do anything to keep that feeling close and consistently felt.

These early impressions of the sport and the relationship between athlete and coach would be the blueprints Pat used for his future success as a coach.

Getting Lost in a Dream

The trumpet that had kept Pat company in middle school and spoke back to him the notes he echoed into it, finally silenced. Instead of being one in a line of chairs sitting in a band room, Pat became an athlete known by name to his coach. Dan provided solo instruction and helped breathe life into Pat's vision of himself.

Dan saw through his horn-rimmed glasses the young men floating by in his classes and in the halls. He saw beyond those boys trying to grow facial hair; he saw their insecurities, their vulnerabilities, and most importantly he saw their capabilities. He made sure that those floating in and out of his office felt included, not excluded. More important than any times these athletes would run would be the time that they felt important. From the least athlete to the greatest, he would explain the sport and offer opportunities for them to invest themselves in their efforts. The law of the harvest rules the world or running. Invest a little and you get a little back; doubling the investment could double or triple the yield.

Nothing was forced or coerced: everything was voluntary. If anyone wanted to push themselves to success, that was their right. There would be no cap to what someone was willing to invest. Pat quickly felt the effects of physical exercise that demanded his best efforts each day. He also felt the joy that came from trying to show his best to his coach.

Part of Pat's dream was to become one of the best distance runners around. Learning as he went, he continued to take care of the details. Pat learned from Dan that he should not envy success, but rather he should emulate it.

Young Pat, in the days before internet, cell phones, gaming systems, social media, and distractions of all types, focused in on finding out more about his passion. It was not enough to have his morning run,

© Lincolnian Yearbook, Tacoma Public Schools

his check in with his coach during the day, and then his afternoon run with teammates. It was not enough to be part of the team and associated with those of like mind and goals; he needed more.

The structure of success he saw outlined by his coach helped Pat see that the future was not set in stone. After school came practice and after practice came homework, then after homework came a chance to run over to the public library. On those dark rainy nights in 1965 Pat would ride the city bus to the Tacoma Public Library. He walked in and found the local papers, turned to the sports section and read up on what was happening with Gerry Lindgren and this new runner on the scene, Rick Riley.

Amidst a sea of books, words, and worlds both real and imagined, Pat picked out the select voices that spoke to him. Words were held silent until he breathed life into them and then they would echo inside of him. Pat shut other doors, other avenues, and focused in on breathing life into his running dreams.

Reading about the success of others gave him hope and reinforced his desire to work.

This would be his great adventure.

These would be his people.

Pat would know them before they ever would know him.

The glow of adventure, of learning, and discovering this world of running, Pat found in the creases and folds of black and white newspapers. Gerry and Rick had come out of Washington State. Pat was also in Washington. This was not some far away dream, but it was only a mountain range and desert away.

The ink of those papers would rub off on Pat's fingers as he turned the pages. But as quickly as Pat arrived it seemed that the library was closing. Pat would quickly close the papers, return them back to the proper place and then carry with him the smudges of statistics, times, and storylines that resonated within him.

The world was at his fingertips.

The world he immersed himself in rubbed off on him.

He stared out the windows of the bus on his return trips home; sitting around people coming or going from late shifts that sucked away their lives.

Night after night the time would come to leave, the lights would turn out in the library, and Pat sat on another bus heading towards home. While he sat on the bus his memory would run over the details he had just read. The relay of his dream revolved around the routines he had outlined to achieve his goals: morning runs, afternoon runs, hard days, easy days, long runs and short runs with all their opposites acting as bookends to one another. These were the high and low notes to a symphony of experience.

Spokane seemed to be the Juilliard of distance running at the time. Rick was still in high school and nearing graduation while Gerry had seemingly won or nearly won every race he entered. Pat decided to put his voice on paper by penning a letter to Rick Riley on the other side of the state. Pat was a sophomore in high school at the start of his career and Rick was a senior in high school on the cusp of setting the national two mile record. As Gerry had been an inspiration to Rick, Rick was now an inspiration to Pat.

Pat, excited by the idea, explained to his mom that he was going to write to Rick on the other side of the state. She did not discourage her son's efforts. She did not put out this fire burning within her son. She did not say no in word, body language, or demeanor. Pat's letter was stamped, addressed, and dropped into the mail.

Time went by.

Pat continued his rituals of running, studying, and heading to the library; feeding the desire to know and be a part of something larger than himself. Statistics and articles on his favorite running athletes acted as food for his dreams; they sustained him from day to day.

And yet days came and went in silence.

Smudges from the newspapers were found on Pat's fingers at the end of each day. He wanted the greatness of Rick and Gerry to rub off on him.

After practice Pat walked through the front door of his house. Sitting on the floor in front of the door sat a letter addressed to him.

Opening the letter carefully, Pat pulled the contents out.

The voice he had only heard through the newspaper which was meant for the nameless, faceless masses, was now directed squarely at him. Pat had thrown his dreams into the unknown and now he was hearing back from it.

Rick kindly responded with training advice and even invited Pat to come over to Spokane.

It was one thing to hope, another to hear a voice from the pictures he had seen; flesh and blood had penned the letter and spoken to him. Pat continued the correspondence and setup a visit to Spokane.

15 year old Pat boarded a bus in Tacoma and sat up all night. He looked out along winding roads and through small towns on his way to Spokane. Pat left the rainforest-like west side of the state. The sky turned purple at night as the bus went over the cold misty Cascade Mountains heading east and chasing the eventual sunrise. The bus went through the dark deserts that lie baked by the sun in the middle of the state. Meanwhile Pat's eyes were alight with the hope of his future; his dream was turning into reality before his very eyes. Finally the bus crested the hills where trees came back into view and the bus descended into downtown Spokane.

Pat would run with Rick and others at Ferris while staying in the dorm of a former Lincoln athlete who was then attending Spokane Community College.

Pat went on training runs alongside Rick. He met Rick's coach Herm Caviness and listened to him speak and explain workouts. Pat even met Tracy Walters and listened to him speak to his team. This world was real and not just had on paper. The dream was speaking back to Pat.

Coaches and athletes, although aligned to different teams, treated this curious journeyman as if he were one of their own.

Eventually it came time to return back to Tacoma. Pat would board the bus, head up out of Spokane, back through the desert, following the sunset, and end up crossing over those same misty Cascade Mountains and end up in the gray skies of Tacoma. The runs back home had a sweet tempo to them upon return. For two full weeks the speed picked up in workouts, the intensity was there; Pat was running on desire.

And just as quickly as Pat returned home to his workouts and routines he would head back to the library. He continued reading the articles old and new, but he did so with the ability to hear the timber of the voices of those he had just met. Letters continued to be sent back and forth with Rick, and money was saved for another trip on the horizon. Back Pat went to the only running Mecca he knew, Spokane.

On one of these training runs with his idol and friend Rick, Pat got lost. Being new to Spokane and unfamiliar with the terrain they had left Rick's house to go on a fifteen mile run late in the day. The only problem was that Pat made a wrong turn and covered something more like 30 miles. Eventually Pat was found just before the Riley's were about to call the police and file a report for a missing person.

Pat came through the darkness, through the Spokane heat, and through a grueling run with a smile on his face. He was chasing his dream, exploring his dream, and even getting lost in his dream. Alive was the belief that anything was possible. Any doubt that may have asked for access to his dreams he learned to push away.

Pat continued to go to church each Sunday with his mom and after church he would run the seven and a half miles out to Coach Watson's house and run the seven and a half miles back home. Watson kept contact with Pat each day, and each day Pat was there, ready to give a report. Pat's sophomore year came to a close with him running 9:51 in the two mile and 4:38 in the mile. As a junior in cross country Pat finished 18th overall, running 11:38 on the Green Lake course. By Pat's senior season he was seventh in state in cross country and lowered his time to 11:21.

Going to the library, to practice, and to Spokane had been like going to church; there was a reverence for consecrated effort and a striving to improve that spoke to Pat.

The only person knowing more about the sport than Pat at the time in Tacoma was Dan Watson who was not just letting *Track and Field News* lie around his office, he was reading, studying, and implementing what he could gain from the Bible of the sport. Dan knew what Gerry and Rick had done, but he also knew what Bowerman was doing at the University of Oregon. Dan wanted one of his athletes to go and learn from the best and encouraged Pat to go there.

While at a track meet in Eugene in June of 1968, Dan told Pat to go and speak with Bill Dellinger, the assistant coach at the University of Oregon. Pat was thinking about running at Washington State University where he had already been accepted. After all Washington State University had Gerry Lindgren who had not lost a championship race yet and they had just signed Rick in 1966; it would make sense for Pat to get in state tuition and follow the men he had read and known so much about.

But Pat, mimicking his mother's ability to never say no, found himself in front of Bill Dellinger at the track meet.

"We would like you to come down to a meet in August we are having if you can find a way. We'll house you in a dorm. I would like for you to walk on to the team." Dellinger said.

Pat, recognizing someone who was being sincere, made sure to save his money for a greyhound bus ticket to Eugene in August.

The meet Dellinger invited Pat to come back to in Eugene highlighted a border battle race between Gerry running for Washington State and Oregon's premier athlete Arne Kvalheim. Pat sat inside Hayward Field just two seats away from Bill Dellinger who had also ran for Bowerman at Oregon. Dellinger was a three time Olympian in 1956, 1960, and 1964. Pat had done his homework and knew who Dellinger was and was grateful to be next to an Olympian. Dellinger won a bronze medal in the 5,000 meter in Tokyo, finishing his career just as Gerry was starting his.

Sandwiched between Tyson and Dellinger was another recruit that Oregon was after. This recruit sat with his big letterman's jacket that had a giant M on it. The meet began and the eyes of everyone were on those running under the lights.

The race began as was typical with Gerry leading from the front. The educated track fans of Hayward Field knew what was at stake and what a win over Gerry might mean for their local team.

The pace was quick, the chants began, and momentum was building.

Pat had to pause and look around at where he was; never had he been with so many people yelling and screaming- and all in the name of distance running. There were a pair of kids not more than six or seven years old pulling on their Dad's arm shouting, "Was that a 64 or a 65?"

These were kids using the parlance of the sport, it was a language they had grown up with, not learned like Pat had through Coach Dan Watson. This connection to running and everything positive associated with it seemed to be in the makeup of everyone in the stands - even the very youngest.

Gerry led the whole race and they were approaching the bell lap; but to everyone's amazement, Kvalheim was still there.

Finally Kvalheim went to lane two and made a move to pass Gerry. The green and yellow jersey was going by the crimson and white; it was all Christmas colors in lanes one and two going down the backstretch.

The crowd went crazy.

A deafening roar filled the final 200 meters as the crowd rose to their feet.

Coming around the bend Kvalheim began to pull away. Down the homestretch they went where Gerry could not make up the distance. Gerry lost a collegiate race, when he had been anything but beatable. An organ could not have touched the bellows that blew out the lungs of those that cheered.

If track was a theology, Hayward Field during the days of Bowerman and

Dellinger would be heaven. That's where Pat was, chanting, stomping, staring, and watching a fantastic meet in heaven. It was a place unlike any other, where young kids spoke the parlance of the sport as if out of the mouth of babes. It was a moment like Pentecost; it was perfect.

As the moment subsided and everyone floated back down to the stadium seats beneath them, Pat turned to the recruit next to him and finally got introduced.

"What's your name?" Pat asked.

"Steve Prefontaine," came the reply.

"Oh, I'm Pat Tyson." Pat said. The two shook hands. It would not be the last time these two would meet.

The smudge marks of newspapers could not compete for what his eyes had seen; a veritable distance miracle. Nothing really could have kept Pat Tyson from attending the University of Oregon after that; except for maybe the head coach Bill Bowerman.

Fitting the Bill

Walking on to a team is no small feats, in any sport let alone cross country and track. Pat, an unrecruited talent who had only taken seventh at the state meet in cross country his senior year and finished with a time that was over thirty seconds behind the likes of Gerry and Rick, was running for his life trying to get on Bill Bowerman's University of Oregon team.

A former athlete of Bowerman's was Kenny Moore, who went on to write a biography on his coach titled *Bowerman and the Men of Oregon.* Bowerman definitely represented the masculinity of the day and age in which he was born. Had some of those athletes that wound up at Oregon ended up at Washington State University, one could not help but wonder if there would have been a separate work titled *Jack Mooberry and the Men of Washington.* Oregon would be a draw for many athletes, including Roscoe Divine, who was one of only two people to beat Rick Riley in high school. Oregon and Washington State needed each other to draw out the best in league matches.

Bowerman and Mooberry had an understanding with one another as coaches. If either had an athlete that they were particularly pursuing then the other would not interfere. When Gerry and Rick were coming out of Spokane, only 74 miles away from Pullman, Bowerman did not pursue. One has to wonder what might have been had both Gerry and Rick been under Bowerman instead of Mooberry.

Bowerman drew inspiration from those whom he chased. Bowerman was on the heels of his predecessor and former coach. Bill Hayward spent 44 years at the University of Oregon, where he coached four track world record holders, six American record holders, and nine Olympians. Bill Hayward was the first permanent track coach at the University of Oregon and was the United States Track and Field coach for six Olympics. Bill Hayward was nicknamed Colonel Bill by those who knew him due to his rough and tough demeanor. To stand tall in Bill Hayward's eyes, Bill Bowerman made sure to give his all. Bowerman's all amounted to quite a lot.

23 Olympic athletes trained under Bill Bowerman.

51 All Americans.

12 American Record Holders.

22 NCAA champions.

16 sub 4 minute milers.

As mentioned before, Bill Dellinger was one of those Olympians, one of those All Americans, and someone that aided Bowerman as an assistant coach in the late 60s and early 70s. Dellinger would eventually take over the University of Oregon program from Bowerman. Each of Oregon's first three coaches had the first name Bill, and each man fit the bill of the expectations heaped upon them.

There are striking similarities between Bowerman and Pat. Bowerman himself had come from a family where his father and mother had separated due to his father's womanizing. Growing up with a twin brother who died young in a tragic elevator accident, Bowerman knew the value of life. He knew what it was like to have a single mother raising him. Anyone on the outside looking in would think that Bowerman would have great pity for what Pat had overcome.

Yet it was not in Bowerman's wheelhouse to simply feel sorry for people. He expected greatness and did not want to waste time on those not willing to work for it. Respect was earned.

Another individual Bowerman was chasing after was his own contemporary and legend in the making, Arthur Lydiard. If ever there was a cornerstone for coaching and ideology with running, Arthur Lydiard was it. Before Kenya's greatness and dominance in the sport of running and before the running revolution of the 1960s there was Arthur Lydiard coaching in New Zealand. Arthur Lydiard was the Rift Valley before it ever occurred in Kenya. On a trip to New Zealand to meet and visit with Lydiard, Bowerman gleaned all he could from this coach that was changing the running world forever. After all, Bowerman's own athlete Dellinger was competing against the Kiwis and again, Bowerman did not want to merely envy success, he wanted to emulate it.

The result of Bowerman's effort to emulate all he understood from Lydiard turned out to be a book on distance running titled *Jogging*. Published in 1967, during the time that Pat was finishing up his senior year of high school, the book caught the imagination and attention of the country. This single book led to what was recognized as America's running boom.

Runner's World Magazine rightfully recognized Lydiard as the greatest running coach of all time. Lydiard's method revolved around creating and sustaining a base through periodization. All the fine tuning of training was focused in different periods that built upon one another. The first period of training revolved around creating a base. As part of that base the expectation was 100 mile weeks of running from his athletes, no matter their respective distance focus. The 100 mile week number was unflinching. 800 meter champion Peter Snell would put in 100 mile weeks all in preparation for a half mile race. The preparation yielded near perfect results and the results spoke for themselves.

In the 1960 Olympics, Lydiard coached Peter Snell to an 800 meter gold medal, Murray Hallberg to a 5,000 meter gold medal, and Barry Magee to a bronze medal in the marathon. In the 1964 Tokyo Olympics Peter Snell would win the 800 meter gold as well as the 1,500 meter gold and is still the only athlete to ever complete that feet.

Bowerman was chasing Lydiard who had changed the world of distance running forever. And so it may not be any surprise that Bowerman had little sympathy or time for an unknown kid from south Tacoma.

As it was, Pat had decided to get lost in his dreams and make the voyage to Eugene and try to compete under the nation's premier coach; the only problem was Bowerman did not necessarily want Pat.

Speaking to his athletes at practice, Bowerman's body language matched the tenor of his message. He used his fierce blue eyes to catch the attention and demand respect of all his athletes. Here was a man revolutionizing the sport of distance running with passion unparalleled.

Nike exists due to Phil Knight, a former Bowerman track athlete, and to Bowerman. Using a waffle-iron to melt and set rubber, Bowerman took to creating shoes for his athletes. The time he took on his shoes for his athletes would eventually be time that was taken away from his own life. The poorly insulated basement and garage area of his experiments kept the harmful chemical odors near. Using tracings of his athletes feet and an experimental understanding of shoe making, Bowerman designed, stitched, and pieced together the lightest, strongest shoes he could make.

Bowerman did not care about the chemical smell circulating from his waffle maker; he was too busy innovating. Bowerman was getting lost in his dream to create the perfect pair of racing shoes for each of his athletes. His innovation did not stop at creating the perfect running shoe, but also creating the perfect running surface. The all weather synthetic tracks that are common today are the handiwork of Bowerman's relentless pursuit of perfection. The tracks at almost every high school and middle school throughout the country are a testament to the man who made running boom in America.

Hard surfaces to race on with spikes digging into them yielded faster times. Hard surfaces and hard facts had faced Bowerman all his life. He did not shield others from hard realities.

The only question in Pat's mind was whether Bowerman had intentionally called him Tim at practice.

If it was deliberate, then Bowerman was trying to tell Pat that his name was not important enough to remember and so he might consider leaving the team. The alternative scenario did not seem any more promising. If it was not deliberate, if it was accidental, then maybe Bowerman was incidentally trying to tell Pat that his name was not important enough to remember and so he might as well consider leaving the team.

Practices started, ran, and ended with Bowerman occasionally barking out splits or instructions to his athletes performing intervals. Repeatedly names like Tim were aimed at Pat without Pat's real name ever being uttered by Bowerman.

Pat was far from the days of Dan Watson. Knowing he was not known was difficult to endure. The dream Pat had gotten lost in, now seemed lost from him.

Yet, practice after practice, Pat appeared. Miles were run, sweat was shown, and small, almost insignificant growth occurred. Pat had to earn his keep. Growing up as a tough blue collar kid from south Tacoma, Pat had some rhino skin. But day after day Pat was called by the wrong name. Those words were real, as short and brief as they were, and they hurt.

Words used internally or externally create or crush dreams.

The words did not hurt as bad as cigarettes being put out on Pat as a kid or the real name calling he received as a youth. Those words did not hurt as bad as the desire Pat had to be on the team.

Practice after practice started and there was Pat, prompt, ready, quiet and respectful to both Bowerman and Dellinger. Pat gave everything in practice and even if it did not look as smooth and good as the top runners, there was no questioning Pat's effort. Bowerman finally tried again to get rid of "*Tim.*"

Pat was told that Bowerman wanted to speak to him after practice. Pat walked into his office and stood before his coach, unsure of what awaited him.

Bowerman informed "Tim" that he wondered if he would like to be the team's manager.

Pat stood on the receiving end of Bowerman's blue eyes that seemed to pierce through him.

Being asked to be the team manager was not an honor or privilege; it was code for *get off the team*. Bowerman knew exactly what he meant in saying it, and Pat knew it too.

With fingers rubbing his thumbs that had touched his dreams, with a mind revolving around the runs with Rick and time spent in Spokane, and with a heart holding fast to his mother's refrain Pat quietly, respectfully, and firmly squared his shoulders.

Pat said to someone in authority, for perhaps the first time in his life, no.

Bowerman looked at the young man before him and exhaled, then nodded his head, releasing Pat from his office.

Only decades later would Pat know how close Bowerman had come from cutting him from the team. It took Bill Dellinger stepping in and saying no to Bowerman for Pat to remain on the team. Bill Dellinger almost lost his own job in the process.

Bowerman used metaphors to make his point. If running were meats, the top chops would be sirloin and prime rib, while the bottom rung, the meat for the masses, would be hamburger. Prefontaine, who had sat by Pat, was USDA choice Sirloin, and Pat, in the eyes of Bowerman at that moment, was low grade hamburger that should be put out to pasture a second time.

Going through the locker room on a Saturday morning shortly after Bowerman had asked "Tim" to become the manager, Bowerman stood frustrated. Dellinger sensed the mood of his former coach and could see the wheels working behind the blue eyes.

"We need to get rid of some hamburgers," Bowerman said while he pulled off Pat's name written along a piece of athletic tape above his locker.

"You're right, we do need to get rid of some hamburgers," Dellinger said while he cocked his head and then pulled off a name of an athlete he knew Bowerman liked. A heated discussion ensued. Dellinger was perhaps the only one that could have talked Bowerman out of cutting Pat. In that instance, Dellinger was the only one pulling for Pat who was pushing so hard on his own.

Pat was suffering his way through practices and trying to adjust to longer distances, higher intensity, and longer workouts. Dellinger, a man who had been to the Olympics three times but did not medal until his third time, knew about hard work, perseverance, and late blooming.

Dellinger knew that success was more than accolades, it was about obtaining attributes that mattered most. Bowerman knew that college was not merely a place to dream; results had to be reached in order for people to be kept on the team. There had to be a rationale for keeping athletes around. Pat needed more time to prove that he was worth the investment of time; Dellinger bought that time by sticking up for Pat.

Bowerman's initial bark towards Dellinger silenced.

Pat's name was taped again above his locker. Dellinger saw in Pat a passion, a work ethic; a blue collar, working class kid who was the type of athlete any coach would want. Dellinger knew the loneliness that came from harboring a dream, and all the elements that could conspire to kill it. Pat was pushing his hardest, he just needed someone pulling for him on the other side.

While Dellinger was training for the Tokyo Olympics he did so in isolation. On the beaches in Oregon, alone, Dellinger would run wind sprints, unknown and unseen from anyone. He saw the same burning desire he once felt staring back at him in Pat's eyes.

The decision to keep Pat proved the right choice. Pat continued to improve. Prefontaine signed on to the team, and a Spokane athlete who had come after Rick, named Randy James who ran at Ferris under Coach Herm Caviness, also joined the squad. With younger, faster recruits that were actually on scholarship and that ran ahead of him, Pat continued to persevere in his training. Improvements came in his running; not by the leaps and bounds he had hoped, but he had steadily improved and moved up the roster so that in his junior and senior seasons he was competing on University of Oregon's varsity squad.

© Pat Tyson Personal Archives; Photographer Unknown

Pat Tyson, bottom left; Bill Bowerman, upper middle left (hands on Prefontaine); Steve Prefontaine, upper third left; Randy James (ran at Ferris High School), upper third right; Bill Dellinger, far right

It was a 35 degree day with clear blue skies at the 1971 NCAA Cross Country Championships in Knoxville, Tennessee. Steve Prefontaine won the race, Randy James came in second for the Ducks, and Pat would be their third runner, coming in one place after Marty Liquori; that same Marty Liquori who was only the third high school athlete to break four minutes in the mile and who would go on to have unforgettable races against Jim Ryun in the mile. For all of the notoriety surrounding the University of Oregon's great coaches and accolades, they had never won a NCAA Cross Country Team Championship up until that race in 1971. Oregon won their first NCAA Cross Country Team title and Pat, the dreamer and hamburger that Bowerman had nearly cut, carried points through to seal the victory.

This is Pat the athlete, having achieved the pinnacle of success for him. To know Pat the coach without a track, one has to know the man that drove him and his athletes to success both on and off the track.

Roommates

The atmosphere of any room can change with the entrance of just one person. What was once a somber mood can be shifted towards hope and happiness with a simple smile. Even when certain people leave a space, there seems to remain the relics of their attitudes, their atmosphere that they carry with them wherever they go.

Sitting in a silver trailer camper outside of Eugene, Pat Tyson scanned the small quarters of his new living arrangement. What he saw stood in contrast to the persona that others had only guessed at.

He saw order.

He saw cleanliness.

Dishes were away and the sink was spotless. The bed was made with sheets tucked tight. The floor was swept without a speck of dirt or dust anywhere. The garbage was empty, except for the fresh trash bag waiting for new abuse. The photo dark room stood at attention.

Parked outside the silver trailer sat a blue MGB convertible two-door coupe. The driver of the car, Pat's new roommate, opened the trailer door and walked in with his long hair and mustache.

Steve Prefontaine, the friend he had met in the stands at Hayward Field a few years prior and who was setting the world on fire both on and off the track, was now his roommate.

No TV, no distractions of any kind, just two young men who loved to run, and came from blue collar backgrounds. Pat went about putting away his shirts, his shoes, his athletic attire, amazed that this world class athlete and teammate sought him out to be his roommate.

When the alarm rang at six o'clock Pre moved as if he were already awake and started to make his bed. Pat, sensing the movement, mirrored what he saw Pre doing. With tired eyes he got himself ready. Quickly, Pat made his bed and switched into his running shorts, socks and shoes, trying to catch up with Pre, who stood outside the trailer waiting.

Off they were on the morning run, just after 6am and setting a six minute pace. The heart that had been resting minutes prior was now up and working.

"How do you feel?" Pre asked as they strode out.

"I feel great." Pat lied.

They kept the quick pace that seemed so welcome to Pre.

"How do you feel?" Pat asked.

"Eh, not so good." Pre said.

The pace kept steady as they made their way down empty and quiet streets. Although Pat was taller and older than Pre, he felt like the younger brother.

In the short time Pat had known, raced, and competed with Pre, he did not see what others had seen, or what future movies would try to dictate: that Pre was self absorbed, didn't like his own body and thought it was never enough. Pat was running beside someone that was fairly intense, but it was a quiet intensity, and a focus aimed outwards more than inwards. Inevitably the conversation revolved around running. Pre would ask Pat what his goal time was for his next race. Pat would state his goal and Pre would then question why Pat had not indicated that he could run a faster time.

"Your workouts show you're ready to rock and roll, what's the worry?" Pre asked. "Why are you a worrywart?" Pre said.

Pat saw that Pre did not worry about fear of failure. This confidence Pat saw in Pre and heard from him instilled a greater hope in himself.

Steve Prefontaine, left; Pat Tyson, right

© Jeff Johnson

It was one thing for Pat's mom to believe in him and allow him the opportunity to travel to Spokane and to meet with Rick, but it was another for Steve Prefontaine, the myth in the making, to speak to him and tell him to believe in himself. Pat said to himself he could do it, but Pre gave the words with command, like he gave his actions with command, and like how he had left his room at attention and standing guard, waiting for his return.

Expectations dictate endeavors.

"How do you think you're going to do in your next three mile?" Pat asked.

"We'll see. I'm a little tired." Pre said deflecting the conversation.

The pace had never let up.

Pre, the man that could speak inspiringly towards others, would hold his own counsel and keep his thoughts to himself. Pre would go deep into others, but he would not let others go too deep with him. Pre had a demanding mother and a father he adored. They were blue collar workers. Pre loved his sister Linda. He loved happy people and liked to keep things light. Pat, although older than Pre, was the little brother that Pre had never had growing up. Pat kept things light and fun, which made him the perfect roommate for Pre.

Part of the way Pre blocked out the surrounding noise was by keeping life simple. He did not need drama and he wanted someone that was also a hard worker and kept an even keel. Pat may have worried over his own performance capabilities, but he kept an orderly, clean, life.

They started and finished their morning runs together, making their way towards home, keeping the conversation light and quick, just like their pace.

Two shirts are associated with Steve Prefontaine, the first one was a stenciled mini-image of Prefontaine running and the words, "Go Pre" above it. The second, now more popular shirt also has two words, yet it was white, with a red octagon imitating a street sign that read, "Stop Pre". The creators of the Stop Pre t-shirts were John Auka and John Gillespie, who enjoyed showing up to meets in Eugene to watch Pre race. They had made the shirts and wore them to the 1972 Olympic Trials 5,000 meter final. These two Johns had even given one of the shirts to Gerry Lindgren who wore it as he warmed up, readying to run against Pre.

Pre saw the shirts, but kept his focus on the track where he would run away with first place. After the win, Pre made his way around the track in victory. John Auka ripped off his shirt and offered it to Pre. Confused by the shirt and the offer, Pre, nonetheless put on the shirt and finished up his victory lap.

Pre admitted he was tired, or sore, but nothing in his running ever seemed to indicate that his statements were true. There was no negativity that Pre allowed to stick to him when he lined up in any of his races. It certainly seemed that nothing would stop him from medaling, if not winning it all. The crowd roared at this rock star of running, but Pat knew he was not the persona wearing the shirt. He knew him in the hours off the track and away from the sport. There is a famous quote of Pre saying that he did not want to let his people down. Pat never heard Pre talk like that in private. Pre may have given that voice to the public for a sound bite, but there was no self-absorption in private.

The Pied Piper, Peter Pan, and Humpty Dumpty

The road from Pat's graduation at the University of Oregon to Gonzaga University is filled with scenarios of what might have been. Upon graduating from the University of Oregon, Pat was offered to coach a the University of Idaho, but he turned down the job. He instead taught middle school students in Shoreline, Washington because he liked their energy. In 1976 Colorado State tried to lure Pat away from Washington. It was not a good time for Pat to leave because his mother had cancer and Pat wanted to stay close by to help. In the early 80s the University of Washington came trying to court Pat to coach their program during the middle of a school year. Pat indicated that he was going to fulfill his current obligation but he might be open to talk once school was let out. The University of Washington did not wait for Pat and made their moves.

After graduating from the University of Oregon with a degree in History and English Education, Pat took his first teaching job at Morgan Junior High School from 1973-1977. The school was named after Thomas Hunt Morgan whose work linking genetics to chromosomes earned him a Nobel Prize in 1933. The school was eventually renamed to Kellogg Junior High School where Pat continued to teach English and Social Studies until 1983. Pat's first real move came when he started teaching at Shorecrest High School, just less than half a mile down the road from Kellogg Junior High. Pat stayed at Shorecrest for three years, from the fall of 1983 to the spring of 1986. In that short span, Pat helped their cross country team finish on the podium at state each year for the 2A classification: third place in 1983 and two first place finishes in 1984 and 1985.

Pat could have stayed comfortably on the western side of Washington, but the desire to journey over the mountains and into Spokane that he had felt in his youth still lingered as an adult. Pat was not the only one wanting to see himself on the eastern side of the state.

Don Kardong's wife Bridget wanted Pat to come and interview at her school. Initially he applied for a job at Lewis & Clark High School and showed up in Spokane for an interview. Pat waited for an interview down at the Spokane Public Schools district office. Pat sat, waiting, with the realization that the end of the day was looming and that he still had to make it back to Shorecrest High School on the other side of the state. He had classes to teach the following morning. Pat sat outside of an office for two hours waiting for an interview that due to scheduling errors never occurred. Multiple college programs wanted Pat and here a high school had a chance at him.

The only other place Pat considered in Spokane was Mead High School, which is part of the Mead School District, sitting on the northside of Spokane. He saw the trails, the climate, and a people ready to run.

Spokane Public Schools missed out on Pat Tyson.

Districts of any size, big or small, can lose sight of what is best for children. Not hiring Pat was an oversight. When you have the chance to learn from someone like a Picasso it becomes imperative that you cast aside the paint by number system.

Mead, at the time, had a superintendent that loved seeking out the best opportunities for their students at all levels and in all disciplines. The school board as well did not stand in the way of excellence with arbitrary rules, regulations, and forms to be followed. The principal at Mead also got behind Pat, as well as other teachers, bus drivers to and from meets, lunch ladies at school, and even the custodians. For that time there was a group of people that were of the same mind as Pat's mother: never say no.

There was good paint and a good canvas at Mead. The people there simply watched a master work at his craft and they tried to learn something and support him in the process. Both Pre and Pat are artists in their own right. Pre said it best, "Some people create with words, or with music, or with a brush and paints. I like to make something beautiful when I run." Pat has coached those words into the hearts of all of his athletes.

Pat recognized opportunity at Mead. His first kids already had morning runs down and a class in sixth period dedicated to running. What they lacked was the aura of what could be. Mead had the first individual state champion, but they did not have a vision like Pat.

Pat made sure to follow Dan Watson's technique of letting them have easy access to *Track & Field News*, and to great running literature. Glossy colored paper does not wear off as easily on the fingertips as newspapers, but the pattern for inspiring greatness Pat took from his own life. He made sure to get his athletes down to Hayward Field, to let them see the Prefontaine Classic track meet, and let them hear the roar of that crowd. Just as Pat bought into the Oregon method of running, so too would his athletes buy into that same method he provided at Mead.

Pre would also say, "A race is a work of art that people can look at and be affected in as many ways as they're capable of understanding." Pat Tyson has spent a lifetime aiding young runners to understand the art of training and racing. He took them to Hayward Field, the living, breathing, Sistine Chapel of American distance running. While there, instruction became easy because the experience of seeing the best imprinted itself on the minds and attitudes of these young athletes.

The first season at Mead consisted of Pat helping his athletes have a clear belief that they ran with their destiny in their hands. The team had finished with a surprising 6-2 dual meet record. Pat made sure to keep his team away from invitational races. That year only two teams would go on to state and the clear favorites were North Central, coached by Len Long, a former teammate and friend of Gerry Lindgren in high school, and Shadle Park.

Early in the season Mead had pulled the upset in a dual meet and beaten North Central who finished the season 7-1. Shadle Park, Ferris, and Mead all finished the season at 6-2.

The qualifying race for state was on the Hangman Valley Golf Course; the site of Pre's last cross country race. Those athletes of Pat's ran inspired.

The final scoring came out as follows:

First place, Shadle Park with 64 points.

Second place, Mead with 81 points.

Third place, North Central with 82 points.

Fourth place, Ferris with 83 points.

Off to state the team went, with a bit of confidence and with Pat determined to make his team feel like winners. The night before the state meet he took the team out to a fancy restaurant and told them to imagine and act like they had just won the state meet.

Pat's inspiration for the dinner came from Digger Phelps of Notre Dame who took on the legendary coach John Wooden's UCLA squad and ended their 88 game win streak. Digger had his team practice taking down the nets and visualize the moment before it occurred. Pat wanted his athletes to feel like winners.

Up and through the first mile of the race Mead, as a team, was in a position to win the state meet. However, most of his team then fell off pace except for a hard nosed sophomore who ended up taking seventh overall. His name was Chris Lewis.

As one sportswriter quipped, Chris Lewis was known to look like an altar boy but to run like the devil. Chris would go on to have two individual state titles in cross country and two individual track titles: one in the mile and one in the two mile. Pat could speak to anyone and no matter their circumstances make them feel like they had something to look forward to and run for.

From that team on, the attitude and culture shifted. Big races were sought out: Foot Locker, Arcadia, Stanford, North Carolina; Pat would take his teams towards experiences these athletes would have never had otherwise.

Wins racked up. Nine consecutive state titles from 1988-1996, then three consecutive titles from 2000-2002

Pat's efforts at Mead effectively raised the bar for distance running in Spokane. Other coaches, competitive as they are in the league, realized that if they wanted to succeed they would have to adapt, change, and improve. The investment of both coach and athlete resulted in both being all in.

Pat was always all in.

There were the weekly pizza nights that Pat had started back at Morgan Junior High and kept going at Kellogg Middle School and Shorecrest High School. At Mead it would be no different.

The highest compliment Pat received came by way of a parent whose son competed for Pat. Ben Allen's father said:

> My kids run for this program. What Tyson is doing
> *is the right thing.* Your kids are going to be consumed
> by this thing.
>
> You may think it is a cult or weird or whatever,
> but these are the kids you want your children to hang
> out with. These are the values you want your kids to
> develop because that is what you are teaching at home.
>
> They are not going to be troublemakers by being
> a runner. You are hanging around with the cream of
> the crop.

Pat did not want running to be the best experience of their life. He wanted his athletes to see the doors that could be opened through running. He wanted them to own all the discipline it demanded.

One of his athletes, that never ran on varsity, later became a navy seal instructor and pointed at Pat Tyson and his time at Mead as being influential to his makeup.

Eventually Pat realized he could retire at Mead. At the same time as Pat neared retirement there was also a potential coaching opportunity at Oregon in 2005. Rumors were circulating that the University of Oregon was looking for a new Cross Country and Track Coach. Pat, the boy who had helped Oregon win their first team cross country title, decided to throw his hat into the mix.

Pat took this opportunity very seriously and went down to Oregon to act as an interim assistant while those with power at the university were making up their minds. During this time Pat was petitioned by Alberto Salazar to aid in coaching at Oregon with his athlete Galen Rupp. It seemed that Pat could follow the line of great coaches, like Hayward, Bowerman and Dellinger who made the University of Oregon, and distance running in America, what it is. The heart of the University of Oregon would stay pumping and churning out people of character and quality. It seemed that Pat had come full circle with his running experience.

But, universities and institutions of any kind can lose track of their DNA and the discipline, formula, culture and environment that made them who they are. The University of Oregon would pass on Pat Tyson who holds within him the DNA, the pedigree and the legacy, if not of Oregon distance running, at least American distance running.

Instead of returning to Mead, Pat decided to take an offer at the University of Kentucky where he would remain for a year coaching their cross country and track team. But the northwest was in Pat's blood. He returned to teaching and coaching at South Eugene High School where he stayed for a year until an opportunity at Gonzaga University opened up.

The full circle that Pat reached revolved around those who had been passed over.

Pat is now at Gonzaga University where he continues to inspire young men and he does so without a track to call his own.

To repeat, Gonzaga University has no track and field. They have a track and field program, just no literal track and field to call their own and practice on.

Pat knew this going into the job and still decided to stick it out in Spokane. It's like taking the film out of the camera that Christopher Nolan is about to use, or the canvass away from Van Gogh, the basketball away from Jordan. But Pat just keeps on going with the same attitude his mother instilled in him, "Never say no." The athletes need to see more than the lanes and the numbers or the times on the stat sheet.

This is just another testament to the artistry that makes Pat who he is.

He needs people, not products.

He works with hearts, not footwear.

As alluring as it is to coach at a top tier Goliath program, there may be some advantages to seeking out and coaching future Davids.

It's the type of attitude and approach that helped him earn the nickname of *The Pied Piper*. Pat's voice instills a vision and belief in all who hear from him because he keeps things simple and sincere. He has been able to speak to his athletes and help them rise up and win every year. He has led thousands of athletes to PR's and some to national caliber achievements. Each year he sets out to help someone do something they have never accomplished before, believing in them before some ever believe in themselves. The principles he uses are the same no matter the age.

It's no different if it's getting Chris Lewis at Mead to win the state title in 1987 or getting Troy Fraley at Gonzaga to qualify in the 3,000 meter final of the Indoor USATF Championships in 2016. Pat develops the talents of his athletes and helps them run up with greatness. It's not a complicated style or approach.

Pat develops his athletes because he needed to be developed.

Another by-product of the running machine of college athletics, is that there are a bunch of humpty dumpties who have risen to the wall of running star status and then been pushed aside by greedy coaches looking for instant success. These coaches believe they can recruit themselves out of any problem or bad season. The once new kid that had potential suddenly did not have a good freshman year and so he is cast aside by a newer batch of freshman who are hungry and ready to go. Tough workouts are tossed at the athletes, with or without forethought, and the talented or lucky survive while the rest are cast aside with next year's recruiting class. Frustrated athletes lose the love they once felt for the sport and some try to find a fresh start.

Pat simply helps his athletes to become born again runners.

His main message to his athletes is to help them believe that they are still a Peter Pan. He wants them to believe that they are young, that they are fast, that anything is possible and that they can fly. But, being in the West Coast Conference and competing against perennial powers in the University of Portland and Brigham Young University, has been no easy feat. It's a tough sell to a teenage athlete to come to a school where there is no track. It is a tough sell to get a kid who qualifies for Nationals in high school to bypass offers from Stanford, Oregon, Colorado, or Arkansas. The young athletes think they need to go to the top programs, and so as a result, Pat is left to find young forgotten athletes and develop them, or find transfers willing to find a coach and not the used car salesman they are leaving behind.

Pat may not have all the fancy facilities but he has his faculties which are all that really matter. Gonzaga is on the rise and Pat is there to see it happen by continuing to aid the overlooked and underappreciated.

As I sat in Pat's office that overlooks the old gym where the Gonzaga Bulldog Basketball team used to play, I saw a few of his athletes come and go.

"They're refugees." Pat said, of the athletes that transfer from different Division I programs. Sitting or standing in his office, his athletes smiled and agreed, humbled and happy to be with their new coach in Spokane.

"They've been cast aside by college coaches unwilling to take the time to develop athletes, and I am here to take a second chance on them, to help humpty dumpty get all back together again," he said.

© Peter Hawkins

The advice Pat offers has authenticity in it due to the adversity he has faced throughout his life. He harnesses that difficulty, makes it relatable and a motivating factor moving forward for himself and his athletes.

Since his start at the program, Pat has done what he has always done: stayed positive, known all of his athletes, speaks to them and their most recent workouts, races and needs. He then forecasts what could be for them. He speaks with unfailing hope at the possibilities for his athletes, and they are all grateful for it.

As whimsical as it is to compare Pat to fairy tale and nursery stories, the reality is that there is true peril involved in those tales, just as there is real peril involved in daily life. The power to lead people of any kind, or even be placed in the position of leadership, carries with it an obligation to give them the very best they need in order to succeed.

Most humpty dumpties that fall from great heights do so without the ability to put themselves or their worlds back together again. Scars, real and emotional, are made in such moments. But, like those stories too, Pat keeps conversations light. He loves to speak with people. He loves to talk about running, to talk about his coaches, to talk about his time with Pre. He never tires of seeking out the undiscovered, insecure, and yearning youth who needs someone to breathe some life into them. By immersing himself with the young, he has stayed forever young. His spirit and demeanor, and even his physical capacity to coach, are a natural outgrowth of his love for the sport and all that it has given him.

That youthful spirit carries Pat onward to this day and allows him to still dream of what could be. For as much as Pat speaks of what could be for others he speaks to himself, his younger self, and he does so like Prefontaine did, like Dan Watson did, and like Dellinger and Bowerman when the time is right. He goes out and tries to do the impossible. Why not have Nick Symmonds show up and speak to his team? Why not get a hold of Alan Webb and have him show up? Why not call up Jeff Johnson, the first Nike Shoe Salesman who coined the term "Nike" and have him speak at the track season awards banquet? Why not have Jim Ryun come to Spokane? Perhaps next year he will get America's last 800 meter gold medalist, David Wottle.

This never say no attitude has Pat looking at the track that is not, and asking himself, *Why not have a track in downtown Spokane?*

The only real challenges Pat faces in building a track in downtown Spokane is finding ten million dollars and a way to keep the track open for the public. Pat would want the track to be accessible to everyone. It does not need to be eight lanes, it could be two or four. The stands do not have to be like a stadium; it could be a place with grass following the curve. Pat sees the track being a place not too big and not too small, a place where it would be somewhat difficult to get a ticket and would be packed with people wanting to show up and cheer the local talent and hopefully some of the world's best. He envisions the track being a place with lights and open to the public so that joggers and runners alike can make use of it when there isn't a meet taking place. Just as Wrigley Field competes with Fenway Park for nostalgic fields of dreams, why not Hayward Field in Oregon and Pat Tyson's Track in Spokane?

In true Pat fashion, he does not want the track to be given to him, or to Gonzaga, but he wants to earn the ability to give Spokane and his athletes simply the best. Pat's efforts inspired others, even coaches, to lengthen their strides and quicken their pace.

Bob Barbero, far right, competing for West Valley High School in 1968

Bob Barbero: The Record Keeper

Standing in his Statistics professor's office on Monday morning at Spokane Community College Bob Barbero was trying to explain to his professor why he was turning in his homework early. The stubborn professor sat with his square glasses and hair parted not wanting to hear any of it. Rules were rules, and these were the professor's rules. If homework was not turned in while the student sat through his class, then that homework would not be counted. It was the morning of November 19, 1973.

"But today is the day of the National Championship." Bob explained breathlessly.

The NCAA Cross Country Championships were being run in Spokane on the Hangman Valley Golf Course and Prefontaine would be racing his last cross country race. The frumpy professor asked Bob if he knew his rule about taking roll.

"You only take roll two times during the course of the semester and if you miss once it drops you a letter grade and if you miss twice you will fail the course." Bob said.

The professor stared at him blankly.

It was a lost cause. This Statistics class was a loss cause. A sports anomaly had come to town and this professor was blind to it.

Bob left his professor's office and did what he thought he should do. He asked his friend to turn in his paper and went to the meet, hoping that roll was not taken that day.

Bob knew his statistics, he had done his homework over the weekend and all along the way since his childhood. He wanted to be a math teacher himself one day. He recognized, just as importantly what he did not want to become. He realized you could learn as much from a bad example as you could from a great one. There are outliers all around us, observed and unobserved that can make all the difference.

Bob Barbero grew up in Spokane, living in what is commonly referred to as *the Valley*. Spokane Valley sits east of downtown Spokane and stretches out and around Brown's Mountain, which separates the South Hill from the Valley. Bob attended Catholic school up until the end of middle school. Bob then attended West Valley High School. Spokane Valley's first high school was West Valley which opened their doors in 1924. Central Valley, the second high school in the Valley opened up in 1927. It would take a stock market crash, a world war, and the rise of the baby boomer generation until two more Valley high schools were opened. East Valley High School opened in 1960 and University High School followed shortly thereafter in 1963. At the request of his middle school coach Bob was told to turn out for cross country once he started high school. Bob asked what was cross country.

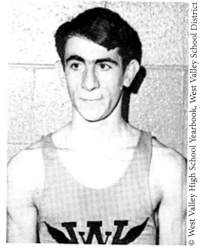

"You like track, right?" the middle school coach asked.

"Yeah." Bob responded.

"It's like track but in the fall time." The coach said.

Of course it was a lie, but it was also half true; so Bob showed up with his track spikes on that first day of practice. The high school coach asked him why he had the spikes. Bob simply shrugged his shoulders and said he heard cross country was like track but in the fall time. The coach, scratching his head, told Bob to leave his spikes and go off on a run with the team.

Bob would run a lot more than he ever planned on running and he would do so with people he knew were good; he was not blind to that fact.

At one event, Bob showed up to a road race that was on the backside of the South Hill of Spokane. The race had been set up by Ken Latting, an older Spokane running enthusiast. Latting would put together masters races and early marathons in Spokane. He would be one of the earliest road runners from Spokane to make the trek and run in the Boston Marathon. He wanted to get the older crowd out exercising and he wanted those who thought their prime had passed to get out and pursue excellence once more.

The road races at that time in Spokane were fairly rudimentary. There were no water or aide stations. The courses were barely marked, and there were not large numbers of people showing up to race. It was probably good there were not more people because it could have been a disaster due to the haphazard planning.

At one event in the mid 1960s the official starting the race had the firing pistol in one hand and the timer in the other. With both hands raised and a nervous command given for the athletes to get set, the gun was finally fired. In one deft movement the official starting the race threw the timer and the starting pistol on the hood of a nearby car. Whether the gun was a starting pistol or an actual firearm Bob never knew but he took off all the same.

The race was an out and back course. The expectation was that the first person back would grab the stopwatch and read off the times for others as they crossed the finish line. Meanwhile, a potentially loaded gun sat on top of the hood of an unprotected car. And so as Bob was coming back to finish his six mile race, there was Gerry Lindgren, standing, holding the timer and shouting out times.

Some of the early experiments in running and road races came from Herm Caviness. He had set up road races during the wintertime and he had also created what he called the Spokane Summer Games. It was an event that was to be treated like the Olympics of Spokane, with the best athletes and all types coming out to race.

Within one of these events was a timed mile race. Each entrant was given a 3X5 card to put their name and predicted mile time on. The race was started and the people took off. No watches could be used by any athlete and no times were read as they passed each lap. The runners had to go off of how they felt and what they knew of themselves. The winner of the event was not the person that ran the fastest; it was the person who knew themselves the best.

Another iteration of road races was the undefined distance. The problem was not that the course was unknown, it was that the people competing did not know who was in their race. There would be a three mile, five mile, and six mile run, but the competitors to each race were all placed upon the same starting line at the same time. The initial phases of each race followed the same course. Everyone started out charging hard, but the assumption in Bob's head was, *Well they are probably running the three mile course and will turn around here.*

The turnaround point came and went with Bob staring at the back of the athlete still charging in front and again, Bob would think, *Well, they are only probably running the five mile race so I am in good shape to win the six mile race.* Yet again, that same athlete would continue on and Bob finally realized they were in his race.

The variables of distance running (time, distance, and space) revolved around Bob's mathematical mind. How much did talent influence the outcome? How much was left to hard work? How did desire sway the final push to the tape?

Bob would train and ponder over the successes of Gerry and Rick. He had seen them run and been at local races with them. Bob would run 1:57.5 for 800 meters at West Valley High School and have the school record, until his only sibling, younger brother Rick Barbero came along and lowered the school record to 1:57.2. And there Bob's name sat in the second slot on the all-time charts of West Valley High School.

The madness of placing second seemed to follow Bob wherever he went. When his team at West Valley ran for the state title during his senior year of high school in 1969, they finished second place. Once more he had to watch as someone else stood on the podium.

During Bob's time at the community college he competed on their cross country and track teams. In order to participate on the varsity squad he would have to challenge the racer just above him in a dual meet on Wednesday nights.

The duals came and went.

Each week Bob challenged, but each week the results were the same: he would not be wearing the team's jersey on race day.

Work, study, and training laid before him each week, exhausting and exhilarating as it all was.

Homework was done. Studying occurred with precision.

Bob was the first person to go to college in his family. He was carving out a path that his younger brother would follow, but it seemed a solitary journey.

Bob needed to see something to hold on to.

Bob finally parked his car and walked down the hill into the Hangman Valley Golf Course on November 19, 1973. Passing buses and vans of all types that showed the trappings of universities they represented, Bob descended towards the starting area.

Bob had heard of the myth and witnessed it on TV, but he had never seen Prefontaine in the flesh.

Striding out with silent fury, Pre ran with his green warmups; his mustache long, his sideburns longer, and his hair pushed back by the wind.

Pre: the man that had run in that famed 5,000 meter race in the 1972 Olympic final in Munich.

Pre: who would forever be remembered charging down the backstretch, trying to wrestle away the lead from Lasse Viren of Finland and Mohammed Gammoudi of Tunisia.

Pre: who would die fading to fourth and be passed in the final yards by Ian Stewart of Great Britain and left off the medal stand.

It was this Pre that was on the course and ready to run.

Bob stood with wonderment like everyone else on the course, speculating about what would happen that day.

In the race were two international challengers. Nick Rose who ran for Western Kentucky but was from England, and John Ngeno who ran for Washington State University but was from Kenya. Both were exceptional athletes and rising stars.

Pre finally ditched his warm up gear and stood with eyes fixed on the course ahead of him.

Pre knew what had happened in Munich, and he knew he still had races to run.

The starting marshal called all the teams to their marks. He raised his gun.

Bang!

A sea of runners escaped from the view of spectators as they ran off in the distance.

When the swell of runners finally came crashing back towards the spectators Bob saw the leaders up front: Pre, Nick Rose, and John Ngeno.

It was too early to tell how the race would unfold.

Again the field disappeared from view.

Bob stood, waiting like others, to see if Pre would be mortal once more.

The course at Hangman Valley was not spectator friendly. The athletes came into view and then disappeared into the outer realms of the course; rising, falling, and turning through the fairways of the golf course. The fairways are long and full of rolling hills that are tree lined in parts.

The next time they came into view Rose had opened up 20 yards of a lead. Back in second and seeming to fade sat Pre.

Pre looked human.

Rose's lead was growing with only a mile and a half left. Perhaps Pre would go down. Gerry's star had come and now gone, so too had Rick's star come and gone; there would be no more Olympic hopes for either of them. Perhaps Pre would fall to a similar fate. Perhaps Munich was all that Pre would ever have.

Rose disappeared from view. Bob watched as Pre faded from Rose's growing lead. Then Pre disappeared from view.

Bob jogged towards the finish wanting to make sure he would have a good view staked out.

The cheers started to come towards where Bob stood. The first runner was coming. Leaning outward and trying to get a glimpse of who was coming towards the finish Bob scanned the horizon.

Pre, who had trailed by 20 yards moments prior now led by 20 yards on Rose. Bob could see it in Pre's eyes.

He's giving everything! Bob thought.

Pre had come back on Hangman Valley Golf Course and threw everything he had left at the line.

Pre won.

Pouring in after Pre came the competition, passing through the finish line.

Bob cheered as they came through but his mind could not move onward from what he had witnessed.

The cheers eventually faded, the awards were handed out, and it came time to leave the race.

Bob walked back to his car wondering over it all again and again. He opened his car door, looking back at the race, trying to replay it once more in his mind.

Bob had just witnessed a real life object lesson on life. He had heard of sacrifice and knew of it firsthand from his own family. The look in Pre's eyes was not foreign but familiar.

Chasing, Revering, Honoring

Bob Barbero's father also went by the American name of Bob, but was born with the name Dominick and he was the son of two full blooded Italians; the Barbero's descend from northern Italy. As luck would have it, Dominick went back to Italy on a trip with his mother Maria near the end of 1939. Dominick was born in America and so he had an American passport. He had grown up with parents that were immigrants to America that worked hard and wanted to live the American dream. The timing of their trip to Italy was ill-fated. They made their trek back to Italy in 1939.

As Dominick and his mother were splitting time visiting relatives between the towns of Candia and Caluso World War II started. There was no travel in or out of the country except by military force. Dominick's mother was safe because she spoke Italian and had an Italian passport. She was back in her home town visiting with family that she had left only years previous. Dominick, although he spoke Italian, felt more comfortable in America and speaking English, which was his native tongue.

Each time the Nazis came to town it would be time for Dominick, only 16 years old at the start of the war, to leave. He would run for his life to the woods. He was not the only one in the town fleeing into the woods and running like a scared rabbit. There was another young person who was his friend that also had to flee for safety. On one such occasion, however, the call to leave town came late. With his friend by his side Dominick sprinted for the woods; shots were fired and his friend dropped from his peripheral vision.

In the woods Dominick would wait, tired, hungry, and afraid. His heart was racing, his mind was trying to keep pace as he confronted the reality that his friend had been killed.

A voice he had heard seconds ago would never be heard again.

He could be next.

There would be roughly 153,000 civilian deaths in Italy during World War II. Dominick had no idea that was the case. He knew that life, to him, meant one more day with family.

When Dominick determined that enough time had passed he would trudge back into the village. Over and over again he would have to flee, and over and over again he survived. Daily he was confronted with the possibility that his life would end.

On one such occasion when Domnick returned to town he rounded a corner to find a German tank sitting there.

Initially Domnick froze.

If I run, he thought, *I will die.*

Domnick continued on his journey by the tank and as he walked by it, the gunner on the side of the tank followed him. No bullets were fired and no one stopped to question him. He had lived to see another day.

Dominick wanted to do more than simply survive.

With disgust for the local atrocities witnessed, Dominick decided to take part in the underground resistance against the Nazis. With dirty bombs, rudimentary explosives, and gutsy timing, 12 trains were destroyed, derailed, or temporarily hampered by the hands of Dominick and those in the resistance. This teenager was doing his best to stand against tyranny.

Dominick saw winter turn to spring, spring into summer, summer into fall, and fall into winter. The seasons changed, but the war seemingly stayed the same. Good information was hard to come by. Rumor and truth seemed mixed. Each day demanded vigilance, and each day brought with it the unexpected. Despite the odds, Dominick continued to live, to fight, to resist. He knew he was not alone in his resistance but the war continued on without any conclusion in sight.

At one point Dominick kept silent in his aunt's attic because he had not seen the troops coming until it was too late. Silent and still, he strained his ears to listen for the movements and sounds all around him. The troops eventually left.

One of those people fighting to take back the land, liberty, and ideology of the world was Bill Bowerman, who had yet to become the coach at the University of Oregon. Bowerman was part of the 10th Mountain Division. He had arrived in Naples, Italy and moved forward pushing the northern line up into northern Italy. It was Major Bowerman that helped negotiate a surrender of Nazi forces in the Brenner Pass in northern Italy. Bowerman, with soldiers of like mind and heart, pushed forward the cause of ultimate victory and helped end the war in northern Italy. Bowerman and others like him on the frontlines advanced with firm resolve in their actions.

They approached the impossible and made it inevitable.

As Dominick's village was liberated and he looked into the eyes of those who still marched onward to more fields of battle he saw the resolve in their eyes and would never forget it. Those moving onward also saw the resolve of those that had been liberated. Both sides were aiding each other.

Two men, an ocean and a continent away from home, held fast to the messages that life was precious and that time was the greatest capital.

Bowerman would return to coach and Dominick would return to America with his mom. Once back Domnick was eventually drafted for the Korean War. He made it to Japan before the conflict there was also over. Once more Dominick Barbero returned home.

He initially worked as an auto mechanic out at Kaiser Aluminum in Spokane Valley, then at a paper mill, and finally for his last 26 years he worked as a custodian at West Valley High School where his kids would attend.

While students silently listened to History teachers recount the horrors of the war, Dominick would be outside in the halls reliving the memories that haunted him. Some days were worse than others. Bob remembers his father being sad or moody on certain days of the year. He would ask him what was wrong and his Dad would simply say it was connected to the war and moments he remembered in those villages.

The man who fought against Germans swept the halls where students, like his children, could learn and hope to see better days. Dominick Barbero never wrote an account of his history, only a verbal testament lives through those who knew him. This would be the message that Bob would keep with him as he approached each day. Seeing the somber look on his father's face and hearing the stories that only came when his father had drunk a little, Bob began to see time differently. His father and other fathers across the world had given him a great gift; he wanted to see the world as they hoped for it to be.

Without men like Bill Bowerman and Dominick Barbero, pushing, pulling and fighting for ultimate victory, there would have been no place for Prefontaine, for Dellinger, and all the others. Pat Tyson and Barbero may have never shared time on the sidelines coaching countless athletes in Spokane, if it was not for those brave men.

Pre's final race before his untimely death was run with a black singlet and the word *NorditaliA* (which is Italian for Northern Italy) arched across the chest. It was a jersey Pre had picked up in Europe when he represented team USA. It was the only time he wore that jersey or any jersey that was black in a race.

Spokane, Washington was home to Sonora Smart Dodd. She started the celebration of Father's Day at a YMCA in 1910. After sitting through a sermon on Mother's Day, Sonora approached her pastor to suggest that fathers be given their own day as well. Her own father had fought during the Civil War and had helped to raise six kids as a single parent following the war.

With that respect for sacrifice, Bob approached his own life with appreciation for the opportunities before him. He graduated from college, had a teaching degree, and was on his way to becoming a coach where he could impart all he knew about the variables of time, place, and desire.

Structures of Success

Each fall in the Spokane Public Schools, elementary students participate in various one mile cross country races at parks throughout the town. They culminate the season at Comstock Park, where each grade level, male and female, race off in an All City race. Literally thousands of little feet take off and circle the winding course, seeing how fast they can cover the mile distance. These children snake their way through the course with beat red faces and grass stained tennis shoes. These small runners wear their school jerseys that are often a few sizes too big. The running bug hits early.

District 81, which includes the majority of high schools in the Greater Spokane League, has this advantage and structure of success set in place. The Central Valley School District, where Bob spent a majority of his career did not have an All City meet.

Each spring in the Spokane Public Schools, elementary students participate in the Fit for Bloomsday program. Each of the schools has a six week program that prepares their students to run in either the Junior Bloomsday Race aimed at children, or the actual Bloomsday Race.

The Central Valley School District did not have the Fit for Bloomsday program in their elementary schools. Bob knew they did not have the built in structures for success. Sitting in his classroom, teaching mathematics, Bob knew the numbers and the structures that were before him and the struggle he fought each and every year.

Bob Barbero, left; Arthur Lydiard, right

Bob saw Pat Tyson speaking to the masses on his team before meets. He saw a tidal wave of 80 plus JV runners warming up on the course. He saw Pat talk to the seven varsity athletes that were Division I bound and that had risen to the top.

The numbers were all in Pat's favor.

Bob would then look over at Coach Mike Hadway of Ferris, with his 12 or so athletes, knowing that five of them would run in the junior varsity race while the seven left were boys that were young men seemingly cut out of wood. Bob knew Mike because he had volunteered to help train with his team during track and cross country while finishing his student teaching at University High School. Mike had found an old trail snaking up Brown's mountain, the mountain that separates Ferris High School from University High School in the Valley. Bob knew firsthand Mike was running as much as his athletes and he looked like he could step on the course and still run like a youth. Ferris may not have had numbers but they had worked like champions, continuing the legacy set before them.

Bob had to convince kids to turn out for a sport that they had not only never heard of, but had never participated in.

Bob's challenge was to try and start a legacy.

Mead's first moment of success with distance running came with Frank Knott winning the first individual Washington State title in 1959. Roger's legacy starts with Gerry. North Central's legacy starts with Tracy. Ferris' legacy starts with Rick and Herm. There was no champion at University High School.

University High School was the team with the colors and title of University of Southern California's Trojan, but they did not have the lights, looks, or makings of an LA script. University High School had a blue collar atmosphere and spirit. The major employer in the Valley was Kaiser Aluminum and most of the families living in the Valley had someone working there. The expectation for many at University High School entailed a future in their father's footsteps working at Kaiser Aluminum, if they were lucky. The title of the school may have been synonymous with further education, but for those growing up in the Valley, it seemed further from the truth. University High School seemed the summation of many student's education.

Gerry's father had worked at Kaiser Aluminum. University was a school full of potential Gerry Lindgrens, but they had no inkling of what could be because there had been no emphasis on running at any level of their education.

Bob set out each year to do the impossible and start from scratch. He went down the hallways, looking inside classes for anyone that showed something resembling the look of a distance runner. He would pull the kid out of class for a brief second and then try to convince them to turn out for track or cross country.

The student would often stare back at Bob with their best impression of a deer looking into headlights. Most times they would ask what cross country running was. He would use the line that was used on himself as a kid, "Oh, it's like track but in the fall time." Then the kid would say they had no interest and Bob would ask them to send out another kid sitting in the class.

It was an uphill battle.

Bob knew he could plan the workouts and help the team succeed, but he also knew he needed athletes that believed in running as much as he did.

Running and succeeding were not as simple as plugging in the numbers with x being the interval done at y speed; there were some variables and intangibles such as passion and legacy that needed to be present. He was fighting a factory line mentality that was set against him. Sure there were students each year being pushed out on the school conveyer belt, but they came with pre-formed thoughts about distance running and the neighborhood they came from.

The hardest part of success is the initial success.

Year after year, Bob would try and get a elementary school training program in place, like the Fit for Bloomsday or the cross country program from District 81, and year after year there would not be teachers willing to sacrifice their time for the students. They did not see the purpose of the program or the spirit in which it was intended. Some even questioned Bob as to why he wanted to see grade school aged children out running.

One year, Bob planned on creating a race for the children to run on Saturday. Bob made his way from one elementary school to another, in the days prior to e-mail, trying to call and schedule meetings with PE teachers. He made sure to have plenty of flyers for the teachers to pass out. One meeting in particular is exemplary of the struggle he faced.

Bob had just finished explaining the flier to the PE teacher standing in front of him.

After his impassioned speech Bob exited through the door and then thought of one last thing to say regarding awards and ribbons being handed out after the races. When Bob looked back over his shoulder and through the window to the PE teacher's office he felt his heart sink.

He saw the PE teacher tossing all the fliers right into a garbage can.

The only thing Bob could do was walk out of the school and hope his next school had hired a younger, hungrier, more impassioned teacher.

This mentality and approach, this factory work, punch card, clock in and clock out system, was as stuck in the schools as it was in the future lives of its students.

Unless that PE teacher and others like them either died or moved, students were stuck with them for the lifetime of that teacher. And in some instances that can mean decades of the same dead end approach.

Bob felt the madness of a system and a people not realizing what they could have if they just elevated their sights. Bob also became more resolute. He felt like he was encountering the children or grandchildren of his college professor who had been ignorant of the anomaly that surrounded them.

The distance Bob would have to cover in order to succeed was longer than others and he knew the eventual victory would be all the sweeter because of it. Doors that could have otherwise been opened were closed to students who never knew they had been cheated out of an opportunity.

Bob knew that such a system was not unique to his school. He knew that there were teachers and schools across the country with the same mentality, but the madness came from knowing that it could be different. He needed a few like minded people to see it through. He needed the volunteers, he needed the start of a legacy, and he knew that once success was started, there would be followers. Bob's first state team title was nearly twenty years in the making.

Perennial

Only 82 runners out of the original 1,198 have participated in every Bloomsday Race since 1977. Bob Barbero is one of those 82 athletes. They call this group of runners *Perennials*. Bob has adopted the perennial attitude of a competitor since his very first moments with the sport.

Bob has always been more concerned about keeping a record for all of his athletes.

At the end of each season, Bob would put together a copy of all the news articles that had been written about the University High School cross country program and its athletes. He would also put a copy of the races and the times run by all his athletes. Pictures of his athletes from various meets would also line the pages of this little booklet he gave each athlete. At the end he would have comparison charts for the all time records of athletes over the years.

Freshman could see how they stacked against previous freshman. Sophomores could see sophomores, and their improvement from freshman year. These metrics were used as motivation for the athletes to have something to hold on to.

He drew on his wealth of knowledge coming from the area. Bob had been in road races with Gerry, he had competed against Herm's teams at Ferris. For a time when Bob ran at Spokane Falls Community College (SFCC) Rick had been the assistant coach working with the distance team. Bob quite literally ran in Rick's footsteps.

The most memorable workout had to be the 200 meter intervals.

Bob Barbero, left; Rick Riley, right

Bob was an 800 meter runner. At the beginning of each interval he toed the line standing right next to Rick.

This time I'm going to do it, Bob thought.

"Ready go!" Rick said, tapping his watch as he led the way around the bend.

Stay with him, stay with him, Bob thought.

50 meters into the 200 meter interval it always seemed that Rick would go from being an arms length distance away to 10 meters in front.

Bob would continually toe that line, knowing of all the previous close calls.

During high school Bob's team had taken second at the state meet in cross country. In practices for the travelling team in college Bob raced off against another athlete for the final varsity spot and Bob always finished second.

Running behind Rick, even in the twilight years of his competitive running, Bob finished second.

Yet, Bob's mentality was never second place.

He knew the results would come, but he needed more time.

In 1982 University finished sixth at the state meet with Shadle Park winning it all. In 1983 University finished seventh. In 1984, University took fifth. It would be five years before University was at state again. In 1989 and 1990 University took second place to Pat's team at Mead. In 1991 they would take fourth while again Mead won. In 1996 Mead was again at state, and again University High School took second to Mead. For 14 years of coaching there had been seven teams to make it to state. Three of those teams had taken second place. There were groups and waves of athletes starting to buy in and then the support system would evaporate after the team did not win it all.

Bob was in a perpetual state of trying to convince his athletes that the time to strike was right now.

When Bob could get a hold of a kid that held promise and convince him to turn out there could be great things. One of those athletes he got to turn out was Seth Mott, who had considered himself a baseball player when he initially

went to high school. Bob convinced him that cross country would help him with baseball in the spring. It was enough to get him interested, and by the time spring rolled around, baseball was left to the sideline while he pursued a future in distance running.

The timing to beat Pat Tyson's program at Mead was at its best in 1997. The Mead School District had finally split Mead High

Bob Barbero, left; Mike Barbero, right; Joe Hawkins, middle

© Peter Hawkins

School into two high schools: Mead and Mt. Spokane. As such, Pat's top runner would now run for Mt. Spokane and not Mead. Pat's stranglehold of over 80 athletes turning out for the sport was now cut in half.

Seth Mott and others recognizing their time to shine was upon them helped lead University to the state title. Since 1963 when University High School first opened its doors, there had been no boys team to win a state title of any kind in any sport. Football, basketball, wrestling, baseball, track, tennis, golf, and soccer had yielded no team championships in the 35 year history of the school.

Bob Barbero came along with his perennial spirit and record keeping mentality. He worked tirelessly for success and finally achieved it. For three straight years his boys cross country program won the state title. The team also won a track title in 1998, 1999, and a second place finish in 2000 by a single point. Both programs started winning and Bob was at its heart.

What added to Bob's enjoyment was seeing his son Mike pass through his program with his friends. As a junior in high school Mike watched from the sideline as his teammates won the first state title. Then as a senior, running as the seventh man, Mike was part of University's second state title.

Mike graduated from University High School and continued his education at Washington State University. Mike's passion for distance running grew out of his father's coaching. Knowing that his times were not fast enough to compete on a collegiate team, but wanting to stick around the sport, Mike asked his father if he could write a letter of recommendation for him.

Bob reached out the Washington State University cross country coach at the time James Li, who was coaching Bernard Lagat. Lagat was at the beginning of his career which eventually spanned five Olympics where he represented two countries: Kenya and the United States. The letter was received in the spirit it was intended and Mike Barbero became an intern with unique access to watch one of the world's best athletes train and prepare for greatness. Mike had his own version of Pre before him on a Hangman Valley course.

Since graduating from WSU, Mike has gone into coaching himself and is working where his father left off at University High School. Mike is also a math teacher. He likewise looks at the numbers, times, workouts and statistics, trying to continue a culture of success.

Mike Hadway: Cut Out of Wood

In the late spring of 1973, Coach Hendrickson of Rogers High School in Puyallup, Washington, sat in his office waiting to speak and not wanting to look at his young athlete and captain to be, Mike Hadway.

Mike just stood there waiting for his coach to speak. Mike's gratitude grew out of the fact that someone like his coach had noticed him and overseen his improvement. Praise did not come often for Mike in either his school or home life.

"I'm not going to be your coach next year," Coach Hendrickson said flatly.

The smile Mike wore while walking in suddenly disappeared.

It felt like abandonment.

"The assistant football coach is going to take over." Coach Hendrickson said.

Mike had a future ahead of him and it involved taking ownership over his own workouts moving forward. Mike's coaching career started in high school and his first athlete he ever trained was himself.

Mike had only picked up running two years previous. A friend of his had explained to him that school got out earlier for young athletes on the middle school track team. Mike, seizing an opportunity to get out of class, signed up for the team.

At his first practice the middle school coach stared at this pale, strawberry blond boy standing in front of him. Mike did not look powerful enough to sprint or lean enough to run distance. Like all middle school kids, Mike looked uncomfortable and like he was not able to fit inside himself. Finally, the coach decided to do what he always did: throw him into the middle of nowhere and see where that took him.

"Two laps," he had said to Mike and the other athletes he did not know where to sort.

Two laps would show one of two things: either the kid could sprint or he could run distance.

So young Mike, the afterthought of the middle school coach, toed the line with all the remaining athletes he did not know what to do with.

The other kids walked up to the line and crouched. Mike, never having raced before tried his best to imitate those around him.

"Ready. Go!" the coach shouted.

Young Mike bolted to the front and stayed there. Around the first curve they went and into a straightaway. Mike kept his legs moving and arms pumping; not really knowing what to do. Mike just made sure to stay in the lead.

Mike rounded another turn.

Mike's heart caught up to his leg's demands and started pounding out blood to fuel the oxygen needed to keep pace.

Into the straightaway and towards his coach with the stopwatch Mike kept moving. Numbers were shouted out to him as he passed but Mike just kept running amidst the confusion.

Mike kept pushing as everything inside him kept pounding. His feet pounded the ground. His brain pounded. His heart pounded.

Mike crossed the finish line on his second lap and heard his coach yell out to him "2:10." The numbers were foreign to him. All he knew was that his legs felt like they were on fire and his arms ached as if they had been clutching a cliff's edge for two minutes. Then Mike realized that no one had passed him.

The middle school coach waited for his last experiment to cross the finish line and then he looked at the specimens in front of him. One by one and in reverse order he went to the athletes and made his comments. Some he put towards sprints and others towards distance events.

When the middle school coach finally got to Mike, who was still catching his breath, he declared, "Son, you are an 800 meter runner."

With that blessing and first attempt, Mike Hadway's running career began.

Young Mike was not certain what that meant, all he was certain of was the fact that he had won and that for the next three days he could barely walk. His muscles had torn in just about every place there was a muscle; his body was trying to heal itself and keep himself from sprinting away again.

It did not work.

The pain remained in every stride but Mike had the pleasure of knowing he had won at something, that he was good at something, and he wanted to feel that again.

Mike continued to run the 800 meter and he continued to win each race. He went undefeated throughout his entire eighth grade season. At the end of the season the same coach that declared he was an 800 meter runner also suggested that Mike turn out for cross country in high school.

In the fall of 1971, Mike turned out at for cross country at Rogers High School of Puyallup, Washington. It is the only other high school named in honor of the former governor. Built in 1968, Mike was entering into a new campus.

What most surprised Mike about high school cross country was the distance. The very first run in high school would be a five mile effort that felt like a marathon and had Mike thinking he might die. He did not die and the practice came to an end.

Rogers of Puyallup is only a little over eight miles away from Lincoln High School of Tacoma if a straight line was drawn between the two schools. Mike was younger than Pat Tyson and at a different school. Despite the close proximity, the schools did not compete in the same league. The famed coach Dan Watson helped Pat earn his seventh place finish at state in cross country and contribute on their state championship track team. Pat was drenched in opportunities to learn about the sport, to be taken to meets, to even have opportunities to talk to coaches and Olympians like Bill Dellinger.

Mike did not have Dan Watson.

Pat also had a mother that supported him in his dream. The never say no attitude was rooted in word and in deed. Mike had both mother and father in his home but he did not have the hopeful atmosphere.

When it came time to go home, it was not to a father like Dominick Barbero or to a mother like Pat Tyson's; Hadway went home to hear "No," and especially in regards to his running. Mike walked daily into a dimly lit house not a home; it had the structure of security but lacked the love.

Running became an outlet, an escape.

Frustrations could be taken out on the roads, hills, and trails that Mike escaped to in his runs.

Mike Hadway's father flew P-38's in WWII, which is the swiss army knife of planes due to its ability to intercept, go on bombing runs, perform ground attacks, night fighting, photo reconnaissance, and radar and visual mapping for larger bombers. Despite manning a craft with multiple purposes, Mike's father was a man with a singular mind. After the war he wanted to open a resort and tourist attraction in Twisp, Washington. He went so far as to purchase a tiny airport out there, but the idea and dream never left the ground. Returning to the hard realities before him, Mike's father went to work at Boeing manufacturing. His one dream had been crushed and so he left that believing to the side and got used to the realities before him. Instead of flying planes he would be on the cold slabs of cement, housed indoors performing mechanical tasks on a mechanical plane. It would pay well enough, and that was enough to expect out of life.

After work, Mike's father would come home to see his son fresh off of practice. Tired from his own days efforts, Mike's father would light a cigarette,

© Rogers High School Yearbook, Puyallup School District

and then proceed to tell his son what he needed to do in order to be successful.

Thinking he knew how to best raise Mike and his sister, Mike's father thought that a job should be found and real work done. With his military mind of seeing a problem and finding a solution it was a matter of making orders and someone taking them. If pieces to life were set apart, then you could fasten them together. To Mike's father, all this running did not accomplish anything. You started and finished at the same spot on the track. Why do it?

In all of Mike's races throughout his life his parents only showed up to two of them. As an act of rebellion aimed at his father Mike grew his hair out and let his father know exactly how he felt.

Mike continued to improve with each practice. He would eventually be the second runner across the finish line for Rogers of Puyallup in the 1971 state meet where he would finish 80th overall and with a time of 13:37 on a 2.5 mile course at Evergreen High School. Not a bad time for a sophomore who had come off the street. The Green Lake course had been abandoned and a more defined course created.

Between Mike's sophomore and junior season he made a huge jump due in large part to regular training. He improved from 80th to 11th overall and 13:37 to 12:31. He again finished second for his team. His team had hoped to win but Mike and his teammate Jim Brewster were the only ones who performed like champions that day. Jim Brewster would go on to win the state track meet in 1973, winning both the 1,600 meter in 4:10 and the 800 meter in 1:53.3. These were impressive times considering Jim was smoking around a pack and a half of cigarettes each day. This impressive talent was not lost on the less talented, hardworking Mike.

Mike was on the rise, Coach Hendrickson had been instrumental in this rise; showing him books on Jim Ryun and Arthur Lydiard. At school and on the roads Mike had found something to pour his heart into.

The team that was winning the state title during Mike's high school years was the Richland Bombers, coached by Max Jensen. The Bombers would win three straight state titles under Max Jensen's command and then two more after he left.

Richland High School's mascot has not always been the Bombers; they used to be called the Colts, Broncos, and Beavers at various times in their history. However, due to the influence of the Manhattan project and the plutonium used to create the atomic bomb, the town and high school eventually decided to change their mascot to the Bombers. Originally the atomic bomb was used as the mascot, but as time has gone on the shift in focus has gone from the weapon of mass destruction to the pilots fighting in WWII.

Members of the community during WWII wondered how they could best help in the war effort. Max Blanchard was one such community member who had a son fighting overseas and wondered how he could help him. After receiving a letter from his son shortly after D-Day, Max's son recounted how helpful the air support had been in their fight against the Nazis. Thus sparked the idea in his father to supply the army with a plane. This effort and the plane behind it became known as "Day's Pay" with the slogan, "Give a day's pay and send a bomber on it's way." 51,000 people that were part of the Hanford site and area ended up sacrificing a day's salary so that a plane could be purchased. After the money was secured, the town purchased a B-17 Flying Fortress, the plane most needed by the Air Force at that time.

This plane could fly 3,750 miles before needing refueling. The cost of this 10 man operating fleet was $300,000.

All told, the plane would fly 60 missions, and take its share of shots while dropping bombs over Germany. After the war, the plane was crunched into scrap and a letter was sent to the Hanford Engineer workers informing them of the results of their plane.

This community banded together and had helped win a war. The children of such a tight knit community, that were service minded and respected authority, were the athletes that Max Jensen inherited in his program at Richland High School.

Mike was in a home and with parents that had created a toxic environment. He needed an out. Running was an escape for him. Yes, there would be disagreements and there would continue to be problems at home, but when he was on the roads, running, Mike found he could breathe again.

That is why when Mike's high school coach decided to leave it felt like a bomb had been dropped on his world. His one outlet for help, the one person who had seen him and believed in him as he rose up to be one of the top runners in the state, was now leaving him.

Tracy Walters, Herm Caviness and Dan Watson are not the kind of men that are in endless supply.

Mike then had to do what he would always do; be his own coach. The books of inspiration from before would now be practical roadmaps for success. If there was a book on running out there, Mike was reading it, then implementing it into his training routines.

Mike was free to test out his limits.

Yet for all his self training and tinkering, he only managed to improve himself to eighth place overall at the state cross country meet in 1973. He improved over his previous year's mark by only four seconds. There was no Jim Brewster to chase and no coach to aid in his endeavors. He knew he had talent and work ethic, he just needed more time to figure out how training worked.

In the late spring of 1974 John Buck, who was the coach at Spokane Community College (SCC), paid a visit to Mike's home. Coach Buck wanted to know whether Mike was serious about distance running. At the state meet in track that year he had finished third place running 4:17.

Mike quickly let the coach in. After a moment of chit chat regarding his visit and desire to perhaps see about Mike joining the team the coach asked if he could see Mike's room.

1974 Men's Cross Country Team - Spokane Community College
Mike Hadway, top left; Steve Kiesel, top third from right

© Northwest Athletic Conference Hall of Fame

Walking into Mike's room, Buck saw books on distance running Mike had read on a makeshift shelf. Coach Buck saw posters and picture cutouts from *Track & Field News* and other sources of various runners throughout time and throughout the world running along the walls of the room. A small sanctuary and shrine to running stood before him.

That was all the Coach Buck needed to see.

Mike was offered a spot on the team. A lifeline out of the gray, the fog, the rain of the Seattle area had come; Spokane was on the horizon and Mike's dreams could take flight.

On Mike's new team at SCC would be one of Dan Watson's other great athletes, Steve Kiesel, who had been an outstanding 800 meter runner at Lincoln High School. Steve would eventually be a longtime coach in Spokane. Steve Kiesel coached at Rogers and Mead High School. While coaching at Rogers, Steve would coach alongside Herm Caviness' son, Chris. They were both able to work with the greatest female track athlete from Spokane, Rebecca Noble. Rebecca would be a multiple state champion, a Junior Pan American Champion and an NCAA Champion.

The team at SCC in 1975 was great.

It was a team that was more than just the name associated with it. At their conference championship SCC's top six individuals placed first, third, fourth, fifth, sixth, and seventh overall. They nearly totaled a perfect score. The team was good enough to beat Washington State University. Mike believes, as well as Bob Barbero and others, that this team was likely one of the top five teams in the country at that time.

Coach Buck eventually left the team. Once more, a coach of Mike's walked out.

Coach Buck's replacement was Max Jensen who had lead those Richland Bombers to multiple state titles over the teams from Spokane.

Running to the Max

In the late summer of 1975 the men's cross country team at SCC met for practice. Notably absent from outside the coaches office was the workout sheet for the week. Also absent, for the time being, was the coach. Mike stood with his teammates, double checking with one another that they had heard correctly what time Max had scheduled the practice.

Finally a large blue van appeared in the parking lot.

Max sat in the driver's seat sporting his mustache and his typical smile. His boyish face always looked like it was in a school picture mode, just waiting for the picture to be taken. Smiling at his athletes who came over to his car, Max killed his engine.

Eventually someone on the team got around to asking the coach what the workout was for the day.

Max, still smiling, informed his team that they would be running long that day.

New to this coach and his way of doing things the athletes wondered what the coach meant by his vague answer.

The athletes were trying to figure out their new coach while Max was trying to figure out his athletes.

Max had his athletes pile into his van. He was going to take them to their run that day.

Into the van piled the team of skinny runners and off they went. With his team loaded in, he started driving out of town. The car ride lasted several minutes longer than any of them thought it would. Finally, Max pulled off to the side of a forgotten dirt road.

Max told his athletes to get out of the van.

Nervous looks were worn on athletes faces as they stood wondering if they were expected to run back into town from this far out distance.

With his head hanging out the window and sporting that perpetual positivity, Max looked at his athletes and finally gave some hint of what awaited them.

Max unveiled the workout. The team was simply supposed to start out running down the dirt road and once they saw Max's van they were to run to it and the run would be over. With that brief explanation Max rolled up his window, turned the key into the ignition bringing his car to life and started driving on down the road.

These skinny men, shirtless, stranded and wearing running shorts, looked at one another confused. Was this some kind of joke?

Mike started heading towards the dust cloud in front of him and everyone soon followed suit. The dust cloud soon settled and the blue van disappeared off in the distance.

Several athletes on the team tried to figure out what lay ahead of them.

Some offered questions, others offered guesses.

Silence ensued as the pace began to pick up.

The next bend came and as they rounded it there was no blue van in sight. They continued onward and more questions and conjectures came pouring out of the athletes.

The *I don't know* answer became a common refrain. Those that were quick to offer comments and questions early in the run, soon found themselves lacking words, or at least the willingness to offer them. The pace was consistent, the time passed, bends in the road came and went, but there was no van in sight. The road rose and fell and twisted and turned.

A guess would be made as to how far they had traveled and then it would be compared with how much time had passed since they started their run. It was 1975 and no one had a GPS watch.

It was a mental exercise as much as it was a physical one; they would need to learn how to survive both elements of running.

Onward they went. They did not know where they were, they did not know how far they travelled. Their eyes kept upward, looking for that blue van. And they kept running, questioning themselves about how far they had gone and how much they had left.

They had run several miles but they did not know how many more miles awaited them.

It was hot out and getting hotter.

Off in the distance it looked like a large vehicle was parked on the side of the dirt road.

Hope sprang inside them as they approached.

However, as the distance shrank between the runners and the vehicle in the distance it became apparent that it was not the blue van.

Some cursed at their new coach not present. Questions again began to creep their way to the forefront of their minds.

How far have we gone?

How much longer can I go?

Turning yet another corner in the road, with trees and brush on either side obscuring the view, Mike could finally see off in the distance the blue van.

As those in the lead pack approached the van they saw the taillights come to life. The pace dropped suddenly, then returned to normal.

They got close enough to the van to almost be able to see the side mirrors. Mike could see Max looking at him, smiling.

The car lurched forward, pulling back onto the road and moved around another bend.

Disbelief and wonder filled those chasing the van.

They kept running on the fringes of their mind, trying to go from keeping pace to surviving. Around the next bend they went and the van was not seen. They kept moving, going upward and downward, hearing the crunch of gravel beneath their feet. Salt crystals outlined where their sweat had been.

Once more Hadway rounded a bend and looked up to see the van in the distance.

The question of distance did not matter anymore and the question of time did not matter either. The only question that mattered was whether the van's lights would come alive again as they approached.

Mike could see the side mirrors, he could see his coach smiling. He reached out to touch the van, as if to make sure that it was there and not going anywhere. Max poked his head out of the side of the van.

"You guys did wonderful." Max said. This would be his common refrain and he would always couple it with his positively beaming smile.

He finally got out of the van and walked to the back of it. He opened up the rear of his van and started filling up and passing out plastic cups of water from the large container he had sitting there. The athletes did not need any coaxing to fill up. Like thirsty thoroughbreds they went back and back again, drinking deeply.

A silent, somber group sat in the van, more gritty than when they had last been in it. The windows were rolled down so the smell had somewhere to escape as they made their long trek back to SCC.

They had literally run to *the* Max.

Practices with Max followed the same pattern as that first day. No workout was ever published to the team beforehand. He would always show up smiling and beaming with positivity, waiting for one of his athletes to ask what they were going to do that day for a workout. Max was always ready to answer with his short single word response.

"Running."

His athletes quickly learned that asking for specifics never yielded any results. They simply prepared themselves for the unknown.

Coupled with Max's smiling was also a complete lack of subtlety. After coaching at Spokane Community College Max would eventually end up coaching at Ferris High School. One time after a hard interval workout with his high school athletes, Max asked them as they were jogging back to school if they wanted a ride. The boys welcomed the rest and jumped in the car. Max ended up making a pair of right turns and the team was suddenly heading back to the park. Once they reached the park, Max turned to his athletes.

"There are no shortcuts to success. Get out and run back." Max said.

The goal was to build up the reserves of his athletes, physically as well as mentally. This approach to running and coaching was a constant. Max was teaching his runners. They should not run off of time or distance, but they needed to run off of feeling. They needed to survive. He wanted his athletes to realize they had more in their reserves than the numbers associated with time and distance. He wanted his athletes to view running differently. In the process of stretching the minds of his athletes, he won over their hearts, especially Mike's.

Coaches came and went in Mike's running career; from his middle school coach, his high school coach, the football coach who took over, then John Buck, and now Max. He had only ran for six years yet he had gone through five coaches. The close of the two year community college experience brought with it mixed emotions.

Instead of a coach leaving him, Mike, due to the end of his two year program had to leave his coach.

Max was not a loud coach, he was silent and full of smiles. He loved to compete and he loved to see his athletes running their hardest. That survival approach to running resonated with Mike, who had survived since his very first run and race.

Of all the coaches that impacted Mike, there was none he took so much from, nor loved as dearly as Max.

It was hard for Mike to then leave SCC and move on to Eastern Washington University. The hardest part was transitioning to yet another coach, Jerry Martin, who did not have workouts as demanding as the ones Mike had just left. Instead of wondering and surviving the elements with Max, Coach Martin's workouts were posted the week ahead of time. Mike and Steve Kiesel, his former teammate at SCC who had also moved on to Eastern, would look at the workouts and realize that if they wanted to be competitive they would have to do more and at a higher tempo. Mike and Steve decided to continue training with the SCC team as a means of staying fit.

Coach Jerry Martin missed seeing his newly signed athletes and called in Mike and Steve for a meeting.

Once more, Mike stood in the office of a coach.

Coach Martin expressed to his athletes that the reason he had recruited them was for their leadership ability. As such he needed his athletes to be present for their practices. If they were to ever become the leaders he wanted them to be they needed to lead by example.

Mike and Steve agreed but asked their coach to not be afraid to push the envelope in practices. The goals that Steve and Mike had were very high and they knew that in order to reach such lofty goals they would need to push themselves to their very limits.

Coach Martin took the words of his athletes to heart and increased both the intensity and the mileage. The only athletes to question the changes on the team were athletes that had been around before the shift. But even their initial hesitation and resistance subsided once the results from such hard work were witnessed.

Eventually graduation came and with it, the opportunity to teach and coach. Mike was now married and while his wife was getting her degree, he was working at Don Kardong's shoe store, *The Human Race*. After Mike's wife earned her degree and secured a job, Mike earned his teaching certificate while interning out at University High School where Bob Barbero was the coach.

Mike then landed a job teaching at Rogers High School. While working there he volunteered his efforts for the track team. However the head coach already had someone working with the distance squad and decided he needed Mike over with the pole vaulters.

Mike had no experience with pole vault, but he had plenty of experience teaching himself how to survive.

The will to do something is more important than the knowledge about something.

The lone student that vaulted for the team improved which was all that could be said from a guy that did not know anything about pole vault.

Mike continued to work at *The Human Race* trying to survive and feeling a little discouraged. He wondered what the future held for him. In walked Max Jensen who asked Mike, "Do you think you could help me coach up at Ferris High School?"

Mike hugged his former coach and said he would.

Max would eventually leave the program and Hadway had his start as a distance coach in 1986, the same year that Pat Tyson started coaching at Mead High School.

Mike taught woodshop in all his years at Ferris High School. His father's mind for engineering stuck with Mike. But whereas his father worked in the cold distant realm of machinery, Mike would work with wood. Knowing wood came with a sense of realizing how different timbers moved and what types of cuts you could get away with. Woodworking taught many of the same principles as running. Woodworking required working with an end in mind, and seeing the end product inside the raw material.

Mike approached his athletes much like he approached his own education. They, like him, would be men cut out of wood. They would be transformed. But initially, upon meeting him and working one's way through his workouts, an athlete felt like their legs had gotten ripped and run through a bandsaw.

Part of the legend of Mike Hadway came out of the names attributed to him by former athletes, "Hard-way Hadway" or "Ten a Day Hadway" were the names that stuck like varnish on Mike. Truth be told, Mike ran with his athletes and pushed the pace in all the workouts. Whereas Mead would have 70, 80, or over

90 athletes, Mike would have only 12 athletes by the end of his first season as coach. Most of his teams thereafter hovered around those same numbers. Only after state championships started to come in did the numbers start to grow, but not by much. Those early 12, like the select few that followed ever after, were all willing to be there and voluntarily submitted themselves to the work and expectations that followed. Just as Max had taught Hadway to survive, so too would Hadway help his runners to rely on themselves and recognize an inner strength and resolve they had not known existed.

Running for these 12 and others thereafter would be a pilgrimage of self-sacrifice. Voluntarily submitting themselves to 70, 80, or 90 miles a week for several weeks throughout a summer, Mike's athletes knew they were embarking on a journey others would not dare to venture into. They too would run to their own max.

Mike did not have any coach that gave him pep talks, that explained to him how intervals should work, or what pace to go on a tempo run. He did not have the free flowing dialogue of ideas that Tracy created for his athletes. He did not have the militaristic approach and outline that Herm created for his athletes. Mike never rubbed shoulders with Pre, Dellinger, or Bowerman and had no stories to share about them. Mike did not have a mother or father who encouraged him.

Much of adult life is lived without mother or father, teammates or coaches and the structures that go with them. As important as each of those relationships and structures are, they can create in some dependency. And suddenly when people are found without them, some are lost. Mike prepared his athletes for the times when they would need to run alone.

The talent Mike tried to develop in his athletes was not only physical but also the mental ability to endure difficulty. He had one coach for a short period of time that helped him run to the max. That single lesson of resilience defined Mike and his coaching style forever after.

Mike's own experience with running was started with a middle school coach declaring that he was a runner. He knew the power and influence a middle school coach could make. Mike reached out to the cross country and track coach at Chase Middle School, which is the main feeder school for incoming freshman at Ferris High School.

Bryce Curray, left; Dave Fuller, right

Dave Fuller: Green Means Go

Twenty year old Dave Fuller sat controlling the machine's movements inside of a rock quarry located on the coast of Ecuador. He sat at his work while silently surveying his past. The foreign had been familiar to him; he had grown up breathing the thin clean air 9,000 feet above sea level.

Dave's parents became missionaries for their church and left the comfort and security of their native state of New York in the early 1950s. They started a medical practice for the underserved in a third world country. Their seven children would grow up in a different world compared to the one that other American children knew. Dave's father was a physician and his mother a nurse. They would physically heal and offer spiritual relief for those seeking either.

Moving the rocks in the quarry, Dave thought over his life and the lives of those siblings he grew up with.

The rocks before him only needed enough pressure before they would break; enough force applied in just the right area and what was solid would split. These rocks would be used to form the base layer of a new road; they would be used for a foundation.

Dave could control the movements of the machine he was in, but he could not control the movement of his mind or the unsolicited summoning of memories, sweet and haunting as they were, that flashed before him.

Growing up in the green of Shell Mera, a full days drive from Quito, had been all that Dave had ever known. Daily he ran ragged over the jungles just outside his door. Running brought with it adventure and opportunity. He recognized, like the local children, when a storm was coming. He knew what the impending rain meant. Like the local children he ran for cover trying to beat the sheet of rainfall blanketing the land. There are feet of rain that fall every year in Shell Mera. Small rivers would open during and after the storms passed through.

He enjoyed the sun that showed after storms. He loved the smell of the earth that seemed to breathe after rainfall.

Dave and his brother Danny, separated by only 13 months, would play together in these small streams that opened up. They would play with anyone that would play with them. Makeshift baseball games would start with makeshift materials for a diamond and Dave would be the base runner for anyone that would let him. Dave loved running the bases and would sprint around as fast as his little legs would carry him. They had nothing but the joy of play and were therefore the richest of children.

If they were not playing games with neighbors, then Dave and Danny were likely out fishing. They had made their own poles, bought a string of nylon from a store in town, and they each had one hook a piece. They went out and dug in the earth to find their own bait and went to the closest river they could find in the jungle. Hours would pass with these two kids unattended in the dense green glades, swimming and fishing. With their catch for the day they would trek on home together, retracing their steps and hauling their fish. Once home their mother would cook their catch for the boys.

Together they would all sit and listen to their father recount the events from the day or the most recent snake bite that their father had treated. It seemed to Dave that there must be a lot of snakes because their father kept talking about another local person being bitten by a snake; but in all his time growing up, neither he nor his siblings were ever bitten by a snake.

There were few days of boredom growing up on the frontier jungle in Ecuador. The trees were green, tall, and thick. The earth seemed as fresh as baked bread. The sky was clear, clearer in his youth than the smog he would see at other stages in his life. As a kid he could remember looking outside their home in Shell Mera and watch volcanic eruptions off in the distance from Sangay, one of Ecuador's most active volcanoes. While attending school in the city of Quito he could see five snow capped mountains, dormant volcanoes, perched in the surrounding distance. It was a land known to be wild, but free. He had known little of heartache or heartbreak.

He grew up on the outskirts of the wild jungle but felt free from the potential terrors it provided.

Leaving Ecuador for America, Dave entered Westmont College, a small Christian Liberal Arts school tucked inside Santa Barbara, California. The world of America seemed so quick, so fast paced, so full of buildings and concrete. Entering college, Dave set about trying to remember the lessons his parents gave in Ecuador. He was faced with the question of what would be his life's work?

Dave settled on a Religious Studies degree, but he would remain unsettled with the direction and purpose of his life. He returned back to Ecuador, far from the college, the campus, and the studies that had seemed so important. He left everything to live with and work for his brother-in-law on the coast, working in a burlap-sack factory and rock quarry.

The rock before Dave, sat stubborn, so unyielding and unwilling to move. The caterpillar only had so much strength and leverage it could muster out of its mechanical wheels and joints. Only so much the engine could whirl and hum out; some jobs were just too big for it.

Dave thought back the day and the hour he could never forget. It was a day just under a year before man would walk on the moon. Yet, Dave felt as far from the moon as he did from the heavens. It was August 8, 1968, the day his sister Susie died from an overdose on medication.

The world he had known, full of wild, free vibrant life had been struck and death had entered in an untimely and crude manner. Dave had to face realities, and he had to approach life, memories, and moments differently.

But the sun kept rising, and setting, and the moon followed suit in the sky. The clouds continued to drop rain, the earth breathed after the water washed away and the sun baked the earth once more. Dave needed to find out what his next move in life should be. He was living with another sister and her husband in Shell Mera, staying with them, working, and living most of his days in isolation at the rock quarry. Nearly a year Dave had sat, day in and day out in the mechanical machine, making mechanical movements, crushing and moving rock.

Should he stay in Ecuador, or should he return to the United States?

Dave continued to work at the rock quarry, thinking over his life, his sister's life, his surviving siblings, and the future that still remained before him. His mind ran over the time he had spent in America, over the time spent in classrooms studying and learning the religion he had grown up in and loved. Yet, confronted before him was a trial of faith that he knew he had to confront.

Coming back to Dave's mind was the story of Gideon from the Old Testament. Gideon had asked for proof of God's will through two miracles. There had been the fleece that was wet while the ground was dry and then the following day the fleece was made dry and the ground was wet. Gideon had received signs; Dave wanted his own sign regarding his life.

Working as he had every day previous, Dave went to work and got ready to climb into his caterpillar to move and split rock in isolation when his eyes raised up and saw someone in the distance wearing a shirt. On the shirt was printed a stoplight and the light was green. He felt that the light being green meant he should go back to the states. Dave continued to work that day and wondered if he would see the worker or the shirt again soon. Days passed and the worker and the shirt did not appear. Dave knew he had received his answer. He ceased to split the rock and quit clawing at the cavern below. He climbed out of his caterpillar, filled with a hope for his new unknown life in America.

Mr. Wonderful

Dave returned to Westmont College sure that he was supposed to be there, but unsure as to how the rest of his life would unfold. During this time he sought out more inspiration from a missionary from Ecuador, who gave him some simple advice.

"Dave, you just got to bloom wherever you're planted." She said.

Not sure where he would be planted, but not wanting to be alone in the process, Dave set out to try and find someone to marry. Five years previous he had worked a summer as a lifeguard while there was a girl in the distance who had worked checking out boats to various campers. He remembered her name was Tammy. He decided he might try his luck; the only problem was he had no idea if she was still at college in Santa Barbara.

Dave went to the information desk at Westmont College.

"I am looking for a person named Tammy, do you have anyone at the school going by that name?" Dave asked.

A binder was opened and a list of names poured over. There were many Tammy's on campus. The first Tammy with the last name did not sound right, but the second Tammy name sounded like the winner and so Dave continued.

"Can I have her number?" He asked.

The attendant behind the counter gave Dave her number and so he called her up. The voice on the other end of the phone definitely was hers and so he had picked the right Tammy.

"Hello, it's me Dave." he said.

"Dave who?" Tammy asked.

"Dave Fuller." he said.

He knew that this would either work, or this girl would think he was crazy.

"Oh I know who you are." Tammy said.

"Great. Well, I was just wondering if you wanted to go to the homecoming game and then go out to eat." Dave said.

"That would be great." She said.

The time and place was arranged and on their first date, Tammy went up to Dave and gave him a big hug.

One of Tammy's roommates shouted out, "Have fun with Mr. Wonderful" as they made their way to Dave's car.

Whatever impression Tammy had left on Dave had been equaled by Dave on Tammy. The two continued to date and Mr. Wonderful proved to be all that Tammy would ever want in a man. The two were married and moved to Pasadena, California.

The joys of marriage brought with it the struggle to find employment. Tammy worked as a substitute teacher during the day and a waitress at night as Dave worked at the Boys and Girls Club of Pasadena.

Remembering his mentor's advice, Dave tried to flower in Pasadena and was looking for any opportunity to go into public schools and become a teacher. While Tammy was subbing one day she heard of a new long-term sub position opening that involved math at the middle school.

Despite never having earned a degree in math, Dave applied and got an interview.

"What's your experience with math?" The principal asked.

"I took an algebra class in high school and a trigonometry class in college that was difficult." Dave said. The trigonometry class he had dropped out of.

"Would you be willing to get a minor in mathematics at the local college as you continue to teach here?" The principal asked.

"Yes." Dave said.

Thus began Dave's career as a teacher.

After achieving the minor in math, Dave and Tammy now had their second and last child, a boy. Surveying their environment they decided that the world of California was not a world they wanted to live in forever. It was a great place to go to school for them, and it was a great place to visit, but it was a concrete jungle that they did not want to be in forever.

Three of Dave's siblings had moved to Spokane and the parents had followed suit. Dave and Tammy had visited and decided they would like to come to Spokane, Washington.

In 1986, Dave Fuller got his first job at Excelsior Middle School, which used to be part of the Spokane Public Schools. Excelsior was a school for at risk youth.

Steve Kramer, far left; Dave Fuller, far right

Dave worked with students confronting a multitude of issues in their lives.

Over the course of his career Dave saw several people, like himself, sitting at the controls to the rock quarry of their lives.

At the time of Dave's hiring there was no physical education program at Excelsior, and so the principal asked him what he would need in order to have a good program. Dave got a list of items he thought necessary and gave it to his principal, who looked over the list and said he could have it all.

Having a stock of supplies was easy, but getting the students to use them and to stay on the field was the tricky part. During one lesson on baseball, there were three students who made a sprint to the fence in the outfield and jumped it.

Dave placed one reliable student in charge and made a chase after the three runaways. They split in different directions and so Dave was only able to track one of them down who then told where the other two had gone and planned to meet up.

The work was demanding, but it was rewarding. For the time that the students were in his class, Dave knew he could provide a shelter from some of the difficulties they faced. He took their struggles seriously, using his own life experience as a daily reminder of the silence attending inner tragedy.

Teaching came first, and coaching came second for Dave. The primary focus would be on the classes and students he interacted with, but if there were an opportunity for both, Dave would not shy away from it. When Libby School needed a PE instructor and a coach, Dave stepped in to help with their cross country and track programs. And likewise, when the new Chase Middle School opened up on the South Hill of Spokane in 1993, Dave taught PE and coached cross country and track. Chase sits on the same road as Ferris High School and is just under a mile away.

Dave soon met Coach Hadway, and was impressed by the stoic, quiet figure who he had heard of due to his participation in the Corporate Cup for Bloomsday. From 1993-1999 Dave continued to coach solely at Chase, trying to prepare the athletes for the future before them if they decided to turn out for cross country as freshman.

Dave kept the workouts fun, but a scaled down version of what they would get in high school. The positive atmosphere Dave created blossomed and over sixty athletes continually turned out each year. The problem Dave saw, was that those same sixty would not continue to turn out in high school. But he coached, he encouraged, and he kept contact with those athletes that did move on.

From 1999-2009 Dave would help as the assistant coach at Ferris, under Coach Hadway. Dave continued to keep his eyes on the prospective talent in his PE classes, and he would continue to encourage them to turn out for cross country and track. During the fall cross country season, Dave was up at Ferris full time after school. During the track season Dave remained solely at Chase, helping those student athletes.

Dave stood in the position like Mike Hadway's middle school coach from years before and could declare to kids trapped inside their own awkward bodies that there was a runner inside them.

Showing the Chase Middle School to Ferris High School pipeline of athletes established by Mike Hadway and Dave Fuller. Over 10 future Collegiate athletes are shown in this picture.

Paul & Ann Hawkins with their seven children

Part Two: Turning for Home

Paul Hawkins was struggling to defeat a much younger, quicker, and stronger opponent. He was facing off against a college aged kid. Paul had been out of college for well over a decade. It was 1990 and he was in a fight to save face. Paul was not running; he was wrestling and trying to choke out his opponent in a judo match. He tried to focus on the opponent before him and not the cheers from his own three children on the edge of the mat.

Paul had his hands firmly around the neck of this college aged kid and his opponent had his hands firmly around Paul's neck. The judo match between the two would be decided by who would tap out or pass out. In a sport dictated by momentum, by speed as well as skill, Paul would use one of his greatest strengths: will. Strength and will had always been anchors that he could rely upon.

Motivating Paul were the looks on the faces of his three boys sitting on the edge of the mat. There these three kneeled; yelling, and cheering him on. With added reserve, Paul looked back at his opponent and decided he would die before losing this match.

Paul did not die and neither did his opponent.

As the boys went home with their father and entered the house, Ann Hawkins, wondered what all the noise was about. Following the commotion came the children and then she finally saw the trophy. Through the three squeaky voices of youth she heard, "Dad won!" and then further acclamations, "And he choked out the guy, it was awesome!"

In walked the man with a sideways smile and a ring of purple and red around his neck. This was the man that fought for his family and tried to keep it all together. He was sporting that same smile she had recognized from years previous. She had loved him then and she loved him now.

As Gerry Lindgren was setting the world on fire in 1964, chasing Olympic dreams and keeping pace with America's hopes in the space race, there was a boy 10 years old growing up in the Spokane Valley who would not be a distance runner; at least not yet.

Paul Gordon Hawkins grew up the second oldest child in a family of eight. Running was not the first thought in his mind when it came to sports: that was reserved for football and Vince Lombardi. He remembered hearing about Gerry Lindgren in the local papers, but he was 10 and running, to Paul, was what you did when you were either hitting someone on the football field, or you were trying to escape being hit.

The only other sport that spoke to Paul was wrestling. Paul knew more about Steve Gannon then he did about Steve Prefontaine. Steve Gannon was a local Spokane wrestler who had Olympic hopes of his own. Gannon would go on to wrestle at Northern Idaho College and help them win a National Championship. He defeated Fred Fozzard, who was a three time NCAA Champion and World Games medalist. Fozzard also had Olympic aspirations on the wrestling mat in Montreal. Gannon had wrestled in Spokane at West Valley High School.

West Valley High School was just under three miles from University High School where Paul attended. Paul was on the same mat as Gannon representing Spokane's All Star wrestling team as they faced off against a touring Japanese National team in the 1970s. Gannon would be the only victor from Spokane. Paul kept the 165 pound match close for the first two rounds but ultimately lost in the third round. He finished his high school wrestling career with a 10-4 record. He placed fourth at districts, and lost in the first round of the single elimination regional tournament.

University High School first opened in 1963. Paul graduated in 1972 but not before becoming involved in every activity available. Paul was the ASB President at school as well as captain on the varsity football team. The team may have had the mascot of the Titans but they were not in southern California and it was not a college level atmosphere. The football team would go 6-2 in Paul's junior and senior seasons taking second to Central Valley High School for the Border League championship.

Absent at University was any sort of tradition of excellence; the first team to win a state title of any kind came almost three decades after the school first opened its doors.

After graduating from high school in 1972 Paul attended a year of school at Brigham Young University. He then served a two year church service mission in Seoul, Korea for The Church of Jesus Christ of Latter-Day Saints. For two years he would wrestle with a language and a culture completely foreign to him and then return home and get back into athletic involvement.

Once back in the states, Paul picked up life on the wrestling mat once more at Brigham Young University. He tried to walk onto the team. Paul eventually discovered rugby and decided to join the team. He was a natural. He loved the constant movement. It was a game of controlled chaos, moving backward before moving forward. His best game came as he scored four tries against rival University of Utah in a win.

Sporting a shiner from the game and smiling as he went to church the following Sunday it is hard to know what caught Ann Newman's attention first. Either way, she could not stop staring.

If timing is everything, then it seemed that Ann Newman's ancestors were very close to missing it. Ann's great grandparents were Bruce Tingley and Ann Dillon. In 1912 they planned on boarding a newly constructed ship heading for America. They stood in line waiting for tickets to board the Titanic. They felt unfortunate that they were some of the first people to be denied tickets, seeing as how they had just sold out. Luckily, they never boarded the boat. In 1912 they would have their first of four children; they named her Ruby.

Ann's grandparents were Ruby Tingly and Hope DeLong. Ruby and Hope were two kids who fell madly in love and decided to get married. Despite their names purporting riches and encouragement, these two would become acquainted with poverty and despair as they happened to be dropping out of high school and getting married on October 29, 1929, the day the stock market crashed.

It was an occasion of opposites. This was not because the stock market had crashed or that a lifetime of happiness started on a day synonymous with depression, but it was because Ruby stood just under five feet and Hope towered over his wife, standing six feet six inches tall.

Ruby would know much of heartache in her marriage. Her third child would die young, her husband would pass not long after, and eventually her last remaining son would die. For over half her life she lived as a widow. Ruby still had both of her daughters to hold fast to.

Marjorie DeLong was Ruby's oldest daughter. She grew up in the Depression and would never forget it. Also not lost on Marjorie was the fact that her mother had never graduated from high school. Knowing that education was power and that she would have to provide for herself, Marjorie not only graduated from East High School in Salt Lake City, Utah in 1949, but she eventually earned a degree in Nursing from the University of Utah in 1954. While finishing up her degree she would meet and fall in love with James Newman. James was the tenth of twelve children and he also grew up in the Depression and used his resourcefulness to help bring money home. James would later join the navy and serve in the Korean War. After the war he returned home, married Marjorie, and started his own business *All Makes Washing Machine Repair* in 1956. He would work at his own business for thirty six years.

Marjorie and James would have four children and settle down in Holladay, Utah. Timing was never conventional and the date of Ann's birthday was no different: February 29, 1956, a leap year baby. The Tingleys, DeLongs, and Newmans just rolled along with whatever dates or problems were thrown their way.

The major tenant taught to Ann and all her siblings was the value of work. Marjorie Newman would seize the opportunity to make extra money by going out at night, after the grass was dewy and search for worms. In her mind it was pure profit. The following morning she would sell the bait to fishermen making their way up into the streams and rivers of the mountains. The only cost was the time needed to search for the bait. This culture of work and opportunities Ann saw and adopted in her own life.

Ann would take up babysitting opportunities to make a quarter an hour, or she would mow the neighbor's yard for three dollars. One summer she helped deliver phone books to people's houses. She did so by running back and forth from the car that her father was driving stocked full of hundreds of phone books. All this money was saved for her future college education.

Eventually Ann had her first working job at McDonald's in the summer of 1972. Ann had been at the job and enjoying the work for two months when the boss said there would be a meeting at the end of the workday and he needed everyone to attend.

Ann worked her shift and wondered what the meeting was about. The boss surveyed the room to make sure everyone was there and then began.

"We are going to have to let some people go. It's not because of anything that you have done, it's just that we are not as busy as we once were and we are going to have to let some of you go unfortunately. I have a letter of recommendation for everyone we're letting go so that you can hopefully find employment elsewhere." The boss did not relish this moment.

Ann thought to herself, *those poor people*. Little did she know she was one of those poor people let go. As one of the most recent hires Ann was also the first to go. She was grateful for the opportunity, and continued to work and save as she got ready to graduate from Olympus High School in Holladay, Utah and then go on to Brigham Young University. She continued to work as a waitress through college while earning a degree in Fashion Design. As Ann finished her degree she met Paul and this couple married in 1976.

In those early years of their marriage money was tight and creativity was needed for everything, including meals and clothing. With Ann's persistence and Paul's strength of will, it was no doubt that their children would reflect something of their character.

Paul's great desire to own a business someday did not come from his father Gordon, who was subject to the whims of the business he worked for. Paul's mentor for business was his uncle, Richard Vidmar, often referred to in the family as Uncle Dick.

Dick Vidmar's business, *General Welding Supply*, was based out of southern California in the 1950s and was started with literally nothing; the people buying from him just did not know that.

As a means of attracting customers, Dick had boxes placed prominently behind the counter of his shop. A customer would come in and ask for a specific part pointing at the box. Dick would make his way towards the box, look in and see nothing and then inform the customer that they were out. It was a true statement. He just never told the customer the fact that in almost all of his boxes that they pointed to, there was nothing. Dick would tell the customer that he could deliver the part to them later that same day if they would pay for it now. The messenger boy would quickly run to a store that did have the part and then charge a small additional fee for delivery.

Dick quickly learned which parts were most popular and as he scrimped and saved he turned nothing but the appearance of parts into an actual business store generating millions of dollars by the 1970s.

Dick had an enjoyment for sports and athletics; Dick's gymnastics endeavors formed the genesis and template that sparked his nephew Peter Vidmar into entering the sport. Paul's father Gordon was more bookish, enjoying reading and questions of academia.

Denied easy access to his uncle due to the distance and lack of money to communicate long distance, Paul learned of Dick's successes through the stories his mother Gloria told over the dinner table. The myth of the man stuck with young Paul, who wanted to mirror his uncle's athleticism and own his own business.

Paul's own father, Gordon, asked him what he wanted to do for a living someday. Paul responded that he wanted to own his own business.

"Get a degree in accounting, it's the language of business." Gordon said.

Paul went about getting his degree in accounting with the belief that by the end of his education he would be closer to achieving his dream of owning a business. Graduation from Brigham Young University came but Paul did not have his own business; he did, however, have a skill set with reading financial statements and understanding the jargon of business.

Paul interviewed at eight of the large accounting firms that existed in the country at that time, but received no offers. At a job fair on campus, IBM showed up and Paul interviewed one last time. IBM offered Paul a position in their accounting division and so, newly married, Paul and Ann headed to California.

Only one year was spent at IBM as Paul worked with their balance sheet sector reconciling the books so that payables and travel expenses all balanced out at the bank. Paul felt that he should get a law degree to go with his accounting degree. He figured that the more degrees he had the more he would understand business and therefore be able to buy a business of interest some day.

Paul was admitted to the University of Puget Sound Law School, located in Tacoma, Washington. Their young family was literally just down the road from where Pat Tyson and Mike Hadaway grew up. Paul, Ann, and a pair of their first kids, Isaac and Emily, lived in south Tacoma.

Law school, as Paul found out, was not an easy endeavor. The professors stood with confidence before the future lawyers in their classes and riddled them with questions. Sitting in class, Paul did not enjoy the questions being asked at him.

Coming home discouraged from a day of learning how little he knew about the muddled legal system, Paul wondered whether the law school route was still right. He had studied the case law but had walked out of class unsure of where he was going.

Sitting in the kitchen, working on a suit to match the shirts she had made by hand, Ann waited for Paul to come home. She stood, hovering over the cut portions and looking at the sewing machine in front of her. They may not have much, but she was making the most of all her skills she had developed over the years.

"I don't know if I want to do the law school thing." Paul said to Ann as he sat across from her on the lone table in their kitchen. They had no couch.

"What?" Ann asked.

"I just don't know if I'm cut out for being a lawyer." Paul said.

Ann, who had gone about the day saving money and taking care of their two kids, looked at her husband who was unsure and wanting to quit. She alone had placed the children down after feeding and tending to them throughout the course of the day.

"The time for deciding about law school has come and gone. That train has left the station. *We* are in it now and *you* are going to do well." Ann said.

"I've read and re-read the case law, and it's just hard. I don't know what the professors want." Paul said.

"You don't have to know everything, you just have to know enough. Keep at it." Ann said, and then added, "I'm not making this suit and shirts for nothing." She believed in him. Paul went back to the books, studying it out while his two children slept.

Ann's resourcefulness would surface again and again as the years in their marriage passed by, proving once more that behind every great man there is an even greater woman.

Ann was in survival mode and knew her husband needed encouragement more than anything else. She also knew that she needed to work and be wise with what little money they had.

When the opportunity to finally buy a couch became available, seven years into their marriage, Ann seized it. She was pregnant with their third child and saw a couch on the side of the road with a sign.

For Sale $5.

Ann saw a good deal. She looked past the fact that this old mediterranean style couch was well worn with stains and fabric fraying. She saw good bones that needed reviving. Knowing that if she spent the five dollars Paul would have to return and to pick it up, she bought the couch on the spot.

Paul went back to get the couch, while Ann went about trying to give it a second life.

Weeks went by and the couch started to transform as Ann went about pulling apart the couch and discovering, in the process, how she would go about putting it back together.

With her featherweight sewing machine, a vision of what could be, and a few yards of fabric, Ann went about sewing and stapling together the family's first couch.

By this time, Paul and Ann were back in Spokane and Paul was starting to sell real estate. During law school, as a means of surviving and trying to figure out his family's future, Paul sat alone in his car in the Nalley Valley of Tacoma. It is named after the owner and settler of the area Marcus Nalley, who went on to start his own development of food products in the Tacoma area. Sitting there Paul felt he should go into real estate. If he was going to own his own business he figured he would learn about the land necessary to facilitate business.

In the race of real estate Paul saw something similar to the Hounds and the Hares. In real estate you only ever eat what you kill. He saw early on that eighty to ninety percent of the real estate was owned by ten to twenty percent of the agents. Most people in real estate wash out because they do not know how to survive initially.

Paul and Ann would master what they termed *The Float*.

Commissions could be lucrative once deals were made, but the time between deals meant that money would have to last. It was like rationing water in a desert and waiting until the next big rainstorm came by to fill up the oasis. They were mapping out their lives in unknown territory.

Paul and Ann stretched the money they made in those early commissions as far and long as possible. They never knew how long it would be until they saw another sale. Living the truth that hungry tigers hunt best, Paul and Ann realized there was a thin line between hunger and starvation. Stretching out from days to weeks to months, Paul and Ann scrimped and saved. In real estate they would be a twenty or thirty year, overnight success. As the sales came and went, children were added to the growing family.

Eventually Paul and Ann Hawkins moved from 27th and Bernard to 75th and Regal in Spokane. They were living on the South Hill and trying to figure out how to raise their seven children: Isaac, Emily, Benjamin, Elizabeth, Peter, Paul Jr. and Thomas. Little did they know they could fill their own varsity cross country team with those seven children.

Paul and Ann relied upon the heritage of those that had gone before them. They looked to their own family legacies of hard work and determination as inspiration. With young eyes looking up towards them, Paul and Ann searched for some template to train and structure their children's lives around. As parents they hoped to teach their children vital lessons that would stick with them no matter the race, distance, or the time of life in front of them.

Isaac Hawkins: The First One

If the Hawkins family had not heard of Mr. McBride, all they needed to do in order to know him would be to track him down as he ran along High Drive Street. This road on the South Hill of Spokane sits atop a bluff. To non-students, Mr. McBride went by Jim. On Friday mornings in the late 1980s and early 1990s Jim could be seen leading a pack of 30 elementary school students on a run who were chanting, "Mama Mama can't you see, Mr. McBride made a runner out of me."

The Ridge Runners were what they called themselves and they were simply following their founding member, trying to stay as fit and active as the man before them. Onward they went, along that ridge that had a precipitous drop as they wound their way down the trails toward Qualchan Golf course below, only to circle back and return again to Wilson Elementary School.

If Paul and Ann had missed Jim on these early morning runs, then perhaps after school they might have seen him leading a pack of kids running to either Comstock Park, Manito Park, or Cannon Hill Park. Sometimes Jim led these young runners to all three parks in the course of an afternoon. Standing at five feet eight inches tall, Jim ran with his graying hair and sinewy build. He had the look of an athlete marked all over him. This old rabbit was hopping around the South Hill, and kids wanted to follow after their kind, cheerful leader.

Isaac, the oldest of the Paul and Ann's children, enjoyed hearing how Jim biked to work all the way from Cheney (20 miles one way, 40 miles round trip). He enjoyed seeing someone who was fit and who believed that anyone could be fit.

Isaac had other sports heroes he saw on TV: Larry Bird, Magic Johnson, Isiah Thomas and the bad boys of Detroit, or Michael Jordan, but those athletes were held behind a screen.

There were no screens with Jim.

He was flesh and blood. Jim's daily effort stood before Isaac in the classroom and ran alongside side him outside of it; Jim was inspiring.

Wilson Elementary School had a program at the time called, *I Can*, which required the students to state the phrase and then complete an action. It was confidence building at the very earliest stage. Isaac was learning what he could do. He wanted to mimic the attitude and belief that he could go great distances and do great things.

Jim was a Spokane Native, who has lived all but one of his 76 years in the Spokane area. Young and active Jim thought football was his future and had scholarship offers, but left the force of the football field for the finesse of classroom teaching. Instead of working with adults, he would work with children. Instead of chasing money, he would chase an opportunity to mold the minds of youth.

Scanning his classrooms over the years, Jim saw snapshots into the culture and community of Spokane and its families. Throughout each school year he would see the students mirroring the home from which they came. Some students had no vision of what could be because they had parents who also had no vision for their own life, let alone their kids. As time went on trends became evident. A decrease in parenting coincided with an increase in gaming systems purchased. A decrease in outside play coincided with an increase in childhood obesity.

And yet, Jim kept biking to and from work, kept swimming, kept training for triathlons and marathons; he kept moving. This Spokane son was a man of structure. He grew up in a day of the trains passing through Spokane. Likewise, Jim kept the trains of his life on schedule. Father of five and with a job to keep, Jim realized his role as a motivator. This great conductor of the classroom knew that others were watching and that he might have a hand in helping these children change the tracks that others had put them on. Jim lived up to the 1930 childhood story, *The Little Engine that Could*. Such was the story and theme of his childhood and life, and he hoped to make sure it was the same for those coming into and out of his classroom.

One such student observing Jim was Isaac. As a sixth grader he started running for fun because he saw Jim doing it and thought he was someone worth emulating. Jim did triathlons and so Isaac decided he too wanted to participate in one. With two of his classmates, Isaac created a team and participated in the Tiger Triathlon. It was an Olympic distance and so Isaac provided the road running while the other classmates did the swimming and biking. Isaac's first 10k was in the books.

Isaac also took the *I Can* approach to his own life and decided that he would have a paper route to save some money. Four years before he could ever drive or officially take on the responsibilities of a job, Isaac had a paper route. This small job taught him skills and developed character that he would need the rest of his life. When the Sunday paper came along with the added weight from advertisements and special reporting, Paul was there, helping his son roll the big papers and deliver them. Isaac would run to the car, grab some papers and then run to the next few houses to drop them off.

Sunday mornings came early for a father of seven who was scrimping, saving, and trying to figure out how to survive. It would have been easier to say no to Isaac and his paper route, but Paul and Ann had a vision of what they wanted their children to be. Paul and Ann did not look at their children as they currently were, but as what they could become. Life was not about what was comfortable or easy for parents, it was about what would be best for the children in both the short and long run of life.

Isaac meticulously saved his money from his paper route. His siblings, Emily and Ben, saw the money being saved and decided they would emulate their brother's example. One route now became three, and with it the demands of early rising and delivery; this meant that Paul was getting up earlier and moving faster in the morning, helping establish the pattern of success these children would need in life. Ann had run to and from the car delivering phone books; her children could run to and from a car delivering papers.

The family only dabbled with an electronic gaming device for one week. A Nintendo game system and *Super Mario Bros.* was purchased one Christmas. However, after a week straight where nothing was seen but the glow of a TV on the faces of children and nothing was heard but the fighting over whose turn it was, Paul and Ann took back the $100 game system. They bought a few cheaper items as a replacement: a basketball, a football, a baseball bat and ball, a pair of gloves, and a soccer ball. These instruments would be the basis of outdoor time after school.

Isaac, like any kid, absorbed the world he was immersed in. Luckily, he had Jim as a model of inspiration. Isaac decided to run around the school, doing laps before the bell would ring for the start of school. He simply enjoyed running because he saw Jim enjoying it. The flashy sports of the day, football, basketball, and soccer, were the sports Isaac also gravitated towards because those were what were on TV. But for Jim, one wonders whether Isaac would have ever taken up distance running.

Isaac's time at Wilson Elementary eventually ended and he went on to Sacajawea Middle School. Isaac saw this as a stepping stone in his life and an opportunity to grow up. Other students his age also saw it as a time to act like a grown up. They simply mirrored what they saw on TV. Partying began in middle school and so too did experiments with drugs, with sex, and with everything associated with being an adult.

The Hounds and Hares game of popularity had begun. For most of these students the emphasis was on being cool, not on school, not on learning, but on wearing what was right, saying the right things, and being with the right people. It was a race to do something more obscene in a grander way than anyone else.

It is very difficult to aid puberty ridden youth and help them engage in positive outlets.

Middle school allowed Isaac his first chance to really be part of a competitive team. He did cross country, then wrestling, basketball and finally track. After each of these after school sporting events, Isaac would read while waiting for the activity bus to take him home. Often he would read biographies of people, especially sports stars. His early favorite was *Bo Knows Bo* a biography about Bo Jackson. While other kids were at home playing early Madden football games moving a virtual Bo Jackson about in silver and black, Isaac was out trying to shape his body and mentality into becoming like Bo Jackson. Isaac knew that he might not have the physical attributes, but he could pick up the mental approach to excellence. Isaac was nicknamed Ike by his siblings, and so Ike was beginning to know Ike while he read about Bo knowing Bo.

Sports for most young men is a language and a way of acceptance. Speaking about sports teams, athletes, statistics, and games is code speak for acceptance. Any kid that can play halfway decent at a sport has instant access to friends within it. Isaac's social outlet was through the friends he earned while playing sports.

All of these sports were enjoyed by Isaac and others like him but his eyes were set on basketball. Turning out for the team, Isaac thought he had a spot on varsity and wanted to be accepted into that group.

The tryouts came and went with Isaac hustling all over the court. Running helped him tire less than those around him but Isaac was at a disadvantage. Specialization in sports was becoming more and more prolific. Young athletes would join AAU squads in soccer or basketball, and they would travel with young teams and compete for young titles. Isaac was not part of any AAU team and did not have the hours of practice that others had. Some of these athletes had already competed with each other for several years and knew each other's tendencies. Their passing, rebounding, and shooting was just that much better because they had participated in those leagues.

Isaac was cut from the team.

It was hard to take. The coach came up to Isaac and offered him the opportunity to be the scorekeeper for the team. Isaac, still upset and a bit embarrassed that he had been cut told the coach he did not want the job.

Typically Isaac rode the activity bus but that day his mom showed up to drive him home. Ann knew the day of cuts had arrived and she wanted to be there to help with her own experience. She knew full well it was easier to build boys than to mend men.

Dealing with disappointment determines much, if not all, of life's successes.

Ann used her life experiences as a playbook to draw from. She had wanted to turn out for the school play and auditioned but was cut. She thought she could win the ASB position of secretary at school and so she ran a campaign and lost. She thought she could be a cheerleader and again went through the audition process. She showed up, learned the routines, practiced the routines, performed the routines, and then was finally cut from the squad.

The one time that Ann did win an event was a position as Speaker of the House in student government. The vote was close and Ann ended up winning by one vote. She had voted for herself. This would be the lesson of her life that she would try to instill in her children: when confronted with a challenge you have to vote for yourself. Much of life is dealing with factors that cannot be controlled; the secret is to give everything to what can be controlled.

And so with experience in being cut, Ann waited for Isaac. She could see disappointment in his face as he approached.

"I didn't make the team." Isaac said as he got into the car.

"I'm sorry to hear that." Ann said.

"I can't believe the coach offered me the scorekeeper position." Isaac said, staring off at the road.

"The coach offered you the position of scorekeeper?" Ann echoed.

"Yeah." Isaac said.

"What did you say, Isaac?"

"I told him I didn't want it. Can we just go home" Isaac said.

"No. I want you to go back in there and tell the coach that you will take the scorekeeper position." Ann said.

"But I already told him no." Isaac said.

"You don't know what will happen with this opportunity Isaac. You don't know what will happen during the season, maybe somebody gets hurt or injured and you are there and they put you into the game. You don't ever say no to an opportunity and this is what you have, an opportunity. You like basketball don't you?"

"Yeah."

"Then this is an opportunity to be part of basketball in some way. You don't know where this can go, but you'll never know until you get back in there and tell the coach you would be honored to be his scorekeeper." Ann said.

She was not speaking to a thirteen year old with hurt feelings, she was speaking to a man who would be a father someday dealing with a kid that had also been cut and would need the words and the resolve to continue onward.

The car had never moved since Isaac got in it.

Isaac got back out of the car, walked back into the gym and went back towards his coach to go back on his renunciation to quit. Isaac would be there at each practice and would do whatever the coach asked him to do.

Ann had known of defeat and known of what internal workings go on when someone is told they are not tall enough, fast enough, or good enough; but she learned to say enough to enough. Her outlook proved prophetic. Isaac was allowed some minutes in a game where he hustled to save a ball from going out of bounds that resulted in him getting an assist. After the play Isaac could put his own name down in the books with a statistic next to it.

It is not hard to imagine why Isaac wanted to play basketball. During his youth he attended the Stockton Camp, named after the hall of famer and Olympic gold medalist John Stockton, who was Gonzaga Basketball before it was Gonzaga Basketball. John Stockton would have a legendary career known for discipline, hard work, and the short shorts he sported while on the court. Besides Bing Crosby, Stockton is perhaps the name most recognized and celebrated in Spokane.

With Isaac's continued efforts to make goals and achieve them, he saw his dribbling, passing, and jump shot improve. Isaac was more persistent in blocking out and rebounding. While attending the Stockton camp one summer Isaac met John Stockton, who refereed the championship game Isaac played in.

Yet the only attributes Isaac would mimic from John Stockton were the determinedness and the short shorts. Running would be Isaac's sport.

Paul stood watching Isaac fail to pass the runner that ran by him in the last hundred meters of the race. Paul stood there and cheered his son on. He saw that Isaac seemed unaware of what was at stake. Yes, it was just eighth grade track and yes, there are more important matters to be concerned with, but Isaac had an opportunity to make it to the city championship. All he had to do was stay in front of one runner who passed him in the last hundred meters.

Paul knew he had a good kid. He knew by the fact that Isaac had set goals to save so much of his money from his paper route. He knew by the fact that he never had to wake Isaac up to get going for the paper route. He knew by the fact that Isaac did not complain about the wind or the rain as he delivered the papers. Paul cautiously approached his oldest son after the race.

"Isaac did you know what you needed to do in that race?" Paul asked.

"I was running in the mile and was trying to run a PR." Isaac said.

"Yeah, you were going after a personal record, but did you know what you needed to do going into the race?" Paul asked.

"What do you mean?" Isaac asked.

"In order to make it to the city championship you had to finish in the top three and you were there up until that last bit when the runner from Salk passed you." Paul said.

Paul was not speaking to a 13 year old who had just missed out on a spot at the city championship. He knew that opportunities had to be seized in the lifetime of the opportunity. In a competitive world, many are passed over by those who know sooner and work quicker to get where they are going.

To aid Isaac in achieving his goals of making it on the cross country team in high school, Paul decided he was going to run a marathon. He did not know anything about distance running but decided that if a little running was good, then a lot of running would really help his son have a leg up on the competition.

Taking inspiration from Mr. McBride who had introduced Paul, as well as Isaac to the world of triathlons, Paul began to run. He lost weight in the process and saw an opportunity to spend time with his son.

Paul and Ann decided to leave the house on 27th and Bernard just as Isaac finished up his eighth grade year. The family moved out to a few acres on Regal Road further out on the fringe of the South Hill of Spokane. The move brought with it a change of schools. Instead of attending Lewis & Clark High School, Isaac, and those that followed after him, would all attend Ferris High School. Paul and Ann knew nothing about the local running scene, but they would soon learn just how lucky their move had been in the subsequent years.

Part of those wanting to get ready for the marathon besides Paul and Isaac were Emily and Ben. Like with the paper route, whatever Isaac did, the others wanted to mirror. It was the Hounds and Hares of being siblings. The first child has instant celebrity status on what is cool and must be followed, and so when Isaac wanted to train with Dad, so too did Emily and Ben.

Isaac was 14 years old during the summer before his freshman year of high school. His sister Emily was only 13 and younger brother Ben was 11. Paul was not sure if Ben could handle such a distance as 26.2 miles. Paul approached running with the mindset and mentality of a weightlifter. If you wanted to be stronger you had to lift more weight. He was afraid that the distance would crush Ben.

With the conditions that Ben could do it, so long as he kept up with his siblings and did not complain, Paul decided he could join the training group for a trial period. The marathon was set; the family would run the Deseret News Marathon on Saturday July 24, 1993.

Isaac, Emily, Ben and Paul all trained for the marathon. They would go out on runs together and they would finish in typically the same order: Isaac, Emily, Ben, and Paul. Emily was competitive and a naturally gifted runner. During one run Emily was leading and was hard charging for home when Isaac came from behind and beat her just as they approached the house. Ben was speeding for home and saw Isaac and Emily suddenly in a bit of a spat.

Isaac had beaten Emily and was letting her know about it, feeling rather proud and cocky of his win. Paul showed up right in time to see his children squabble and quickly put an end to it.

"If you win, you never, ever, rub it in someone else's face. That is not what you should ever do and I don't want to ever see that again," Paul said.

Paul was speaking to what could be. He did not know what was going to happen with his kids and the success they might someday enjoy; but he wanted them to be people that were humble winners, not the type of characters that boasted their successes like major sports athletes on TV. It appeared Isaac had been watching too much of the Detroit Pistons basketball team growing up.

Race day would come and the little family showed up to race. Isaac and Ben would end up running together, and Paul and Emily would run together.

The race organizers ended up creating a new category because of the 361st person to pass the finish line. Ben would be the sole victor and placer in the 11 and under category, clocking a time of 4:28:12. Just one second behind Ben was Isaac finishing 362nd overall and second out of three runners in the 12-14 age group. Isaac had waited for Ben a few times as he went to the bathroom in porta potties and so his time would have been closer to the four hour mark without those stops. Ben and Isaac had made a pact to run the race together, but in the last ten meters, Ben broke away from Isaac to be the first family member to cross the line, and the first Hawkins to ever complete a marathon.

Emily was the sole runner in the 12-14 girls category finishing 424th overall with a time of 4:59:03. Paul was the 65th place finisher in the 35-39 year old category and finished 423rd overall with a time of 4:58:44.

Tired, chafing in areas, and dehydrated, these four had done it; they had run a marathon. These four joined the rest of the family during the vacation in Utah and then returned back to Spokane.

A week after returning home from the marathon in Utah, Isaac was told that there was someone at the door who wanted to speak with him. It was early morning and standing in the doorway was Zack Ventress, the captain of Ferris High School's cross country team. As one who was not only surviving but thriving on Coach Hadway's program, Zack instantly saw potential in Isaac when he heard that he had just completed a marathon.

Freshman Year

1993 marked the eighth year that Mike Hadway and Pat Tyson were coaching at their respective schools in Spokane. When Mike and Pat competed as athletes at their respective high schools they were on the western side of Washington and were only separated by eight miles. Now as coaches on the eastern side of the state their teams were only separated by 13 miles. Their coaching styles and approaches could not have been more different, yet they both found a way to get results.

Pat Tyson, whose nickname was the Pied Piper, had the ability to recruit and make believers of anyone. Once a prospective athlete heard Pat speak, it was hard for them to find reasons not to join the team and want to dedicate themselves to running miles upon miles. Running became cool and learning from Pat became a privilege. In 1993 Pat Tyson had his largest team ever assembled with 93 athletes. He was only seven athletes (one last team) shy of his goal of 100.

Mike Hadway, whose nickname was Hard-way Hadway, or ten a day-Hadway, also had one of his largest teams in 1993. He had 19 athletes at the start of the season but that did not stay that way at the end. His soft spoken demeanor and approach spoke to the athlete who was motivated, who was hungry, and who was already running with his eyes upon the future. The ideal athlete for Mike Hadway was the kind of kid who would read on a bus, who had an early morning paper route, and who did everything the coach asked because he wanted to.

A varsity squad in cross country is filled by seven runners. Pat Tyson could fill 13 full teams of athletes with a few left over. Mike Hadway had one varsity team and one junior varsity team by the end of the season. The picture crews that were required to take the team photo for the yearbooks at each school would both use a wide angle lens: for Mead it was to fit everyone into one picture, for Ferris it was to make the team look bigger than the numbers in it.

Pat's goal was to get 100 athletes, Hadway's goal was to get 100 percent from his athletes.

Out in Spokane Valley at University High School, Bob Barbero had far more athletes than Hadway and far fewer athletes than Tyson, but he was trying to figure out how his squad was going to compete and believe they could hang with these teams. His team had moments of brilliance followed by moments of bafflement.

The state meet in 1992 had ended with the top individual spot going to junior Matt Davis of Mead, then second place was senior Ezra Ellis of Ferris and third was senior Ryan Cross from University. Mead had gone on to win the team title in the lowest point total ever in the history of the state: 20. A number that has never been touched before or since.

Hadway and Barbero had the same struggle: their top athletes, who finished second and third at the state meet, were both graduated and gone. Adding to their trouble was the fact that Matt Davis was still around and the clear favorite to win it all again. As a junior Matt had won the three mile course by 25 seconds and had set the course record.

The best was yet to come for him.

If it was just Matt Davis that these coaches had to worry about, it would have been one thing. But the reality was that Mead's entire 1992 varsity team had only one senior on it.

Mead's seventh runner, who finished 17th overall at state and ran 15:38, would be back.

There was no wonder as to why Mead was ranked #1 in the nation by Harrier Magazine. They were that good. They were perhaps the best team that ever ran in high school cross country history.

In seven years time Pat Tyson had nearly created long distance perfection. He had entered the league in 1986 and in his first year as coach took Mead, a team not expected to finish higher than middle of the pack in the GSL standings, all the way to state. His second year at Mead in 1987, the team did not qualify for state. He had the fastest runner in the state in 1987, the individual winner, Chris Lewis and he was only a junior. Those that had been around saw the Mead train getting ready to pull out of the station and Pat Tyson effectively yelling, "All aboard!"

As numbers on the team increased, the times dropped and Mead had not only the fastest runner in the state in 1988, they had the fastest team.

What were the first four years like for Hadway? In 1986 Ferris as a team did not qualify for state and they had no individuals qualify either. In 1987 there was no team accompanying their super sophomore Stuart Burnham at state. Hadway's third year in 1988 brought with it junior Stuart Burnham taking third overall, and the team not only making it to state but taking second to Mead. With 1989 on the horizon it looked like Ferris might be able to challenge Mead; the only trouble was they failed to get out of the regional meet. Only Stuart Burnham would be sent on as an individual runner to compete at the state meet for Ferris. Stuart Burnham in his senior year placed seventh overall and watched as Mead had three of the top four runners in the race and took the team title. University had edged out Ferris in regionals and took second as a team at state to Mead in 1989. Again in 1989 Mead had the top team and the top runner, with Greg Kuntz winning it all.

These second place teams were very good teams it was just that Mead was that much better. In other states, these second place teams would have been state champs, they just happened to be running against Mead High School and Pat Tyson.

1990 brought with it another Mead title, with University taking second. It was hard to get any traction for the second place team because they were good, but they were not the best. Mead kept winning, Pat kept coaching to the athlete he once was, speaking to that "never say no" attribute that he imprinted on the minds and hearts of his athletes. The Mead machine was up and running, and it

Isaac Hawkins, left; Skiy Detray, Mead jersey

© Peter Hawkins Personal Archive

steamrolled everyone. 1991 was another Mead title with sophomore Matt Davis as the top athlete. 1992 was like a song stuck on repeat, Mead won the team title and had Matt Davis atop the podium now as a junior. This was the backdrop to what had been going on prior to Isaac showing up in the late summer of 1993.

Zack Ventress as a sophomore had qualified for state in 1992 for Ferris and he finished 15th overall. He was a believer in the Hadway approach to distance running, and he wanted to see Ferris win it all. Fellow teammate and captain Cameron Copher also ran as a sophomore for Ferris and was also an individual qualifier who took eighth overall at state the same year. Yet it was hard for Cameron to see how it would be done when there were four Mead runners that finished ahead of him. The team with the neon green jerseys were the ones to beat and they could be seen from a mile away, both in person and in the stat column.

Zack and Cameron knew that for Ferris to have a chance they needed everyone they could get to turn out and they needed them to be tough. They needed a calloused athlete. Isaac, fresh off his marathon, seemed to Zack and Cameron like one more member of the team they needed.

At the end of the first week of training in late August there would be what was referred to as a time trial. It is an intersquad meet determining who was on varsity and who was not. The top seven individuals to cross the line were on varsity and the rest were put on junior varsity for the first meet. The varsity squad could change throughout the season based upon shifting times of athletes at meets, but this first time trial would decide who would run varsity for the first meet of the year. To be a freshman and running varsity can be exceptionally tough, especially when placed on a competitive team, in a competitive city, with some of the most competitive coaches in the country.

The time trial came and went without much notice at home. Isaac did not inform the family of the race. He had biked three miles to Ferris on a Saturday morning, ran the time trial, and biked three miles home to announce that he was on varsity. What that all meant, he had to explain. He would be running on the team and travel to Oregon to compete in a week's time.

Initially Paul wondered whether time out of the classroom on Friday and travelling to Oregon for the weekend was a good idea. But he did not want to crush his son's enthusiasm either. Isaac had just proved that he had learned his lesson since his last race in middle school; he had learned what he needed to do to qualify and he had done it. Paul did not realize what this could mean for his family.

Paul had never had a kid in high school. He had six younger children that would soon be in the position of Isaac. He had yet to grasp the significance of the opportunity before him as a father and for the family in general. Isaac went on the trip and the family stayed home for the weekend. It would be two in the morning on Sunday when Isaac finally came back home; yet he was full of enthusiasm.

On the next morning's paper route, there Isaac was, bubbling over what had occurred in the previous thirty six hours. As Paul listened to his son while he came and went from the car delivering papers, he realized what this could mean. His son had more structure, more drive, and drew inspiration from the fact that he could work hard in the offseason. And so the family would go to all the meets from then on; they would show up and support Isaac. Paul would hitch his family to the Ferris running train for the season and see what places it took them to.

Paul did not know much about distance running, but he would follow his children and learn from them. There would be many benefits from running, and physical exercise was just one of them.

Sticky Buns

After the invitational in Oregon and getting used to racing in a field of over 200 athletes, Isaac assessed his situation. He felt excited by what he could accomplish going forward. He enjoyed seeing what Ferris had done and he enjoyed learning about this rival Mead and the significance of their accomplishments.

After the race, the team piled into Hadway's green Astro Van, cranked up some Led Zeppelin, and started their way back to Spokane. Isaac had never heard of Led Zeppelin, the Doors, the Eagles, Tom Petty, or any of the music blaring as they drove along the Columbia River heading back to Spokane.

Eventually the team rolled into Ritzville, Washington to stop and get a bite to eat. They were just over an hour outside of Spokane and it was late, but they were also hungry. The team decided to eat at Perkins and so they sat around and got their order in; the only thing that they still had left on the menu when they finally got to their seventh runner was sticky buns. The name brought with it a few laughs and a nickname ensued for the season. From then on Isaac would be sticky buns.

The hazing brought the team closer together, it was not meant to be destructive and it was nothing that seriously harmed anyone; although they did toe the line.

On a separate weekend coming back from an invitational the team again stopped in Ritzville to refuel. Again it was late at night, and everyone was tired, sleepy, and stinky; everyone except for Cameron Copher. He saw an opportunity for a joke.

"Hey Isaac, come here," Cameron said, standing beside the back end of Hadway's car and the back end of a neighboring trailer.

"Stick your one finger here and the other one there." He said indicating two spots at the end of a long metal object.

Isaac placed his fingers on the instrument. The next instant was filled with yelling and jumping by Isaac.

Hadway, inside, looked over his shoulder as he was paying for the gas.

Cameron Copher had just used a cattle prod on Isaac. Volts had gone into and out of that poor freshman, but he was more than awake for the rest of the trip. The season was electric and Isaac was beaming with joy.

As much as that prod zapped him, Isaac was being branded as one of the guys on the team. The social aspect of running unites everyone. They are out there on the roads, running the same miles, going through the same intervals, and testing themselves against the same clock. There is great joy that comes from spending that special time with those of like mind and heart.

One of the most memorable moments for Isaac during the course of the season was watching the SunFair Invitational. One of the unique aspects of this race is that instead of running one varsity race, there are seven varsity races run. The teams put all of their seventh best runners in one race, the sixth best runners in another race, and so forth. There are seven flights of races. It is a way to see how one team's fifth man measures up against another team's.

At this race Mead's team would run and win all seven races. In the forty plus year history of the race, no team, except Mead's 1993 squad, has ever had all seven of their athletes win all seven races in the same meet. There was no doubt in anyone's mind that their team was a cut above everyone else.

While at this meet, Isaac saw Matt Davis run. In previous meets against Mead, Isaac had been in the race and only seen Matt surge to the lead and then disappear. Isaac was able to watch as Matt Davis leapt to the lead and then never let up. While watching Isaac said to himself, *That's how you are supposed to run when you get good. You take it from the beginning and you never let up.* Isaac the athlete was Isaac the student, taking notes on what to do.

Finally the short cross country season was coming to a close. Mead won regionals and Ferris took second, they would be moving on to the state championship held in Pasco, Washington on the Sun Willows golf course.

Paul and Ann Hawkins made sure to bring their six other children to the event. Those siblings standing and cheering on were Emily age 13-8th grade, Ben age 11-5th grade (he was held back one year), Liz age 9-4th grade, Peter age 7- 1st grade, Paul Jr. age 4, and Tommy a year and 8 months old.

On that sunny cool day in early November, the Hawkins clan stood behind the chain link and other makeshift fences watching as the race began and the runners disappeared. As a group they migrated, like all the other spectators, to the 180 degree turn just after the first mile. Mead was clearly in the lead. They waited and cheered for the Ferris boys running in red and white. Isaac was in the middle of the pack. When he appeared the family cheered and then followed the masses that went to another chain link fence to see the two mile mark. Again, Paul and Ann corralled their kids as they made their way through the sea of people at the event.

If Matt had a lead at the mile mark, he had an ocean at the two mile mark. It seemed that there were two races being run, Matt's race and then everyone else.

Again, Mead was dominating, again Isaac was in the middle of the pack. Finally the fans raced over to the fence by the finish and the Hawkins family was no exception. The kids squeezed their way through others to get a view of the race.

Matt Davis would set the course record running 14:09 and he would beat the second place runner, Micah Davis, his brother, by 37 seconds. After Micah passed the finish line, then came Rob Aubrey of Mead in third. Mead's fourth runner to come in placed eighth overall, and their fifth man finished far back of where he typically ran. Had the team run as they could have, then their point total would have been lower than the 20 they had set the year previous. However, coming away with 31 points scored was still impressive.

Isaac finished 86th overall. He was Ferris' fifth runner in that day, finishing 60th in the team scoring and clocking a time of 16:19. Ferris placed third in the state and Isaac climbed the steps of the podium to have his photo taken with his team. After the race, Isaac got a hold of the results and started to decipher their meaning. He did not look to times, he looked to grade levels. He counted and found that there were only six freshman faster than him in the state. Isaac had been inspired by what Matt Davis could do, and believed that he could improve six spots in less than three years time.

While Isaac was ascending and descending the podium with his team, Paul thought back to how a few months ago his boy was not making it to the city championship and now here he was standing on the podium of the third best team in the state. Paul may not have understood running, but third place was something he could wrap his head around. Although the state championship was over, that did not mean the season was complete. For those interested there was a regional race still left and a chance at Nationals.

While Paul was thinking about the transformation in his son Isaac, his other children saw the uniqueness of what their oldest brother did and the attention he received for it. They too wanted to run. There would be races to the parking lot, mimicking what they had just seen. All of the Hawkins kids were caught up looking at the podium in that moment and wondering what could be.

Foot Locker

The season was over for a month but Isaac and the team kept training like they were preparing for the state meet all over again. The next meet for them would be the Foot Locker Western Regional Race held in California. High school aged runners from all over the western United States would show up and race for the chance to be one of the lucky eight runners to represent the Western Region of the United States. Those eight runners competed at Nationals, held in California in just another week's time.

Don Kardong and the governing body overseeing Bloomsday had decided to sponsor local athletes who had worked hard over the course of their seasons and have a shot at making it to Nationals. They have since used money from the Bloomsday Race to provide airfare and hotel accommodations for the top runners from Spokane coming out of the region.

Isaac had not made the cut in his freshman year to have Bloomsday pay his way down to the race and so he wanted to dip into his paper route money to pay for the event. Paul, wanting to come along and see for himself what this all meant, told Isaac to keep his money in the bank; he would pay for the both of them to fly down.

Top runners from the GSL and some of their parents went down to this postseason race to see if they could have a shot at Nationals. The parents from these various teams intermingled and stayed in the same hotels.

It just so happened that Paul would share the floor of a hotel room with Wayne Davis, Matt and Micah's Dad. While with Wayne, Paul asked questions about his kids, about Mead, and about Pat Tyson.

"Oh, Pat, well he was Pre's roommate in college." Wayne said.

"Who's Pre?" Paul asked.

There was a lighthearted chuckle by some of the parents. Their laughter was not to be mean; they laughed at the innocence with which Paul had asked the question. It was like the main character in the movie *The Sandlot* asking who

Babe Ruth was to baseball. "Heroes get remembered but legends never die" was the line in the movie. Prefontaine was both hero and legend, but Paul just did not know this at the time.

"Was he somebody that was good?" Paul asked.

"Yeah, he was alright." Wayne said as he looked at Pat Tyson who was in the room.

Pat kindly walked over to Paul. He gave a brief history on Prefontaine, the University of Oregon, Bill Bowerman, and how he fit into all of it.

Paul was living up to the advice he had given to Isaac in that pre-All-City Race. Paul was gaining that education and starting to know where it could all go and what it could all mean. He was grateful for the kindnesses shown to him by the other parents as well as the coaches. These were good people, this was a good environment, and this was a place he would want all of his kids to be. The atmosphere of acceptance radiating from coaches and athletes was empowering. There was fierce competition amongst the athletes and coaches that lasted as long as the race was run, but before and after there was always great camaraderie.

The day of the race finally came and there would be several races based on grade level: Freshman, Sophomore, Junior, and Senior as well as what is labeled the Seeded Race. The Seeded Race was for anyone vying for the top eight positions to run at Nationals in a week's time and to represent the Western Region. Matt Davis, his brother Micah, and the Mead runners would all be in the Seeded Race.

Isaac would run in the Freshman Race to see how he stacked up against the freshmen on the west coast. Isaac ran tough and finished 10th overall in the Freshman Race. The wheels that had started to churn seeing the state results added another bit of data to be processed. *Of those that could show up to the race*, Isaac thought, *I am the tenth fastest for my grade level on the west coast. If I continue to practice and train like Zack Ventress and Coach Hadway have told me, then I will improve and I can be one of the best in my grade.*

The Seeded Race was run that day and Wayne Davis had two reasons to rejoice, both of his sons had qualified to run at Nationals. A quarter of the Western Regional team was made up of one family and one coach. Mead. Pat Tyson. The Davis brothers.

Returning home and excited from their trip, Isaac made sure to tune in to watch on TV as the Foot Locker National Title was being broadcast. Isaac had a VHS tape ready to record the race and study it later.

In the race the runaway winner was Adam Goucher, who would be a future Olympian in the 5,000 meter. Taking second was Meb Keflezighi who would be a future silver medalist in the Olympic Marathon in Athens. Coming in third was Matt Davis. The boy that was crushing it in Spokane was truly one of the best in the country. Micah, Matt's younger brother, also did well finishing tenth overall. Two brothers were in the top ten in the country. It was an amazing accomplishment.

The season finally came to an end, but it was the beginning of the chase for achievement for Isaac. Gone were the days of dreaming about basketball. Here his hard work was rewarded and not held up to the subjectivity of a coach. Time was the only variable for measurement and Isaac could control that through his preparation. Running rewarded the worker. Isaac knew all about work.

Isaac was off to the races in finding out all things that dealt with running. He subscribed to *Track & Field News*. He read up on all the runners that he had heard about through his coach and teammates. Isaac was running down the same road that Hadway, Tyson, Barbero and others had gone down and he was loving it just as they loved it.

Winter training came and Isaac averaged around 50 miles a week in the offseason. The mileage was good for a freshman, especially considering he still had his early morning paper route and the fact that he had early morning seminary at his church. Isaac's days started near four in the morning. The papers would be delivered as he ran his route, then Isaac would run off to seminary, and eventually to school.

After six periods of classes where it was important to keep his grades up, Isaac would hit the roads after school with upper classmen Zack Ventress and Cameron Copher. If Isaac was going to be the best, what better training partners than his teammates who were already faster than him.

Track finally came and Isaac improved on his time in the mile from middle school and ran sub ten in the two mile. He ran fast enough to qualify for the district meet, having run one of the 16 fastest individual times in the city. However, Isaac's track season would end there. He did not continue on to regionals. He finished 13th in the two mile race as a freshman.

The Mead boys had top finishes in the distance races in track at state. One athlete finished second in the 800 meter at state, in the mile they were first, second and fourth, then in the two mile they finished first, second, and third. With points only from their distance crew alone they might have been able to win the state track meet. As it was, the full team competed in various events and Mead won the state track meet easily. They won without their lead runner Matt Davis who was recovering from an injury.

University had one runner in the 800 meter final who took seventh.

Ferris had two runners in the two mile, Zack Ventress and Cameron Copher taking fourth and fifth in the two mile. They were only seconds off of those Mead runners who finished first, second, and third.

Another offseason came and with it the hopes of breaking Mead's current win streak of six state titles.

Sophomore Blues

The summer before Isaac's sophomore season was a time of preparation. Isaac went with teammates and others in the GSL to participate in the Oregon Camp. The University of Oregon has a running camp that their college promotes for high school talent to show up and participate in. Pat Tyson, who ran at Oregon, had kept in touch with the former Assistant Coach who took over when Bowerman retired. He took his boys to meet Coach Bill Dellinger. Mead's boys would all be there and so would the top athletes from other teams in the GSL.

After that weeklong training experience, Isaac also attended a running camp up at Whitworth University in Spokane, which is where he first ran into Rick Riley. Isaac asked all sorts of questions about his training.

"Near hundred mile weeks." Rick said, as casually as if he had just opened up and handed out some M&M's. It seemed as simple and easy as eating candy to Rick. Isaac saw that the workload had to increase. He knew he had to be wise about raising his mileage but he took note of future goals he wanted to achieve.

Isaac kept his notes in his running log. He gave a title to the routes he ran each day, along with his daily mileage, and then ended each run with a positive statement focused on how he was closing in on his goals.

The sophomore year looked promising. Seniors Zack Ventress and Cameron Copher were ready for a rematch against the Mead boys who had swept them in track. Juniors Paul Harkins and David Schruth had improved from the previous year. Isaac as a sophomore was still delivering those early morning papers and going to early morning seminary. Perhaps, they thought, this was the year that Mead's dominance would end. Mike Hadway had a core group of guys that worked hard to prepare for their future, but they could not plan for everything.

Hangman Valley Golf Course. Cameron Copher, left; Isaac Hawkins, right

Incidentally in 1994, the Washington Interscholastic Activities Association (WIAA), in an attempt to try and make the cross country field a little more "competitive" at the state meet, decided that Spokane could only send one team to state and the top three individual runners.

It was all done as a means of keeping things "fair" for everyone. It just seemed a bit ironic that the city and state that had produced Gerry Lindgren, who ran against Soviet runners in the Cold War, was now instituting socialist principles.

The district championship, which decided which team would go to state, was held at Hangman Valley Golf Course on Saturday October 26, 1994. It was the de facto state meet. Whatever team won would be the winner a week later down in Pasco.

Mustering that miraculous comeback spirit was coach Pat Tyson of Mead; knowing full well that the end of the title run could occur with each season. These athletes were running on the same Hangman Valley Golf Course where Prefontaine ran his final cross country race representing the University of Oregon.

The high school race started amidst a light rain and the runners from nine GSL schools took off. After the first mile it was clear that Micah Davis, now a senior, was opening up a lead for Mead. Right in the mix and running second was a red jersey, Ferris' Zack Ventress, followed by another Mead runner, senior Skiy Detray. A small gap ensued and then there was an orange jersey, Lewis & Clark senior Kevin Rickard, who knew his team was not in the running for state and that if he was going to make it he would have to claim one of those top three spots. Right on his heels in fifth place was sophomore Isaac Hawkins. Right behind Isaac was senior Cameron Copher of Ferris.

Isaac knew what was at stake, yet he also held the firm belief that the team might actually win it. With three guys in before Mead's third runner, and with the firm belief that Paul Harkins and Dave Schruth would be running their best, it seemed that Mike Hadway's team of David's would finally land the blow to beat the Goliath.

Through two miles in the rain the positions did not change. The rain kept coming but could not douse the hopes welling up within the families and fans of Ferris. They were going to do the unthinkable. State was within their grasp.

With a half mile to go, again the rain poured and Isaac, this lone sophomore was still in fifth place with only seniors ahead of him. In the course of a year it looked like he had moved up and closed a huge gap; chasing Matt Davis' ghost and his flesh and blood brother Micah Davis.

With just under a quarter of a mile to go Cameron Copher made a surge and went past Isaac.

Isaac did not respond. This was his teammate and no Mead runners had passed him since the first mile. In Isaac's mind their team was going to win.

The initial reaction of the Ferris supporters was jubilation. Mead had three runners in the top eight positions, but Ferris had four runners in the top nine spots. Ferris finally appeared to have Mead like numbers.

The only problem was that Ferris' fifth man, junior Dave Schruth, finished sixteenth overall, two spots away from Mead's sixth runner. There had been a pack of three Mead runners, Mark Mohrland, Morgan Thompson, and Mike Lee, who were between the bookends of Paul Harkins and Dave Schruth. Added to the misery were the two Lewis & Clark runners that snuck into those bookends as well.

The final numbers of the top three teams were as follows:

Mead 1, 3, 8, 11, 12 = 35

Ferris 2, 5, 6, 9, 16 = 38

Lewis & Clark 4, 10, 14, 26, 39 = 93

Mead would go to state, but the race there was a formality; they were state champions before they even showed up to run at the Sun Willows course.

The only remaining hope was that Isaac would be one of the three individuals to run at state. That list, factoring out the Mead runners who as a team qualified, was as follows:

1. Micah Davis - Mead
2. Zack Ventress - Ferris
3. Skiy Detray - Mead
4. Kevin Pickard - Lewis & Clark
5. Cameron Copher - Ferris
6. Isaac Hawkins - Ferris

On a day when only one team and the top three individuals would go on to state, Isaac was on the second place team and he was the fourth individual.

The pain of defeat was real.

The rain kept falling, and the awards ceremony went on. Ferris had to go up and claim their second place trophy.

Mead's dominance would continue another year. Another title would be printed on the backs of their team sweater; this would be seven years in a row.

Thoughts raced through Isaac's mind. *Had I responded to Cameron's surge, had Dave broken up that group of three Mead runners, had Paul passed the*

Mead runner and Shadle Park runner . . . these thoughts fell like the rain, with incessant pounding.

Had the state's athletic governing body not interfered with their brand of fairness for a year, one has to wonder what could have occurred at state. In the subsequent years and due to rightful kickback from the league, there would be four teams coming out of a regional race with the GSL going up against schools from the Big IX conference. Had there been four teams going to state, Ferris would have been in the bunch as well as Lewis & Clark and North Central.

Had Mead been allowed to run their next seven, out of the 69 they had on their JV squad that year, then they would have scored 132 points and knocked North Central out of the fourth position.

In the junior varsity race that competed before the varsity race, the top 12 finishers were all from Mead. The first runner and school to break up the dominance was sophomore Andy Brown from Ferris. He was followed by two more Mead runners, a junior Craig Toribara from Ferris, a Mead runner, and then finally a third school entered the picture with University's Peter Gay finishing 18th. 15 of the top 18 positions were all from Mead. Mead had 69 junior varsity runners, Ferris had 8. The numbers tell the story and those numbers are what carried Mead away and off to state.

Isaac and his teammates that did not qualify went to watch the state meet. They watched as Micah Davis won the race. They watched as four of the top six slots were all from the GSL. They watched as Mead walked atop the podium having scored 46 points. They saw second place at state went to Richland High School scoring 121 points. Zack Ventress placed third overall and Cameron Copher placed 6th overall.

Isaac stood and saw that he could have been fifth or sixth in the state meet. He could have been standing there, having passed 80 slots from the previous year. Isaac's only consolation was that he was a sophomore and he still had two more years and opportunities to run at the state cross country meet.

The WIAA's experiment at fairness did not work. The GSL's three individuals they sent all finished in the top ten to go with two athletes from Mead, so five out of the ten people on the podium were from one town. Mead crushed it while the likes of everyone else lagged far behind. 3A teams-Kurtis, Kelso, and Oak Harbor-all were able to run in the race and score 300 plus points in the process. The state meet that year was merely watered down greatness. Had Mead been allowed to send their B team, they likely would have been fighting for second or third place when pitted against the likes of Richland and South Kitsap.

At Foot Locker that year, Isaac would finish 60th in the Seeded Race. Micah Davis, who had run at Nationals as a junior with his brother, failed to make it to Nationals as a senior having an off race at the Western Region. However, his teammate Skiy Detray did qualify for Nationals.

Isaac decided what he needed to do was increase his mileage. The most mileage he would hit in a week during his winter training was 80 miles. The increase in mileage brought with it the increased hope that much better results would follow.

In track, there would be the district meet, where the top 16 individuals competed in each event knowing only eight would go on to regionals and from regionals only four were sent on to state. Isaac qualified for the district meet in both the mile and two mile events. However, he would only make it to regionals in the two mile and at regionals he would finish fifth place. Again there was disappointment.

At state, Mead's Micah Davis and Skiy Detray would flip flop first and second place finishes in the mile and two mile with their wins coming less than a second apart from each other. Zack Ventress would take fourth in the mile and drop out of the two mile. Sitting in the stands, absorbing the moment in the Lincoln Bowl, sat Isaac. He was in the stands and staring at the same track where Pat Tyson had run growing up. Since the bitter race at regionals, Isaac finally looked at the grade level and not the times in that race. What he found was that he was the top sophomore in that race and the only people in front of him had just finished their last high school race. Next season could be his. Walking out of the Lincoln Bowl Isaac vowed to return. And so his offseason began.

A Summer with the Golden Arches

After the state meet, Isaac went over to watch the Prefontaine Classic, a race held each year honoring the running legend Steve Prefontaine. It is the premier track meet of the year held in the United States. The best athletes from all over the world descend into Eugene, Oregon to compete at Hayward Field.

Isaac entered into a race amongst collegians and ran a 5,000 meter time of 15:13. It was a good time for a sophomore, and one that was only 40 seconds off of the then PAC 10 qualifying standard at that distance. Isaac even beat a few college aged runners.

After the race and the effort, Isaac bought a shirt to remember the moment. It had Steve Prefontaine on the front wearing his last race jersey, the black singlet with the word *NorditaliA* arching over the top of it.

While on his way out from his purchase, Isaac saw Frank Shorter signing autographs. Having done his homework, Isaac knew who Frank Shorter was and what he had done and so he got in line to meet the man who last raced with Pre. Isaac did not have anything for him to sign and so he simply took off his shoes and asked him to sign them. Frank obliged this happy young running enthusiast. With homage being paid to the great running Mecca of the United States, and having feet blessed by Shorter's signature and the shield of Pre on his chest, Isaac returned back to Spokane and a second job.

Whether or not high arches in your feet indicate speed or distance prowess is not proven or known. A Hawkins family myth associates high arches with speed and it just so happened that Isaac had the highest arches on his feet.

The disappointment that Isaac felt over the results of his sophomore seasons brought with it a burning desire to work harder. Remembering the notes of the previous summer, when Isaac had met with Rick and how he had indicated 90 to 100 mile weeks as being the way he achieved his success, Isaac set out to mimic that effort.

Effort was what Isaac realized was his gift to himself. Effort: that ability to work, to endure, and to continue onward could be drudgery or delight. The morning paper route had continued throughout his years, now it was time to add more to his plate. While trying to fit 1,000 miles into the three months of summer before school started and cross country began, Isaac tried to add another job to keep his schedule full.

Looking for work, Isaac applied all around the area to various stores and fast food restaurants. The only place that contacted Isaac asking for an interview was

McDonald's located on 29th and Regal. After a brief interview Isaac was hired.

Isaac prepared the food; he would not be the face taking orders from customers. He worked, preparing everything unseen and at a frantic pace.

Everything had picked up pace for Isaac. His running had increased in both mileage and intensity. He was not only running farther than he had run before, he was running faster than he had run. The stride was lengthening while it also quickened. Isaac's height had increased, his muscles developed to keep pace with the demands of his heart and mind.

Papers needed to be delivered each day, McDonald's never seemed to slow, and Isaac had to squeeze in a morning and afternoon run. The days felt like weeks and the weeks felt like days. The life of each day started before sunrise and continued beyond sunset and runs were had in silence. The world would demand their news and their food, but before they paid their price for them, Isaac was paying the price for his dreams and it was all or nothing.

Standing at the fry bin, during the middle of the summer, on a hot July day, with sweat pouring out of him, Isaac felt within him the words *This must work*.

He had finished his morning run and he still had an afternoon run ahead of him, but right now he had to run to and from the fry bin to fulfill orders.

All of the running around, all of the work, all of the effort had to pay off. This was not something that was done merely to fail. The exhaustion was real, but the realization he came to was exhausted: *This must work*. Isaac had to have the success.

As the order for fries came and went, the order in Isaac's life came into balance. He would survive the training and be made stronger for it. No one saw the miracle of work, they only saw the fruits of it.

Demands do not crush people, they make them.

Junior Year

No one had to encourage Isaac to go faster on the cross country course. He was ready to race; so too were his teammates Paul Harkins and Dave Schruth. If Paul or Dave wanted colleges to look at them they would both need statements to be made their senior year. Zack Ventress was off to Princeton and was running in the Ivy League; they knew what was on the line. They all knew that they could sweep first, second and third places at state and that was their goal. They wanted to beat Mead. They wanted it all, tired of having to always place second. This was Isaac's second chance and for Paul and Dave their final chance.

Isaac was successful in achieving his thousand mile goal. He had more than a thousand positive associations with his running. Each mile had carried with it belief in what would shortly occur. At home Isaac had created a miniature state podium above the entryway to his room. On it were his goals: State Individual Champion, State Team Champion, Foot Locker Western Regional Champion, National Champion.

Lofty goals for a kid that had not made it out of his own district or region in track the previous two years. He had never even won a race, and yet he was aiming for victories at the highest level. The only time Isaac had made it to state was when he was a freshman during cross country. Isaac visualized running at the state meet with every run and workout. In his mind he had run the course thousands of times and thousands of times the results had been the same: he won.

The season started off with tragedy however, as one of Isaac's teammates, Craig Toribara, committed suicide. Unseen to the world were Craig's struggles. He felt deeply and decided to end it all. All on the team and in the community were brought closer together.

Running was again a gift.

The first meet of the season was down in Oregon at the same course Isaac had run as a freshman. The family all made it to watch Isaac run this time. The race course was not spectator friendly. The teams would all run out and disappear in a wooded trail section near the school and then surface near the finish as the course ended on the track.

Isaac had a strong start, set into a strong pace, and then never let off the pedal once he was up and moving. He was opening up a lead and beating everyone. The only problem was the course was not well defined. Isaac made a wrong turn and ran an additional quarter mile. Once he figured it out he got back on course and ended up taking second place.

The work had been hard and taxing, and now the racing seemed easy. There would be dual meets and invitationals every week but the results kept coming back the same. Isaac would take out a strong pace, hold a fast pace and never let up. Running against Rogers' best, win. Against North Central, University, Central Valley, East Valley, West Valley, he again won. Running against Lewis & Clark, Gonzaga Prep, Shadle Park, Isaac and his team wracked up victories. Even running against Mead, Isaac won.

Regionals came and it looked like Mead would finally be dethroned. After regionals, Ferris had walked out with the team victory and with the fastest individual beating Mead 73-88. The win was sweet. Redemption seemed so near. The work, the effort, the goals seemed to be lining up and all coming to fruition. The team that had only fifteen in comparison to the near ninety up north was solid. Hadway's crew were cut out of wood; they were stained and only needed a final coat of finish.

State came and with it, the preview of the course the day before the meet. The team ran the course collectively and then broke up as individuals to revisit certain parts they wanted to run over again and focus in on. Isaac found himself with nerves and wonder as he ran through his mind what he wanted to see the following day.

It was all so close.

During the early part of the previous week there had been a two mile time trial on goal pace for the state meet. Isaac had wanted to go through at 9:20 for two miles. He believed if he went through at that pace on the rolling hills of the state course, that he would be on pace for the win. The practice had gone exactly to plan. Isaac had run 9:20 on the track. But running on grass would be slower and going up the hills would be taxing as well. The only help would be the added adrenaline of running at state.

That night in the hotel, Isaac surveyed the previous year, the paper routes, the work at McDonald's, the early sessions at seminary each morning. He had been awake and attentive to all of it. Isaac still needed some comfort.

He opened up his Bible to Psalms 23 and read:

> *The Lord is my shepherd; I shall not want.*
> *He maketh me to lie down in green pastures:*

he leadeth me beside the still waters.
He restoreth my soul: he leadeth me in the paths
of righteousness for his name's sake.
Yea, though I walk through the valley of the shadow
of death, I will fear no evil: for thou
art with me; thy rod and thy staff they comfort me.
Thou preparest a table before me in the presence
of mine enemies: thou anointest my
head with oil; my cup runneth over.
Surely goodness and mercy shall follow me
all the days of my life: and I will dwell in the
house of the LORD for ever.

Hangman Valley had been in his mind, but that would be the past. Isaac had a calm future ahead of him.

The state meet started with the firing of the gun and 152 individuals storming up the first hill not 50 meters into the start of the state race. Mead's neon green charged from one side, Ferris' red charged from the other. Up the hill they went and disappeared from the view of the Hawkins family and others who had come to support their teams. The coaches, with those families, made their way towards their first viewing of the race, just after the mile mark. A sea of runners had disappeared, and a sea of families and coaches went chasing their team.

Before the athletes would come into view, there would be the voice of the announcer echoing over the loud PA system.

"Coming through the first mile, leading is Hawkins of Ferris, followed by Harkins of Ferris, Fayant of Mead, and Schruth of Ferris. It looks all Ferris at the front."

Cheers from families supporting Ferris cried out.

Worried looks from the Mead families were seen.

Into the hairpin 180 degree turn they came and with it the noise of everyone cheering for their athlete, their boy, their brother, their son, their grandson, their nephew, their friend. And out they all went, athletes and spectators alike, towards the two mile mark. Again the athletes disappeared towards the silent

© Peter Hawkins Personal Archive

outer rim of the course and the families and coaches nervously speculated with one another as they raced over to view the two mile.

In the distance the athletes came into view and the announcer came back.

"Hawkins of Ferris is well into the lead now, coming through two miles in 9:20." Cheers from the Hawkins family and the Ferris families.

"Following Hawkins is Harkins of Ferris, holding strong in second." More cheers.

"Then there is a group of three, it is Jason Fayant of Mead, Matt Kerr of Kennewick and Dave Schruth of Ferris." It looked like Ferris was running like the Mead teams of the past seven years.

Isaac passed by the spectators with only a mile to go. Harkins went by chasing his chance to try and catch his teammate. The three went by with Schruth, Fayant, and Kerr all trading places. Then came the pack and cheers, yells, and encouragement followed before a mad sprint by all to the finish; athletes and spectators alike.

Cresting the final hill Isaac rose and then sprinted downward to the finish in first, clocking 14:40.4. Then came Paul Harkins: 14:56. The next three had been battling with the end result being Fayant of Mead finishing third in 15:02, Then Kerr of Kennewick in 15:05 and Schruth of Ferris in 15:07. Ferris had not swept as planned but 1,2,5 was still amazing.

Families and spectators alike had different digits on their hands up or down reflecting the team that had their runners in. Everyone was trying to keep score in their mind.

"We had two in before their one, and three in before their two."

"There's a Mead runner, was that their third or fourth one?"

"Here comes a guy from Ferris, he's their fourth."

It was a work in mathematics, of estimates, of what might be.

And the runners poured in. On the opposite end of the finishing chute the athletes poured out and were welcomed by families hugging, supporting, and congratulating their athletes. Sweat had come from not only the athletes but the families as well who had sprinted to the locations to cheer on their boys.

"I think we did it," became the common refrain from various athletes and from the two opposing teams.

The ban that had put only one team coming out of Spokane had been lifted after only one year. Had the ban been in effect, Ferris would all but have been assured the victory having won regionals that year, but 1995 was not 1994.

Teams finally made their way to the podium to await the results. First they would call up the individuals.

Of the ten slots on the podium, six were from the GSL: three from Ferris, two from Mead and one from North Central.

After the cheers and celebration, after the picture was taken, the voice of the announcer came back on.

"In 16th place from Olympic with 438 points," the list continued to be read with everyone waiting and wearing nervous looks upon their faces. The last three names would be read, but only after each team had first ascended the podium to get their picture taken.

"In third place with 127 points, from Richland, the Bombers." A group of athletes wearing green and yellow apparel walked up the pyramid of steps.

While the picture was taken, Hadway and the Ferris boys looked around, waiting with solemn respect for the moment.

"In second place with 65 points, from Spokane, Washington..." the announcer knew how to draw out a pause.

"Ferris High School."

As heads shook and eyes looked off into nowhere, the Ferris boys climbed the pyramid to claim their second place trophy. Meanwhile there came bedlam and excitement from Mead; they had done it again. Eight years in a row, going against their toughest competitor and closest call yet. Respectfully they shook hands with every Ferris athlete as they came off the podium and then went up to claim the championship trophy that they had brought back and forth from the event for the past seven years.

"Your champions with 54 points, Mead High School."

Ferris had their top three just where they needed them to be, but their fourth and fifth runners, junior Dana Harper and freshman TJ Marshal, finished 28th and 30th in the team scoring. Every point matters and every position counts with the top five athletes. Mead was the better team that day.

Mead's fifth man that day was none other than Lee Hodin. Lee, like Isaac, had also ran at the Hangman Valley golf course the year previous. He also had not gone on to state. He was in the junior varsity race a year ago and had finished 27th in that race running 18:00. At state, a year later and as a senior, he ran 15:49 and finished 28th in the team scoring. Ryan Wiser, Mead's third runner in had also been at Hangman Valley, running junior varsity, but he had taken second there, running 16:47, and at state as a junior now, he finished 14th in the team scoring, running 15:31. Everyone had been fighting for improvement, and they all saw it. Mead won, having a stronger core of guys from top to bottom.

Everyone in races are chasing their dreams. For some it was to beat Mead, for others it was to be on Mead's varsity.

Isaac returned back to Spokane, able to check off one of his goals, an individual state championship. The team championship had not come, but next on his list was Western Regionals and then Nationals.

The Foot Locker Cross Country Championships were previously known as the Kinney Cross Country Championships which started in 1979 and were sponsored by Woolworths. The name changed in 1993, when Matt Davis had taken third.

The race and event was the only National Championship in any of the high school sports. With the country divided into four regions: Northeast, Midwest, South, and West, Isaac looked to do what no other individual in the Western Region had ever done: win as a junior.

Prior to the Seeded Race, some runners opt to have their name read and then they can run in front of the crowd. Typically the state champions from various states and from various divisions show up to have their name read. Isaac did not need to hear his name announced before the race. He did not need to run in front of people and have them cheer him. He was there with his goal in mind.

The race started, Isaac went to the front and held a small lead. Instead of the state meet, it was like having 11 state meets, all at once. To qualify for Nationals, Isaac would need to finish in the top eight. Skiy Detray, who ran for Mead the previous year, had gone on to Nationals when he had only finished fourth at the state meet with a time of 15:00. Isaac had run twenty seconds faster on the same course. It was well within the possibility to make it to Nationals.

The first and second miles flew by and Isaac was there in the lead. It was not the largest lead, but it was a lead nonetheless.

McDonald's, the boy with the paper route, the kid who had been cut from the basketball team, the boy reading on the bus, the kid who had completed a marathon; it was all continuous effort done in the dark, in isolation, without anyone watching.

Now he had the eyes and attention of thousands there at the event.

Down the homestretch he flew and crossed the line in first. The first ever junior in high school to win the Western Regional. His time was not the effect of a down year in the Western Region; his time would have qualified him for Nationals in any of the previous runnings of the race. Isaac had not only won the race, but he was now a clear favorite heading into the National Championship only a week away. Spokane would send yet another runner to Nationals.

Going someplace Isaac had not gone before, he relied on the words of someone who had. Coach Hadway's only other athlete to compete at Nationals at that time was Stuart Burnham, who was his first great athlete. Hadway got Isaac in touch with Stuart, who had run the Balboa Park course in California and let them speak to one another. Stuart advised Isaac to go out with the leaders but to not push the pace. When you put the very best together, you could go out too fast and end up dying.

Isaac saw the wisdom in the words of someone who had gone before. He also saw in the tapes he had recorded since his freshman year that it was true; some athletes had gone out and then clearly fallen back into the pack.

Isaac shifted away from his winning strategy of going out hard and daring others to try and hang with him. He opted to wait until later in the race to make a strong push for the finish.

With his hopes on the line, the gun was fired, the teams ran off and Isaac held true to the previous advice. He went out with the leaders but he did not force the pace. Abdul Alzindani from Dearborn Fordson High School in Dearborn Michigan, and Sharif Karie from West Springfield High School in Burke, Virginia were vying for the lead early and Isaac was right on their heels. Isaac stayed in third position, but was uncomfortable not running hard from the gun. When it came time to shift gears late in the race, the runners who had already separated continued to do so.

Isaac was in third place with just over 80 meters to go. Nine guys would pass Isaac on the way to the finish. Isaac finished 12th in the country. Two of the athletes to pass him were future collegiate teammates Jonathon Riley (tenth place) and Gabe Jennings (seventh place); both would also be future Olympians.

The season had ended, not with a national title, but with experiences and doors open that had not been opened previously. College teams that had not registered the letters Isaac had hand written in his freshman and sophomore years, were now well aware of the boy from Spokane with a paper route and a job at McDonald's.

Junior Year Track

Returning from the warm weather of California to the sleet, snow, and wind of a

Spokane winter was a bit of a letdown. Yet, Isaac realized he had accomplished, in part, almost all of his goals and he still had another year of high school to reach his goals.

Eager to get back out and train Isaac kept running, but slipped a few times on the icy roads in Spokane and had his first major injury, a calf injury. Wearing an air-cast Isaac continued to train but there was a nagging sense of doubt chipping away at him. Instead of being the boy flying in under the radar, Isaac was the one with the target on his back. Isaac was the one they were all gunning for, teammates and competitors alike.

The confidence that came from training and preparation was now in question. Could he perform like a champion, not having the miles he was accustomed to?

The track season started and Isaac was beaten. It did not come because of a wrong turn on the course like in cross country. Isaac had been a strong runner, but not necessarily someone with the fastest foot speed. His ability to endure just slightly more pain for a longer distance had been his strength. In track the distances were shorter, and the competitors many.

Isaac however, still had goals. He wanted to win the mile and two mile in track and complete, in essence, the triple crown of high school racing: state cross country champion, state two mile champion, and state mile champion.

Isaac qualified for state in the mile and two mile and so he was, at least, in a position to be in the race for those titles.

The state meet is a two day event and in the first day there would be the mile run; the event where Isaac was least confident in his foot speed. The race started and Isaac stayed near the front pack, but one runner went out and grabbed a big lead. Through the first lap they went, through the second, and now the one who had gone out fast started to come back to the pack. The third lap was coming to a close and the chase pack was catching that lone runner. With two hundred meters to go, Isaac saw that if he were going to win he had to go in that instant and he had to give everything he had.

This must work, came back to him.

Willing himself and coming back with confidence, Isaac surged. He passed by Jason Fayant of Mead who had grabbed the lead, and now Isaac lunged towards the tape with legs arms and everything he had seemingly swimming down the homestretch. Isaac had done the improbable, he had come from behind and he won: 4:13.25, Fayant was second 4:13.96. This would be the first and only race from which Isaac would cry. He had done it. He had proved to himself that he was still there and it could still happen. The worker could win.

The next night in the two mile, Isaac again hung back, reserving the energy he had left in hopes of having one last hard charge to the tape. With two laps to go, Isaac made his move and held on for the victory, running 9:13.04. Again Jason Fayant placed second with 9:16.98. The triple crown completed, Isaac stood again on the podium recognizing that he still had one more year to do it all again.

© Peter Hawkins Personal Archive

Senior Year

Hadway was excited by what Isaac had accomplished. This boy who had gobbled up all of his workouts, who never questioned, never said no, never stopped giving his best in every workout, and who seemed to have endless energy to draw upon was an athlete he had for one more year. He knew Isaac wanted to win it all and he wanted to help him get there.

120 miles a week looked to be the base point. The best runners in the world

can touch such limits so why not go with the best in the world? For two straight weeks in the summer heat of Spokane, Isaac would put forth his best efforts to try and run a total of 240 miles. Isaac did all his running each week on only six days of effort not seven because of a religious observance of the Sabbath day. So 20 miles would be logged each day for six days straight. One day of rest would be had, and then, six more days of 20 miles each.

Isaac wanted to win the Western Region and set the course record. He wanted to win Nationals. He wanted to go sub four in the mile, he wanted to go sub 8:43 in the two mile. He wanted it all. He dreamed big.

Yet, as with all things, the unforeseen elements play a part in determining destiny. The work that had brought success, brought with it a pounding on the body of an 18 year old.

Isaac started his senior year winning every race and setting course records on almost every course he ran. He was beating times of Matt Davis, Chris Lewis, and other Mead greats. Isaac was seemingly setting the world afire. Gearing up towards state, however, he seemed to feel more tired than usual.

Gone was the paper route and the job at McDonald's. The money he had saved over the years was plentiful, and the offers from universities interested in Isaac had started to pour in. But still, Isaac felt like he was running on empty at the end of a workout or a race.

He was pushing the pace as he always did and performed at the very highest level, but internally he knew that something was amiss.

The state cross country meet came and with it an individual victory where he ran 14:39. He was only one second faster than the previous year. Isaac wanted to break Matt Davis' record. It was the last year that the state meet's distance would be three miles. After Isaac's senior year the official distance of the state meet would move up to 5,000 meter (3.1 miles, the standard national course distance). Isaac felt sluggish as he passed the finish line, well ahead of everyone.

Mead won the team title yet again, with University High School taking second. 11 out of the top 18 finishers at the state meet were all from Spokane. Again a deep fast bunch poured out of this small city.

Isaac continued to train for Western Regionals and Nationals that were on the horizon. He was still on pace to achieve his goals. Perhaps it was just an off day, and still a good off day to have in comparison to what others have on their off days. Isaac finally decided to have his blood sampled to put to rest the nagging fears inside his mind.

The results came back and Isaac was anemic.

He had pushed his body to its limits and his body was trying to slow him down. There were not enough healthy red blood cells coursing through his well tuned body. The results were that he felt sluggish.

At the Western Regional Race Isaac would have to fight like he had in the mile race in track his junior year to secure a spot on the team heading to Nationals. Isaac took fourth at the Western Regional. The race was an indication that a National Title would not be in the works. At Nationals Isaac would finish 26th and a future teammate and Olympian Gabe Jennings would also be having an off day and finished 27th.

With a careful watch over Isaac's diet and adding iron to his system as a means of combating the anemia, Isaac continued to train and prepare for track. The toughest workout he would complete was 40 X 400 meter on the track.

With it came quick results. At state, running in that Lincoln Bowl, Isaac ran the mile in 4:07 and the two mile in 8:56, winning handily in both events. The triple crown of racing had been won yet again and there was a future of running ahead of him.

Various teams showed interest, but the foremost was Stanford University. They were the fastest team in the country and had won the National Title that year scoring 46 points. Comparatively it would be like playing basketball at Duke for Mike Krzyzewski or Nick Saban from Alabama ringing up and offering a position at quarterback. Stanford was not only going through a distance renaissance it was also Stanford, one of the most prestigious universities in the country and they were offering scholarship money.

Even with the offer, Isaac was still unsure where he should go. Paul and Ann took their son out to dinner to help put in context what it meant to have the coach at Stanford calling their house. They knew that this opportunity did not happen to everyone; everything in their upbringing and in their associations growing up indicated that doors like Stanford do not open everyday. After the dinner, Isaac decided he would call up Stanford and tell them he would be coming there in the fall of 1997.

In the spring after Isaac's freshman year at Stanford he received a missionary call from his church to serve in the Manila, Philippines for two years. After his missionary service, Isaac returned to Stanford University where he continued to compete on their cross country and track teams. Isaac earned a Bachelors in English and then went on to law school at the University of Utah. He now works in Spokane with his father, continuing the family business.

Isaac has also involved himself in trying to revive Spokane's running scene. He worked alongside Herm Caviness to try and bring back the Spokane Summer Games which they did in the summer of 2014. They hope to make it a permanent staple of the town. Isaac is also trying to revive the Junior Bloomsday Race which had been discontinued. He hopes to provide rich opportunities to his four children as they make their way through Mullan Road Elementary School on the South Hill of Spokane.

Emily Hawkins: The Second One

Watching and waiting one year behind Isaac stood his younger sister Emily. She had watched him win while she was discovering what she could accomplish. The boy she could almost beat on training runs for their marathon when she was only 13 was someone she saw developing in front of her and believed she could catch.

Isaac had set the pace and expectations high for everyone to follow. The Hare that she chased did not live in another age, did not go to a different school, did not live in another neighborhood; it was a brother living and breathing just twenty feet down the hall in the upstairs bedroom.

Isaac's place as the first child in the family could never change and he experienced everything first. Emily's eagerness to follow Isaac and engage in everything he did started at an early age. Isaac had a paper route. Emily followed suit in getting her own paper route. Isaac had a job in fast food working at McDonald's; Emily got a job working fast food across the street on the other corner of 29th and Regal. Instead of making burgers she was making pizzas at Little Caesars. He was tall and had dark hair, Emily was short and had blond hair. Whereas boys perform better the older they are due to the maturation process and added strength, girls typically perform better the younger they are due to the lack of maturation process. Despite the differences and difficulties Emily faced, she showed the same fight she displayed at 13 when she fought to break free from Isaac's pace.

The women's distance running scene in Spokane took only a few years to develop. It coincided with the rise of Title IX in 1972. The first Washington

State Girls Cross Country Championship was held on October 21, 1973. It was held at Granger High School and was only a 1.5 mile distance. There were no individuals or teams from Spokane at the event. There were two races for girls that day. The AA division had seven schools competing with only 45 runners in the race. The A division race had only four teams competing and the field consisted of 34 runners.

In 1975 Spokane started to send girls teams and individuals to the state meet. The location changed to Lake Sammamish State Park in Issaquah, Washington and the distance increased to two miles.

Jan Weitz was the lead runner for West Valley High School in 1977 and helped her team win Spokane's first AA girls division state team title. Coach McLachlan guided the girls team to the win. He also helped Jan's sister become the first female individual state champion.

In 1978 Judy Weitz of West Valley High School won the AA division race and helped her team finish fifth overall. Judy's sister Jan finished fourth in the race. The girls racing out of Spokane had to try and catch the legacy that the Weitz sisters started at West Valley High School.

Isaac had to look across town and into the history books to find the ones he wanted to compare against. Emily did not have to look far for her competition, she had to look only across the hallway at school.

One of those athletes from across the hall at school for Emily was her teammate Jennifer (Jenny) Smith. She was the same age as Isaac and was also a year older than Emily. Jenny was not one who slowed with age. She sought out Coach Hadway for workouts because she knew he got results. By the time Jenny graduated in the spring of 1997 she became the National Scholastic Outdoor mile champion and held the then meet record in the mile running 4:45.33. At the same meet where she would be crowned the nation's top prep female runner, Jenny would also finish second in the nation in the two mile running 10:28.66. As Isaac raced around the track doing insane workouts, there would be a pack of guys on the team trying to either catch Isaac or not let Jenny pass them. She was the real deal.

Jenny and Emily's coach at Ferris was Wayne Gilman. Most people associate

Wayne with his 32 year coaching career in basketball where he had a 522-276 record. They think of the five state high school basketball championship games he helped his teams reach. Some even remember Wayne from his days as a basketball player at Eastern Washington University in the 1960s. But whether it was on the wood floor or the grass of a golf course, Wayne Gilman knew how to condition and prepare his athletes for future success. He guided the girls cross country team at Ferris to a state title in 1991. Not many coaches can win state titles in two different sports and with different genders, but Wayne did. Unfortunately, colon cancer took Wayne in 2001, just shortly after leading Ferris' boys basketball team to yet another state

Left to right - Steve Kiesel, Mike Hadway, Emily Hawkins, Jenny Smith

© Peter Hawkins Personal Archives

championship game. Wayne was the coach for both Jenny and Emily.

Even though Jenny Smith was the national high school mile winner in 1997, she did not win the mile in track at the Washington State meet during her senior year. She was beat by her Ferris teammate Kristen Parish, who ran 4:52.63 compared to Jenny's mark of 4:55.13. It was an off day for Jenny, but with Ferris' girls squad at the time, off days meant second place. Jenny improved by ten seconds at the national meet, but her strength was in the two mile, where she did win the Washington State meet in 10:43.6.

Kristen Parish's victory in the mile was great, but what irked her was her fourth place finish in the 800 meter race at state. She was outkicked by another Ferris teammate Missy Blackshire who won the race in 2:10.27 compared to Kristen's 2:13.21.

Those three girls Jenny Smith, Kristen Parish, and Missy Blackshire scored

43 points at the state meet in their various events. These three athletes constituted Ferris' Girls team at the state track meet in 1997. They placed second, only losing to first place by seven points. Those were the girls Emily chased since her freshman year. Kristen and Jenny were both a year older, but Missy was Emily's same grade.

Emily competed on a very talented team. In Emily's sophomore season in 1995, as the boy's team had finished first, second, and fifth, and lost to Mead, the girls race was even closer and involved three teams vying for the title, not two.

Ferris' first four runners across the finish line that day were freshman Jill Johnson, followed by junior Jenny Smith, then sophomore Emily Hawkins, and finally junior Kristen Parish. Their finishing positions were: 6, 7, 14, and 15. That 42 was a great number to start off with for the first four runners coming in. However, as with all cross country races the fifth runner counts. Ferris' fifth runner in the team scoring that day was senior Theresa Lyons who placed 33rd with a time of 19:01. The Ferris girls team scored 75 points that day and finished third.

Second place was Eisenhower, beating Ferris by just one point, scoring 74. First place was Snohomish scoring 70 points. Eisenhower and Snohomish's top finishers were both sophomores; Ferris' top finisher was a freshman. Snohomish's team did not have a senior in their top five; they were younger, smaller, and faster. Whereas with boys the teams can build from year to year, with girls teams it is often in reverse; the best years may be as freshman and sophomores.

Emily's junior year in cross country featured a team with talent at the top, but lacking depth. The team would fail to move on to state but their three top runners would qualify as individuals: Jenny Smith now a senior, Emily a junior, and Jill Johnson a sophomore. Jenny was a clear favorite to win having not lost a single race all fall and having won at regionals.

It appeared that Isaac would be the winner on the boys side and Jenny would be the winner on the girls side. However, Jenny went out too hard while fighting a late season muscle strain. She set a blistering pace for the first mile and opened up a huge lead before running into oxygen debt. She suffered through the last half of the race gutting out a courageous 13th place finish. Emily would catch Jenny on her way to 12th place. The smartest race of the three Ferris runners was run by the youngest, Jill Johnson, who finished 7th overall and found a spot individually on the podium.

Emily would be fighting time in ways that Isaac had not fought it. Yet her solution to the problem of time would be the same as Isaac's: work.

Emily sat during the state track championships at the Lincoln Bowl during her junior year. She saw not only Isaac's dominant performance but also her teammates triumph and fight for victory over each other on the track. The headlines came, the celebration was shared, but Emily was left watching and had only one year left to prove herself.

Going into Emily's senior year of cross country it was not clear who would be the favorite for the title. There were four sophomores and three juniors all in the top ten. In a year's time there could be a freshman that could come through and beat them all. Emily was not a clear favorite, or even a favorite to win, since she had not even made it to state in track any of her previous years running.

Emily was observant. She saw Isaac's success and work ethic. She was initially surprised by Isaac's small paper podium with his goals written on it before the start of his junior year. She saw the paper and thought to herself, *How is he going to become a state champion this year when he has not even won a race?* Emily saw Isaac's effort, his goals and the alignment of his will to succeed. Once he won for two straight years, Emily said to herself, *I should try to do what he did and it might work for me.* She wrote her goals down on paper and included positive quotes and affirmations.

Then she went to work.

With the clock ticking away on her time in high school, Emily had one last summer to give to her dream.

The formula for success that Isaac had used would be the one that Emily adopted. The mileage increased and the tempo went with it. Consulting with Hadway Emily made a training program consisting of high mileage and high intensity on select days balanced out with rest and recovery runs.

Never before had Emily ever even come close to running 90 miles a week. During that summer Emily touched that number.

With confidence elevated Emily entered the season, under the radar and without any expectations, except those she put upon herself. The season started off with the typical Shadle Highlander Invitational and Emily started off the season with a win.

It would not be the last.

The state had upped the course distance from three miles to 5,000 meter (3.1 miles) and with it came fresh course records. Emily's wins were course records. She only lost one race the entire season, a race in which she ran sick.

Entering into the state race, Emily had done all that she could to prepare. There was no illness, there were no injuries, there was only Emily's eyes up and ready for the next bend in the course.

The gun fired and again, the Hawkins clan migrated with family and friends that showed up to watch the race. The migration began again. First to the mile and a half mark and the wait for the PA announcer to echo out a status update.

"Leading at the mile mark is senior Emily Hawkins of Ferris." Cheers sprang up. In the hunt behind her were a pair of juniors and a sophomore. Emily was holding fast to her training and her desire to win.

The Hawkins family again wound their way towards the fence overlooking the two mile, as well as the coaches and other spectators.

The family stood at the chain link fence and tried to spot the white jersey and the blonde ponytail come around the bend.

"At two miles it is still the senior, Emily Hawkins of Ferris, opening up the lead now." Still those younger girls trailing Emily were in the hunt.

Once more the shift of fans occurred and the mass of people shuffled over towards the finish on that cold day in November. The Hawkins kids pushed against the chain link fence and threw out their squeaky voices to their sister with yells and screams of delight. Emily was coming down the last hill with no one in sight and she crossed the finish line in 18:34.9, a new course record.

One of the first to meet Emily at the exit of the finishing chute was none other than her younger brother Paul. The local paper was there for the moment and snapped a picture. The younger generation was looking up and seeing their future hopes.

Emily walked up the podium having achieved her goal. After state, Emily

competed at Foot Locker Western Regional with hopes of going to Nationals. She ran tough and finished 24th overall. Within the top eight that went on to Nationals there was one freshman, one sophomore, four juniors, and two seniors.

Wrapping up her season Emily received offers from colleges across the country to come and visit their university. Emily went to various schools but ended up going from the Northwest to the northeast, settling in on a full ride scholarship to Boston University.

Emily earned a degree in Elementary Education while competing at Boston University. After graduation Emily married Nathan Smith and they live in southern California. As her husband practices patent law, Emily volunteers her time towards her children's school programs. She has created her own running group as an after school program. She too is trying to provide opportunities for her kids and anyone else in her community.

Tyler Byers: Iron Wheel

During one warm summer day in 1992 Tyler Byers, age 10, sat in the back of a boat speeding along Loon Lake in Washington. He looked out the back of the boat to see Jim Martinson gliding from one side of the water to the other. Jim had his usual big smile, and with it a yell that carried over the roar of the sloshing water.

"I love being disabled!" Jim shouted.

And back Jim glided over the water. He flew up the wake and flipped about, twisting around and enjoying the moments of air time, as half his body was without use.

Tyler had never heard someone shout with such glee that they loved being what others considered a disadvantage. Jim's shouting and sheer joy struck Tyler, who looked down at his shrunken legs, made such by having been born with sacral agenesis (a disability caused by a malformed sacrum).

Jim Martinson was a Vietnam War Veteran and a friend of the Byers family. Martinson became a paraplegic due to his service in the military, a mark he would carry with him throughout his life.

Jim finally let go of the rope, and waited for the boat to come by and pick him up.

"Tyler you wanna try?" Jim asked.

Tyler got secured in the single ski, fell out the back of the boat and held to the rope. The engine roared to life. Tyler held tight and rose out of the water feeling the same words Jim had shouted moments earlier rise up within him: *I love being disabled.*

Tyler had such a moment on the back of the boat due to his mother Ann's determination to see him live. After delivering Tyler, the doctor told Ann it would be easier to let Tyler die due to the doctor's fear of Tyler's future inability to self feed.

Ann saw a flash in the eyes of her first son.

This first time mother at twenty-two years of age would not let her son die. She loved her son and would do anything for him.

Ironically, one of the best decisions Ann made was to let Tyler struggle. She did not hover about performing every task for her son, but rather she let him figure out the world around him. He would not have the full use of his legs but he had a perfectly good mind and ability to move and develop the rest of his body.

When Tyler was almost three, he welcomed a younger brother Joseph into the world, and at almost age four he welcomed the last of his brothers, Ryan. These three amigos would roll about together on the floor. Words like disabled and able bodied meant little to kids, let alone brothers. They defined themselves by their play-time rolls.

Legos did not come prepackaged with the words, "able bodied use only." They were there for anyone to use to create worlds. Tyler and his brothers snapped pieces together bringing to life their imaginations.

After five years of marriage Tyler's parents divorced. Ann's husband was losing himself to drugs and other issues that were not worthy of emulation. Ann continued to support her three young children as she eventually met and fell in love with Tim Byers, an honest, hardworking man. While playtime was left for Tyler and his brothers to shape imagined worlds, the end of play time brought with it a world that was being shaped by their mother and adoptive father.

When it was time to clean up, everyone helped, including Tyler. If anything, he would have to set the example to his younger brothers.

Eventually more physical activities took place over the mental imaginings of youth. Basketball and wrestling soon took center stage and with it, Tyler throwing up shots and using the strength of his upper body to try and pin his younger, albeit larger, brothers.

Joe and Ryan quickly realized they would have to give everything they had in order to try and pin their older brother. Sometimes they would succeed, other times they would not.

The chores of cleaning up inside were not the only routines expected for everyone to participate in; Saturday brought with it time in the yard pulling weeds. Tim walked out in the yard to see his sons working and reminded them why they needed to work.

"You're not getting paid to be here. Your payment is working around the house and us feeding you." He said with a bit of humor.

The three boys looked up and listened to their father, then returned to the weeds. Their tiny hands continued to gnaw at the ground. Crawling about in the yard, Tyler made his way around, grumbling like his brothers and any child would. There would not be a separate set of rules to live by for Tyler. Once the job was complete they could go back to playing, but work needed to have its proper place for all of them.

Routines of work and play continued. The toys were brought out, the play started, rough-housing occurred, and then time was up and the chaos needed to be brought back to order. The toys and all their parts were brought back and if there were any apology needed from one brother to the other, it was given.

Wherever their mother went, so too went Tyler, Joe, and Ryan. If it were to the store or park then they all went. Life continued for them, as it continues for anyone, one day at a time. Clothes were worn, marks were made, and kids continued to grow through the wash cycles of laundry and the spills of spaghetti slurping. All the boys' hair kept growing like the weeds in the yard and it would need to be cut. The movements and seasons of life, with all the small details occurred for the Byers boys just as they occur for anyone.

Eventually, Tyler headed off to school, that unknown world that Joe and Ryan would have to wait to see. Tyler attended Mullan Road Elementary and rode the bus just like any other kid. He was the second stop on the early morning bus route to school, the first stop being at the Hawkins. And so as the Hawkins kids got on the bus, so too did Tyler and eventually his brothers. They lived on the same road and so they rode the same bus.

Tyler's wheelchair was placed in the back of the old yellow school bus and Tyler would walk using his arms to maneuver through the aisle, touching the fake leather seats and making his way towards the back of the bus. Everyone else would get picked up on the route, and then file off, and there Tyler would be ready to maneuver back through the aisle, with arms gripping that fake leather as he made his way to the front of the bus. Then he was back in his wheelchair and off to the basketball court where he hoped to put in a few shots before school started.

Tyler would figure out how to navigate the terrain around him and he had been doing so his entire life. At the age of four, he figured out how to snow ski, at the age of nine he finished his first Bloomsday Race. Observant as any young child is, Tyler looked at those older, stronger, and faster than he was and tried to figure out how to catch up to them.

At Tyler's first Bloomsday he caught a glimpse of the elite wheelchair racers. They zipped around with their three wheeled racing wheelchairs. Their arms were bulging as they ripped up the roads before them, heads down, helmets ready, and sunglasses covering their eyes. These warhorses of work were churning out incredible speed. There was no self pity, no doubt, no fear, just these men and women wheeling themselves forward with iron wills.

I want to be like them.

This thought kept rolling around Tyler's mind as he saw one after another pass by. These were his people. What they did spoke to him.

Standing alongside Tyler at this time were his parents. They observed their son's reaction and knew it came from a real place. They also knew about the considerable cost to purchase a new racing wheelchair. But their sacrifice became a bargain when they thought of what it would mean for their son.

$1,900 later, Tyler at the age of nine had his first racing wheelchair.

The wheelchair was put to use during cross country training in the fall and Fit for Bloomsday training in the spring. Out of Mullan Road Elementary little flocks of students could be seen sprinting or jogging.

Out near the front of the pack was Tyler Byers, trying to chase down a boy one year younger in school than him but who was the fastest runner at Mullan Road Elementary-and who happened to be his neighbor-Ben Hawkins.

East and west of the school these two would go. One run east of school, named *Monster Run* due to the long hill leading to the bottom of Regal Road, was a run that lived up to the hype. Tyler glided towards the bottom, getting a head start on the return trip, while Ben looked up and saw the gap he had to try and close.

As Ben's legs went to work, Tyler's arms did their best to keep pace.

Gripping and releasing, Tyler found his rhythm in every revolution. The pacing of it all was relentless: the catch, the pull, the release, back to the catch, the pull, the release. Uphill, gravity pulled against Tyler and so he fought against it, revolution after revolution. Upward he went, earning everything one push and pull at a time.

Momentum is made of tiny, continuous movements and Tyler knew it. He had to stick with his efforts, from one moment to the next so as to keep his momentum; there would be no shortcut to success. And with every tug, pull, and push Tyler's muscles became taut and his arms began to bulge. Tyler was not the only one to notice the difference in his physique.

As everyone readied for the PE test at Mullan Road Elementary, Tyler received the only help he would need that day, and that was merely to be placed on the chin-up bar. Once on the bar he started doing chin-ups. Ms. Coffin the PE teacher stood by, as a class of sixth graders looked on.

"One, two, three, four" Ms. Coffin kept count with a clipboard at her side.

Eyes of some twenty odd school children watched mesmerized as Tyler rose and fell on the bar.

"Fifteen, sixteen, seventeen" Ms. Coffin continued like a metronome.

Already Tyler had beaten the best mark that day: sixteen pull-ups by a female gymnast in the class. The eyes of all his classmates were stuck on him. Entranced they watched him rise and fall.

"Thirty-one, thirty-two, thirty-three." Ms. Coffin said as Tyler began to slow.

As if the trance of the moment had finally been lifted Tyler's classmates, with their squeaky voices, started to encourage.

"Come on Tyler, you can make it to forty!"

"Hold on Tyler!"

"You can do it!"

Their shouts rose and so did the red color of strain through Tyler's arms and up through his neck near to his head. They were seeing something that most of them would never do.

"Thirty-four" Ms. Coffin said.

Tyler's young arms were burning.

"Thirty-five" Ms. Coffin said.

Tyler would give one last heave and rise again.

"Thirty-six" she said.

And Tyler fell off the bar to the mat below. Gravity was something Tyler pushed against, just like everyone else. He had wanted to get to forty, but thirty-six was still the school record and one that would never be beaten.

At Sacajawea Middle School Tyler would again have the opportunity to engage with the chin-up bar in the PE test and as an eighth grader he was again helped up to the bar where he started to rattle them off with precision and ease.

"One, two, three, four," McLaughlin rattled off, as if keeping pace for professional dancers. The first ten went by before McLaughlin took a breath.

Awkward young middle school students with freckles and pimples watched, standing in their gray and black PE uniforms, letting their insecurities disappear for a moment as they too were won over by Tyler's unapologetic will, rising and falling before their very eyes.

"Twenty-three, twenty-four, twenty-five" McLaughlin continued to rattle off the numbers.

Up and down Tyler went, arms bulging.

"Forty-one, forty-two, forty-three, forty-four, forty-five."

It was on the forty-sixth one that Tyler finally broke the pace he had kept. His arms were zapped, but his mind said there was still more.

"Forty....seven," McLaughlin said.

Hanging on the bar Tyler searched inside himself trying to find more.

"Forty...eight," McLaughlin said.

Again the student's with pimples and changing voices realized the exceptional effort being displayed before them and so they started to cheer.

"Let's go Tyler!"

"You can do it!"

"Get fifty!"

Tyler held fast to the bar and tugged once more, that long, sinew shocking pull.

"Forty...nine"

Gravity yanked Tyler back down but his arms held fast to the bar. There would be one more to fight for. The slow pull upwards began. Gravity's pull was constant, but Tyler's will was just as constant. Slowly, but surely, Tyler continued to rise.

"Fifty."

And Tyler again fell from the bar.

He had improved and set another school record. The classmates, mesmerized and excited by the effort, then retreated back into their insecurities and volunteered one another to try and follow up Tyler's efforts on the bar.

During Tyler's time in middle school he continued to explore sports and tried out for the wrestling squad. In a time when others are ruled by insecurities and a fear of isolation, Tyler crawled out on a mat with his wrestling singlet on, casting both of those feelings aside. He had wrestled with brothers his whole life, why not wrestle against others on the mat? And so with his incredible upper body strength, Tyler wrestled, chalking up some pins, as well as some disappointing losses. The wins were far more than the losses on the mat; he was an exceptional multi-sport athlete.

To and from school Tyler went, with classes to study for, tests to take and projects to do. His academic mind was as strong as his arms. Good grades and near perfect marks continued to follow Tyler; there was no problem that he would not tackle. The assignments were difficult, but Tyler did not relent. His grip on his grades mirrored the grip he had in all his training.

Tyler knew that others looked at him, but he did not want to let the wheelchair define their perceptions of him. He did not want it to be a big deal, especially as he entered the world of high school at Ferris.

High School: Raising the Bar

On the first day of cross country practice in 1996, before the season or school had started, Tyler did not tell Coach Hadway that he was going to be there. He did not want to explain anything to his new coach, or try and control his

expectations. He did not want Coach Hadway to see him as a liability.

Tyler wheeled himself around and saw Coach Hadway, standing in the parking lot with the ten guys who were strong or crazy enough to show up. Standing next to Coach Hadway as he surveyed the area was Isaac Hawkins, a senior who stood with legs marbled out of the miles he had logged away.

Coach Hadway spoke to the inner athlete, the one hungry for more and who came seeking their own evolution. Coach Hadway's eyes touched upon Tyler and continued looking at those who had the guts to show up to his practices.

Tyler would be treated just like everyone else. He would have his times recorded like everyone else, and like everyone else, time would be the indicator of improvement. Coach Hadway would cut Tyler out of wood, just like he did anyone else that showed up.

Little did Tyler know there had been no wheelchair racing in the state of Washington up until that year. This chapter of racing would be his alone to write. And so he would tackle the events before him, as well as the practices, moving off as fast as he could, trying to separate from those that followed.

During Tyler's freshman year he showed up to meets but his courses had their own outline, usually on the roads, and he would disappear, a one man race, fighting against himself and the clock. Times improved and the season progressed all the way to state.

At state Tyler's freshman year he won. There were only three other competitors but he completed the 1.9 mile course in 8:43. Second place was a minute and fourteen seconds back. Tyler was in a league of his own. Yet it was bothersome for Tyler that the race distance was not three miles like others at the time, or the 5,000 meter distance that the high schools in the state of Washington would make the following year.

What impressed Tyler the most about his freshman year was his experience on the track trying to chase down Isaac during his 40 quarters. Coach Hadway would indicate the start of another quarter and they would take off.

Isaac would open up the lead and Tyler would chase, trying to catch this multiple state champion in front of him and try to keep ahead of Jennifer Smith, the nation's best female runner in the country, behind him.

Tyler was impressed by the amount of hard work, the dedication, and the focus to do something exceptional. The standard of hard work he saw and he chased it down the backstretch of lane one. Tyler wanted to apply that work ethic to himself.

In the middle of the summer offseason Tyler continued training. Up and down Regal Road Tyler went, pushing against the gravity that had made Isaac a champion and that was in the process of proving Emily's mettle.

On one early morning, Tyler was working his way, going six miles an hour up the hill in front of the Hawkins house when he heard something rising above the din of his wheels turning.

All of a sudden, 100 meters from the crest of the hill, Isaac burst past Tyler. Isaac was finishing up his run and with a sideways smile he jogged from the top of the hill back towards the driveway, to see Tyler wheeling up.

Tyler realized Isaac had seen him from a distance at the bottom of the hill and tried to catch him. Tyler saw the effort and the smile of hard work and respected that.

In competition nothing is given to you.

And with a wink to Tyler, Isaac walked down the driveway for home, watching as Tyler continued his trek up the hill then down towards his home.

Although Isaac had graduated, this would not be the last time he would be just out of Tyler's reach. Each year as Tyler got on the track, he could see in his mind's eye the ghost of Isaac Hawkins running just in front of him. Year in and year out, with each practice, Tyler was trying to chase the man who impressed him with his wholesale dedication.

Each fall Tyler competed in cross country and each spring he competed in track. But Tyler wanted to race against more than the same handful that were in wheelchairs in the fall and spring and he wanted to see more than the same handful of parents that were the only ones watching the races. These moments showcased only individual recognition. Sure he could go off and be the Junior National Wheelchair Champion in the 100, 200, 400, 800, and 1,600 meter, but he wanted more than individual achievement. The points Tyler won for his events were not added to any team total at state in cross country or in track. He raced in the Ferris team uniform, but his points were lonely ones, isolated ones, not totaled with teammates; his reliance was aimed at himself.

Wrestling is a sport that has no separate standard for anyone. You put two people on the mat and let them wrestle for points, for pins, and for pride. Tyler turned out for wrestling all four years at Ferris High School. His efforts were watched by teammates and his points were added to team titles. He knew the exhilaration that accompanied the refs whistle signifying a pin, and he knew also the despair of time running out; two points short of the victory.

Tyler felt the tug of defeat as he sat in the stands, having to watch the final of the Missoula Invitational Wrestling Tournament. He sat and watched, reliving his own semifinal match over again in his head.

Tyler had dropped his weight to 98 pounds, cutting away at his already defined arms with a chisel. In his semifinal match, Tyler had taken the lead early in the first period and grew it through the middle of the second. However, some careless mistakes and some reversals by an opponent seeking an opportunity for the title meant that Tyler was only up by a point heading into the final seconds of the third round.

The tournament had been long and Tyler fought, but within the final five seconds his opponent scored another two points and took the lead as time expired. Tyler would watch the finals from the stands with everyone else.

He had been on his way to the top but now he watched from the bottom.

Ferris' team was talented and coached by Tim Owen, one of the six legendary Owen brothers who are all known in the northwest for leading their teams to state titles and some to national championships. Tyler would show up to practice each day and be ready to give his all. The grip he had gained from the countless revolutions of his wheels in road races proved helpful on the mat.

Tyler would grip his opponents in his weight category but he seemed to have the strength of someone several weight classes higher.

When it came time for the team to jog in the hot sweaty upper room of the Ferris gym, Tyler found himself doing push-ups instead.

For thirty minutes his teammates would run around, and for thirty minutes Tyler would do push-ups.

Fifty, fifty-one, fifty-two, fifty-three.

Tyler kept track in his mind. Up and down he would go as teammates went around and around. The second hand on that clock seemed to move so slow.

Two-hundred and four, two-hundred and five, two-hundred and six.

If Tyler was going to have a chance he had to keep his strength up and his weight down. Muscle weighing more than fat made it a tricky battle to fight.

Five hundred and eighty-five, five hundred and eighty-six, five hundred and eighty-seven.

Fifteen more minutes till the time was up.

Tyler was ahead of the pace he would need to sustain if he wanted to reach his goal. He could not look at the clock and let it rule him. He confronted the burning in his arms, clamping down with resolve. Around and around his teammates went in that small upper room, while Tyler only felt the fire of pushing himself up and down.

Seven hundred sixty, seven hundred sixty-one, seven hundred sixty-two.

He did not want to let his team down. The loss in the tournament had been a loss with points on the line. Had Tyler been in the final, maybe he would have won the tournament in the 98 pound section.

Nine hundred fifty-seven, nine-hundred fifty-eight, nine hundred fifty-nine.

His weakness in the last match had been his inability to endure to the very end. How could he have let up at the last moment?

Nine hundred ninety-eight, nine hundred ninety-nine, One Thousand.

"Time," shouted Coach Owen. "Back to first positions," he barked.

Teammates, sweaty and exhausted, found one another and got ready to wrestle.

"Go!"

Tyler was back against Doug Baker, the reigning district champion and second place finisher in Washington State 4A wrestling.

Leverage, muscle, and determination rolled about from both sides on the mat that practice and every practice.

The pursuit of excellence is relentless.

After winning a varsity match against Ferris' league rival, Lewis & Clark High School, Tyler went over to the chin-up bar to celebrate. Once more someone posted him on the bar and he did the rest.

He was ten shy of doubling his effort from eighth grade. Tyler did 90 straight chin-ups; his all time best.

The season continued and Tyler had stacked up an impressive 21 and 10 record. The losses hadn't been by much and the wins came through his vice-like grip.

One of the more memorable matches for Tyler came against Gonzaga Prep. Tyler was set up against an athlete from their team who was a little person. Both teams lined the mat and cheered as the small person in blue and white ran around Tyler in his red and gray. The match was hard fought on both sides but Tyler won this varsity contest.

Everyone has something to wrestle with or against.

On to regionals Tyler went, hoping to win a state championship in wrestling to go along with his multiple state championships in cross country and track. At regionals, however, Tyler would lose and finish sixth overall; the top four finishers moved on to state.

College Years: Aiming for Athens

Tyler left the mat of high school wrestling and would not return to that sport, but he did continue on with his first love, racing. Clocking a 14.9 second time in the 100 meter and posting a 13:01 in the 5k at the Junior National Championships, Tyler showcased his range and speed to do it all and wheelchair recruiters took notice. The national competition, to Tyler, equated to competing at the GSL level; the real competition in wheelchair racing was on the world scale. The two main collegiate schools for wheelchair racing at the time were the University of Illinois and the University of Arizona. Illinois had been the storied program of the past and Arizona looked poised to be the program of the future.

© The Fuze Magazine, Marilu Lopez Fretts

Tyler decided to go to Tucson, Arizona where it was warmer, having had enough of Spokane winters. Tyler's 4.0 GPA and National Merit Scholar achievements, coupled with scholarship money from the university meant that Tyler would not have to work through college. His wheelchair and academic endeavors were working for him and paid for everything.

Losing no time to workout with his new teammates, and having wheelchair teammates to train with for the first time, Tyler was amazed at the efforts of two athletes on the team: Troy Davis and Cheri Blauwet. Both were training for the Sydney Olympics.

Cheri had grown up in small farming community of Larchwood, Iowa where the population did not reach over a thousand. Due to an unfortunate farming accident, Cheri would be paralyzed from the waist down at a young age. With some encouragement by a local high school coach who had seen a wheelchair race, Cheri decided to try the sport. This was before Cheri would go on to Paralympic fame and have her own Visa Card commercial narrated by

Morgan Freeman. Before the glory and medals came the test of Cheri's mettle. Like Tyler or anyone chasing success, she found work, toil, sweat, and tears worked wonders. The day-in and day-out revolution of rigorous routines were molding her to greatness. It was a labor of love.

Like Tyler, Cheri had an outstanding appetite for academics. Fueling her mind as well as her body she earned a degree in Molecular Biology from the University of Arizona, with a 4.0 GPA. She then went on to Stanford University's School of Medicine before ending up at Harvard Medical School. Cheri currently is a Fellow in Sports Medicine at the Rehabilitation Institute of Chicago. She also currently serves as the Treasurer of the United States Anti-Doping Agency (USADA), hoping to create a clean sports environment for everyone.

Tyler's other teammate Troy Davis was born with all his ribs broken, his legs broken, and a broken arm. He was born with osteogenesis imperfecta, or brittle bone disease, which is a genetic disorder. The third child of eight, Troy grew up living life like any of his siblings and hoping for his opportunity to shine like anyone else. At the age of 12 Troy discovered wheelchair racing and was hooked like Tyler and Cheri; just itching for something to call his own.

After delaying his collegiate career for a two year church service mission in Houston, Texas, Troy returned to school and competitive racing.

It was at the University of Arizona that Tyler learned about being a great teammate in wheelchair racing. He would help pull Cheri, Troy, and other athletes along, allowing those behind to draft on him. Eventually his teammates would charge by and Tyler had his turn to rest.

With bodies that may seem broken to others, these three went out each day with the only thing that mattered: unbroken wills. With their indomitable spirit and years of training underneath them, Cheri and Troy went off to Australia and the 2000 Paralympic Summer Games. Tyler watched from home, looking to see what his new teammates could accomplish.

Troy would compete in the 100, 200, and 400 meter events, and earn a bronze medal in the 4X100 meter relay.

Cheri would win a silver medal in the 100 meter and three bronze medals in the 200, 400, and 800 meter races.

Tyler saw their success and gained confidence from the fact that he had been on the same track with these people. The reality of racing in four years at Athens came home with force as he saw his teammates and their medals.

Tyler's freshman year was spent almost anywhere but his dorm room. He had chosen one of those "easy" majors, Mathematics Engineering, to fit inside his already simple schedule. From classes, to working out with the best wheelchair racers in the world, and then back to studying Tyler went, only to take another break to fit in some wheelchair basketball during the winter. Regularly each semester, Tyler made sure to volunteer time at the local retirement home. There were only two weekends spent inside the dorms during his entire spring semester of his freshman year.

After going about this hectic pace, Tyler decided he needed to be more choosy about the races he entered. During his freshman year Tyler competed in the Boston Marathon, where he finished 16th overall, clocking 1:53:25. It was a great time considering he was only eighteen years old. The winner of the race that day was Ernst Van Dyk from South Africa, who had a wingspan of nearly seven feet. He was born with congenital absence of both legs. 2001 marked the first of 10 victories in the Boston Marathon for Van Dyk.

The next marathon for Tyler was the Los Angeles Marathon, where he would finish 18th. The winner in that race was Saul Mendoza from Mexico. Tyler knew Saul well, having seen him race at Bloomsday over the years in Spokane, where Saul would win from 1998-2007. Saul would be a six time Paralympic medalist, earning two golds, one silver, and three bronze medals in a career spanning Paralympics from Seoul, Korea in 1988 to Athens, Greece in 2004. Saul Mendoza and Ernst Van Dyk would make up the Mt. Rushmore of wheelchair racing. Tyler competed in these races and challenged himself to rise higher than he had before. If he were going to make it to the Paralympics, these would be the men he would meet there.

Returning back to Arizona, Tyler prepared himself for the New York Marathon and other races, making sure to keep his grades up and to serve in the retirement home.

At college Tyler saw the difference his parents had made in his life. Amidst Tyler's movements to and from his activities, he saw other students who had disabilities. The hands off approach of his parents had liberated Tyler, whereas some parents, he saw, hovered over their kids with disabilities. As a result these people could not rise above the circumstances around them. They did not know how to study or structure their lives. Their sights were never elevated and their attitudes never changed. As a result, many of these student athletes, Tyler saw, struggled to make it from day to day and season to season.

With gratitude for the gift of each day, Tyler continued to train and he continued to improve. The grip he had on his wheels grew stronger as he pulled himself through the seasons. Athens was on the horizon.

Whereas most runners max out at 100 to 120 mile weeks, wheelchair racers can log more time and miles away; some exceeding 250 miles a week. Tyler had to know his limitations, and rarely did perform double day workouts. Listening to his body, he saw that he could only go up to 120-130 miles a week before his body started to break down. His efforts had to be high quality at every turn.

Fit and readying himself for Athens, Tyler was invited to the IAAF Track & Field World Championships in Paris, France in 2003. Prior to this race, Tyler had set the American record in the 1,500 meter at a race in Switzerland wheeling himself to 3:02.59; a record that would last for five years. With his name in the record books and the promise of fast times, Tyler was invited to compete in Paris. The wheelchair 1,500 meter final would be raced during the able bodied track meet.

70,000 people filled the stands to watch as Tyler wheeled himself through the tunnel and into the stadium. Never before, nor since, had Tyler been in a stadium with that many people ready to cheer on the world's best. Looking up he saw himself on the big screen alongside Saul Mendoza and Ernst Van Dyk.

The boy who had been attracted to the sport as a nine year old, was wheeling around now with the legends of his sport.

Tyler was one of ten finalists and the only American in the field. He was excited and nervous to be on the world stage representing his country. The only problem Tyler faced was the weather.

Racing and training in Arizona, Tyler became accustomed to dry conditions. In Paris it was raining. Tyler tried to adapt quickly to the conditions at the time and put pine tar on his racing gloves, but as he went around the curves he could not catch his wheels as he was accustomed to which disrupted his rhythm. Tyler would finish last in the race with an uncharacteristically slow time.

Tyler returned to America and continued to train. Athens neared and Tyler was selected to represent the USA in the 800, 5,000, and 10,000 meter races, and the marathon. Unlike the able body trials wherein the top three finishers with qualifying standards go on to represent the USA, wheelchair racing has a committee overseeing and selecting its athletes. The committee analyzes average times a wheelchair racer has in their respective events. Someone with the fastest time may not have the higher average, and could be left off the team.

One of Tyler's teammates at Arizona had a faster 800 meter time than Tyler, but he was not as fast as Tyler in the longer events, and was not selected for the team. This teammate took it personally and decided to give up wheelchair racing entirely, because he was not selected to go to Athens.

Quitting is a choice made by anyone.

Tyler did make it to Athens.

Athens, the birthplace of the Olympics, would be the host nation in 2004. The motto of citius, altius, fortius (stronger, faster, higher) had been the reality of

© Tyler Byers Personal Archives

Tyler's life. He had trained for four years, ready for his goals to be achieved.

For all of Tyler's training, he was not prepared for a mistake he made a month before the Paralympics.

Prior to heading over to Athens and in the midst of his training, Tyler saw a banner asking for those in the local community to give blood. Seeing himself as someone that gave when someone was in need, Tyler wheeled his way towards the donation station and sat ready to give a pint of his blood.

Tyler's already small body took a significant blow when he gave his blood.

In a day and age in which more and more athletes lose themselves in the attempt to win at all costs and cheat through steroids and blood doping, there was one athlete who lost because he was doing the opposite; he was trying to give some of his blood to someone in need. Blood doping occurs across all sports, able bodied as well as disabled. There are mind games and trash talk that happen in the Paralympics and wheelchair racing; it's just that Tyler would not sink to that level.

Tyler ended up failing to advance from any preliminary round. He had competed in the Paralympics representing his country, but he wanted to be back in four more years; Beijing would be his next opportunity.

Coming back to the states after Athens, Tyler, now twenty-two years old, received news that the University of Arizona wanted to have him hired as the head wheelchair racing coach. Tyler, the athlete was now Tyler the coach. His new responsibilities included selecting and registering his athletes for meets as well as planning workouts. He also had to navigate the logistics of how to get everyone to and from their locations. It was yet another task tossed on his already full schedule. Tyler just rolled with it.

Instead of focusing on himself as an athlete, Tyler had to turn his attention to athletes. In some of them he saw a desire for success coupled with discipline, and in others he saw talent wasted. Some did not show up to practice on time, or they would skip practice, and finally there were some that just did not want to push it at practice. The focus on the team brought a dip in individual success for Tyler.

Another factor leading to Tyler's slowing on the track that year came from the love of his life Analee Olson. Tyler had known Analee since Spanish class at Ferris High School. Tyler sensed that there may have been some interest from Analee but he was nervous and shy. He had never been to a school dance and never asked a girl out before. Tyler had waited and waited for the opportune moment to ask Analee out on a date. The moment almost came too late when, after graduation, Tyler kept in contact with Analee and finally asked her out on a date.

During Tyler's first year at Arizona, Analee was at Washington State University. After that first year, Analee transferred down to Arizona where she and Tyler continued to date until he proposed and they were married in 2004.

Marriage, school, coaching, and training took up all of Tyler's time, and during it all he had to try and prepare for his career after school.

Post College: Work, Family and Country

After graduating with a degree in Engineering Mathematics, Tyler accepted a position at IBM in Tucson and continued to coach, hoping to prepare athletes on the team for the New York Marathon. Prior to graduation, Tyler had applied and interviewed with the CIA for an analyst position. Weeks went by and he heard nothing from the CIA. Tyler worked 60 hours a week: full-time at IBM while coaching part-time at the University of Arizona. After practice one day, Tyler saw he had a missed call from the CIA.

Tyler called back and was informed that the CIA was still interested in him. They wanted Tyler to fly back to Langley, Virginia and to go through another interview. Tyler flew back and sat through a polygraph, an interview, and some more questionnaires. Then Tyler left and returned to Arizona, waiting for another phone call. Days turned into weeks, and weeks into months before Tyler heard again from the CIA. They wanted him on their team.

Tyler accepted the position and with his wife, Analee, they set off for Virginia.

Tyler's work involved air to ground missile operations, aerospace analysis, data analysis, and a bit of programing. Going through the entry to the building each day, Tyler saw the American flag. He took pride in knowing that he was working for the American people in an effort to keep them safe. Tyler loved his work and he loved the people he interacted with each day who were of like mind.

Tyler continued to train in Virginia and adjust to his new life. It was difficult to balance, work, training, and time with Analee. As Tyler came home, Analee was off to work, putting in night shifts at the Children's Hospital Emergency Department. Tyler would hit the roads, throwing in twenty mile efforts on a

Tyler Byers, far left, competing in a heat of the 5,000 meter race in Beijing

daily basis. A majority of Tyler's training was a solo effort, alone on the roads. It was a lonely trek to China.

In 2008 Tyler again made the Paralympic team. He would compete in the 800, 1,500, 5,000 meter and marathon. This time Tyler made sure not to donate blood.

Beijing was different than Athens, primarily because the stands were packed with spectators every night. Athens had been filled with mostly empty seats in the arena, whereas in Beijing it was bustling with spectators at every event.

Tyler made it to the 1,500 meter semifinal round. He was one race away from being in the finals. One round away from a shot at the podium.

The race had gone well. Tyler was in the mix and starting to make his move down the backstretch on the last lap when the back-strap to his chair broke free. It would be like being spiked and tripped up. The momentum was lost and the seconds started to slip away.

Tyler glided home through the finish.

The only final Tyler would take part in was the marathon, where he would set his lifetime best in the distance. Lining up in Tiananmen square, Tyler thought over the history, over the man who had stood against the machine.

With the Paralympics drawing to a close, Tyler found himself in the chow hall of the Paralympic village. Prior to entering the games Tyler weighed 105 pounds; after leaving China Tyler weighed 115 pounds and the extra weight has never left.

Tyler has since left the grind of competitive wheelchair racing. After a three-year stint in Australia as an Air Force civilian, Tyler moved back to the United States, and was working in Denver, Colorado for a short time. He has since moved back to the Spokane area with his wife and kids. He works in the private sector as a data scientist. His oldest son was born in 2011 and he now has four children.

On Saturdays Tyler spends less time cranking out 20 mile rides and more time with his kids helping them grasp hold of those growing opportunities. And Tyler makes sure to take the same approach his parents took with him. If they are at the park and his child falls, he will let them pick themselves up and get back after it. Resistance is what made him and he will let it make his children as well.

Ben Hawkins: A Longer Race to Run

The first two Hawkins had both won at least one state championship. Rarely do you find such talent and work ethic in one person in a family, let alone two people. Members in the community took notice of the Hawkins family and wondered what the future held. Isaac and Emily were champions and next on the rise were another brother and sister duo that were also set one year apart in school: Ben and Liz. The question on many people's minds once they heard that there were more Hawkins was *Could this be a rewrite of the first two?* The fact that Ben had run a marathon at age 11 only added to the fodder and expectation that this kid could be a phenom.

Ben, as any younger child will do, followed along with his older siblings. If Isaac liked cars, Ben would like cars. If Isaac thought basketball was cool, Ben thought basketball was cool. So, it was no surprise when Isaac ran down the wood floor hallway as a second grader and slid to a stop saying, "That was awesome," that following behind him in his shadow came Ben, sprinting down the hall likewise saying, "Awesome!"

Emily had joined the fray as well and ran down the hall sliding. Then it came time for Isaac and Emily to go off to Wilson Elementary. This was one thing that Ben could not do, but one day, his mother informed him, he too would go off to school. He just had to have patience in the meantime.

Ben decided to practice running down the hallway and sliding. Each time Ben ran he went a little faster and slid a little further.

Unfortunately, Ben's exuberance carried him further and faster than his young mind could calculate. Before he could stop himself at the end of the hallway he was heading towards a wall that had plate glass windows outlining the door to the house.

Ben shoved out his arms straight ahead of him to stop himself. One hand hit the door, the other arm went through the plate glass.

Ben looked down to see all the way to his bone. He saw muscle tissue. And then he saw blood start to puddle.

Ann, hearing the break from the kitchen, came around the corner to see her son's arm through the window. She instinctively grabbed a clean cloth, went to Ben, and carefully helped him pull his arm back out of the window. She wrapped the arm tightly with the cloth then picked up her son and put him in the car. She raced down the hill to the hospital.

44 stitches later, Ben was back at home and with the firm caution not to ever run on the floors and play that game again. He was lucky no main artery had been hit in the cut or else he likely would have died.

During the time his arm was open, Ben had looked inside himself. He saw his flesh, blood, and bone, in a way that most humans will never see themselves. As life would go on, Ben would be hard charging for doors in his life, hoping for them to open by the time he arrived.

Well before Isaac had ever won a state title or been in the hunt for one, the Hawkins family attended a Hawkins-Vidmar family reunion. Paul's mother Gloria had been one of three children, all with the last name Vidmar. One of her brothers was John Redd Vidmar, a wonderful man who contracted polio later in life and would actually attend the famous race of Gerry Lindgren beating the Russians in the LA coliseum.

John would remain in California where he would raise his six children. The youngest son would be none other than Peter Vidmar who ended up winning two gold medals and a silver in gymnastics, representing team USA in the 1984 Los Angeles Olympics. He would be part of the only men's team in USA history to win the gold medal in the team all around competition. Peter would win another gold medal in the pommel horse, and a silver medal in individual all around competition.

While at a family reunion, several years after the Olympics, the families and cousins were all on the beach jumping, wrestling, and horsing around. Peter Vidmar took note of how his cousin Paul's boy, Ben, seemed to have excellent body control. He could do flips, cartwheels, handstands and seemed to be exceptionally strong for a child his age.

Recognizing talent when he saw it, Peter then remarked to his cousin Paul, "Your son looks like he may have some natural skills with gymnastics that you may want to take a serious look at." It was like having Michael Jordan as a relative telling a family member that he thought they were good at basketball and that they should see where it could take them.

With the confidence of a gold medalist gymnast's remark, Paul asked Ben whether he wanted to try gymnastics.

While Isaac and Emily were exiting middle school and running in their freshman and sophomore years of high school, Ben blazed a trail of his own with gymnastics. Younger siblings Liz and Paul also saw the fun that Ben had swirling and twirling through the air. They too wanted to try gymnastics.

Ben started his gymnastics career at Northwest Gymnastics in Spokane, but he quickly plateaued and heard that there was a better coach at the rival Lilac Gymnastics. Ben and his siblings made the switch.

Ben's new coach at Lilac Gymnastics was a man named Stoin who had defected to the USA from the eastern block of Bulgaria. Allegedly Stoin was the inventor of the one-armed giant, a move in gymnastics in which the competitor goes around the high bar and makes a complete revolution with only one arm holding the bar. Stoin said he was not credited with the move because he was not the first to showcase the move in international competition.

Once Stoin defected to the USA he joined up with the circus as a means of making money. Doing flips from various bars in routines he delighted audiences. Eventually Stoin left the circus and got into coaching gymnastics.

When Ben first arrived at Lilac Gymnastics he could not do the splits entirely in either direction. He quickly learned why the eastern bloc countries had dominated the sport of gymnastics.

Stoin came up to Ben and leaned on him as he attempted to do the splits. With clear expectations and a thick accent he said, "Don't whine about it, just do it." If Stoin was not leaning on Ben physically, he mentally tried to push Ben and other athletes to work harder. Within six short weeks, Ben could do the splits in any direction.

Ben's skills began to improve in all areas: pommel horse, rings, parallel bars, high bar, and floor exercise. Ben's muscles, which were already more defined than any kid his size, seemed to grow larger and more defined. His body was transforming and reflected his coach's bulky build.

Within the basement of the Hawkins home one could see handstand competitions taking place amongst siblings, to see who could stay on their hands the longest. Ben would walk about the room on his hands. He would go over to a wall and start doing handstand push ups. To aid their son's abilities Paul and Ann also invested in an Ultra Dome Pommel Horse that they placed in their basement.

Ben was the only one that had strength, speed, and the balance necessary to use the device. He would only place his hands upon the curved surface and then spin his legs about while keeping his upper body centered over the middle. Ben's legs would scissor out in various directions as his bulged arms and shoulders expanded and contracted. Ben's legs were keeping time revolving repeatedly about the dome. His body control was exceptional; he was a raw talent.

Paul also saw in his son a talent that could be used in wrestling. Paul knew that strength went far in wrestling, and he saw that gymnastics had made Ben stronger. And so with that encouragement, Ben decided to pencil in wrestling to go along with his gymnastics and his early morning paper route.

Ben's practices in middle school wrestling were limited to the first ten minutes because he then had to jump in a car and travel to gymnastics. For those ten minutes he would practice, he mostly just free styled his way around.

Ben knew he was strong from gymnastics but he did not realize how strong. Prior to his first match he walked to the center to shake hands with his competition and thought, *I'll probably lose.* He logically believed that since he had not practiced he was at a disadvantage.

The match started and Ben's opponent went to lift him into a double leg takedown. Ben instantly and instinctively maneuvered his hands around the boy's head and twisted in the air so that the momentum carried his opponent to the mat. Ben was on top and only needed to squeeze his opponent with a submission hold. Ben flexed his muscles performing this makeshift half nelson and the opponent went limp on the mat, due to lack of oxygen. Ben had won, off of innate ability and superior strength. The match was over before thirty seconds had passed.

Left to right - Emily, Paul, Ben, and Isaac Hawkins.
Before the start of the Deseret News Marathon.

© Peter Hawkins Personal Archives

From then on, Ben knew that if he could get a grip on someone the match would be effectively over. And match, after match, after match, he had the same result as that first one. The *I'll probably lose* philosophy quickly shifted to *I'll probably win*.

Before future matches against his middle school competition Ben would do handstand push-ups on the mat. He could hold the handstand as long as he liked and walked about on his hands just as easily as he walked about on his legs. If Ben was not physically dominating the match he had already maneuvered psychologically a win against his opponent. Knowing that his competition was watching him, Ben struck fear into his competitors.

This toughness came out of curiosity. Knowing his body as well as he did, Ben wondered what his limits were. After reading up on his great uncle Peter Vidmar, Ben discovered that one of Peter's coaches had him do leap frogs around an entire track. Peter said that the next day he was barely able to walk due to the soreness, but the experience lead him to believe that he was strong and could perform difficult tasks.

In this spirit, Ben wanted to see just how strong he really was. On Friday nights while his parents were out on their date night Ben was trying to figure out how long it took him to do 1,000 sit-ups. His best time was just over twenty minutes. Another endeavor revolved around how many sets of ten dips he could do. Twenty-seven sets later he realized that 270 total dips was his limit before he could not complete an entire set. Ben liked testing his limits.

At Sacajawea Middle School they had an all-time fitness chart. Ben wanted make the list in chin-ups. His 30 were outstanding, but they were second best to that boy living just down the road from him, Tyler Byers.

One notable incident with Ben and the size of his arms came as he was walking down the main hall at Sacajawea Middle School. A female student asked Ben if he could walk down the hall with his hands down by his side. Ben, confused at what she was asking, said to her, "They are down at my side." The girl explained to him that they were not. In reality his lateral muscles had gotten so big that his hands did not naturally rest by his waist but stuck out. Ben was a man amongst boys, a middle school sized action figure.

Again, Ben did not practice wrestling for more than ten minutes on any given day, due to his gymnastics schedule. Matches were where he really learned all about wrestling. Before each match athletes shake each other's hand. Ben made it a point to grip the opponent's hand and let him know how incredible his grip was.

Time in the gymnastics realm had increased his ability to grip not only the rings, the pommel horse, the parallel bars, or the high bar, but also his competition.

In one particular match, Ben lifted his competitor into the air and went up into the air himself and then followed on top of his competition and body slammed his competitor knocking the wind out of him. The match was stalled, but not before Ben's teammates erupted from the bleachers as if they had seen a pocket Hercules in their presence who had lived out a WWF move they had seen on TV.

The rival coach instructed Ben that he could not lift someone up like that and bring them crashing down as he had done. When the match resumed the deflated opponent quickly cooperated with Ben and was pinned. All told, Ben only lost one match in middle school; it was during his seventh grade year against a wrestler who truly knew what he was doing on the mat; everyone else got tossed around like a rag-doll.

Ben's ambitions to figure out his limits like he had read about Peter Vidmar doing had its drawbacks. One day during his ten minutes of wrestling before he headed off to gymnastics, Ben decided to take on the team's only heavyweight, big Joe Green. Ben had beaten everyone so why not take on the biggest challenge. Joe Green weighed well over two hundred pounds. Ben, all of just over 100 pounds of him, went to make the same WWF throw he had done in his last match, but in the process nearly threw out his back. Shoots of pain charged up his spine that caused him to be ineligible to compete at the Spokaloo Tournament (The City Championship). The competition rejoiced at the fact that the freak of nature from Sacajawea Middle School was out of the tournament.

Uphill Both Ways

When Paul and Ann decided to move out on Regal Road, they chose a piece of land near the top of a hill. They chose the land because of the pretty view and because it was affordable; they did not know that such was a geographical gift to their future distance running children.

Isaac started incorporating hill repeats at the end of his morning runs during his sophomore year. He figured the resistance of covering the 600 meters from the bottom of Regal to the top of it (which was where the house was located) would be great strength training.

Running away from the Hawkins home one immediately descends in either direction on Regal Road, and then has to climb up either Regal Road or they have to eventually run out from the bottom of the Palouse Highway. The old adage about going to and from school, uphill, both ways, was something that was literally true for the Hawkins family. Runs always ended uphill when starting from their home. The resistance made for great strength and great runners. If athletics were to be the school Ben went to, it would be uphill both ways, no matter which sport he chose.

© Peter Hawkins Personal Archives

Ben, with his gymnastics, his wrestling, and his running, sat in a unique position. He was a relative latecomer to competitively pursuing each of the sports. As an eighth grader he traveled with his club gymnastics team to various meets, competing as far as Portland, Oregon. However, there was a certain social isolation Ben felt from other students.

Gymnastics was not a school sponsored sport and so no one knew about it, nor did they take much interest in it except when the Olympics were showcased every four years. When someone at school is on the basketball team, the baseball team, or the football team, there comes a certain amount of knowledge, respect, or social awareness that is not present with a sport like gymnastics. Most of the guys on Ben's gymnastics club were younger and had started far sooner than Ben. He quickly caught up to their skill level but figured he needed to have started gymnastics at the beginning of grade school, not the very end of it as he had done.

Wrestling also presented a unique challenge. Sure he had physical gifts to go out on the mat and handle his competition, but the level between middle school and high school brought with it an increase in intensity. Ben loved to throw others on the mat, but he did not like his own head being shoved against the mat. His own head always seemed to rattle after a match, even when he was the clear victor.

Cross country was something he had competed in since grade school, yet had not taken too seriously. He had run because Isaac and Emily had decided to try it. Ben was one of the fastest at Mullan Road Elementary. He completed a marathon as an eleven year old, but he did not take running seriously until he saw the success of his siblings.

Ben sat perched atop his own hill and whatever he descended into, he would have to return going uphill, both ways. The choice was Ben's alone to make. Paul and Ann had instructed all of their children that their middle school years were a time to try out their talents in whatever arena they saw fit. They were instructed that once they entered into high school, they needed to specialize in something and stick with it.

If Peyton Manning is your older brother and you are Eli, then you are going to want to throw the pigskin. Isaac's signing with the best distance running university at the time, Stanford, signaled a promising running career ahead of him. Emily's full-ride scholarship and state championship also weighed on Ben's mind. He had, after all, beaten both of them in that marathon.

Ben had sat with his younger brother Peter on the hillside of the Lincoln Bowl and recorded Isaac's mile and two mile races at the Washington State track meet. With their two young squeaky voices they provided commentary as Isaac started out in his race.

It was evident through their commentary that they were not just wishful thinkers, hoping their brother did well; they had a sound understanding of the sport at ages 13 and 9.

"What pace did he go out in?" Ben asked.

"70 for the first lap." Peter said.

"Slow, slow, slow." Ben responded.

It would be hard for Ben or for anyone to walk away from a sport in which he just saw siblings win. Crowds watched Isaac and Emily only in competition,

Ben saw them in the hours before sunrise. He saw them under the dark purple sky when they were all delivering the morning paper. He sat at dinner with Isaac and Emily, hearing how their latest workout went that day. These were two people he had played basketball with in the driveway, baseball with in the backyard; he had covered a marathon, if not literally, then also developmentally in his childhood experiences.

Isaac would read books and Ben would peeking over his shoulder to see what it was about. One of the few areas of interest that were solely Ben's involved making model airplanes from different eras in aviation and shooting off self made rockets. Ben's mind gravitated toward flight, towards the mechanics involved in it and the speed to push back against gravity. Ben read Chuck Yeager's biography detailing his position in the cockpit and breaking the sound barrier.

It all seemed so logical, so mathematical, for Ben in his approach to running. Isaac had started taking running serious as a freshman; if Ben took it serious in the fall of his eighth grade year, then the results Isaac had experienced Ben could experience an entire year sooner.

With Isaac excelling in his senior year of cross country, Ben turned out for eighth grade cross country. Former teachers of Isaac and Emily at Sacajawea all quickly claimed them as their own.

"Oh, you're Isaac's brother," became the common initiation to a long list of anecdotal stories about how they just knew Isaac and Emily were bound for something great. How he had sat in their math class, or social studies, or science class. Everyone wanted to claim the success of Isaac or Emily and share in the associations with it. Ben just knew they would say the same of him someday.

Ben's running times in middle school were near his older siblings. Isaac was not winning races in middle school and he never competed in the All-City Race. Ben took second or third on his team during cross country, but after a winter of running, while simultaneously competing in gymnastics and wrestling, Ben began to see results from his training during the track season. As part of his own winter training, before his track season began, Ben would bike from Sacajawea Middle School to Ferris High School and then participate with Isaac and the Ferris team during their track workouts.

After working out with high school athletes as an eighth grader Ben became the fastest runner at Sacajawea and started to win races. Clocking near 5:20 in the mile, and running in All City, Ben felt confident that he already had a leg up on where Isaac had ran. Isaac sunk his teeth into running in high school, Ben had sunk his teeth in during middle school. It only followed, in his mind, that the results would come as well.

Early in the fall of Ben's freshman year he was the fastest freshman on the team. However, as the season progressed, fellow freshman Andrew Ice who was latent with talent finally coupled his abilities with Coach Hadway's workouts and started to pass by almost everyone. Ben continued to fight to try and join the varsity ranks. Yet, as soon as he would get on he would be bumped off. There were four seniors on the varsity squad, two juniors and one lone freshman, Andrew Ice. An older group was getting ready to graduate. The junior varsity squad was stacked with freshman due in large part to Assistant Coach Fuller. His work with middle school athletes at Chase prepared them for Coach Hadway's tough workouts.

Ben would watch from the sidelines at the state meet in 1997 as his sister Emily, then a senior, won the state cross country girls individual title. Following her race, he watched as the Ferris boys team lined up and ran a rather poor showing, taking sixth overall. The highest finisher for Ferris was Dan Schruth, Dave's younger brother, who took 29th overall. It was an off day for the team.

Brad Lewis, a junior, and Andrew Ice, a freshman, both came in with the same time and were only seconds back from Dan. Andrew was the second highest placing freshman at the state meet that day.

Coach Hadway stood with mixed emotions. His workouts and skill elevated Emily Hawkins to an individual state title. He had helped Isaac win state multiple times, he had helped Jenny win state, and win the national championship in track in the mile. He was helping Tyler win multiple state titles, but his teams could not come together for the victory. In 1997 Pat Tyson's Mead team was finally beaten by Bob Barbero's University High School squad. Gonzaga Prep had taken third as a team that day. The GSL had swept the top three spots, while the Ferris team could not seem to find their stride.

Barbero's University boys team title was the first time any boys program at their school had won a boys state title of any kind in any sport. They placed three of their runners in the top 11 spots, and had their fifth runner in before Ferris had their first runner in. During Isaac's rise individually and Mead's improbable run of titles, University High School had a large freshman and sophomore class that bought into Barbero's belief that they could run with anyone. On courses that had top 10 times for each grade level throughout the years, many new names were added at this time. Had anyone looked to the JV All City race in 1996 to see what was happening, they could have foreseen the shift.

Mead's 67 JV athletes would end up being divided in half at the start of 1997 due to the opening of Mt. Spokane High School, making their new JV squad total around 33. University's JV total was 34; Ferris' JV total was 14. Typically, the team with the largest pool of runners to draw from does the best. The more athletes competing against each other, the greater the competition. If Coach Barbero at University could get a big buy in from multiple athletes, then there would be that opportunity to do the unthinkable: beat Mead. One of those on Barbero's team was his own son. It was doubly special for Coach Barbero to see his son make the jump to varsity and to see his team's numbers swell.

Pat Tyson at Mead began the season without his top runner, Tom Becker, because he now attended Mt. Spokane High School. In 1997 Tom Becker was the individual state champion, edging out University's Seth Mott by three seconds. Even if Mead had Tom Becker as their runner that day, they still would have lost to University.

Pat faced a second problem besides having a smaller pool to draw from. His second place team was full of six seniors and one junior. The lone junior was their seventh man, finishing 66th overall. One of those in attendance at the state meet in 1997 was Ian Johnson, who ran in the 3A division. His family would be moving to Spokane during the summer and in an effort to go to one of the premier schools, University seemed an ideal place having won. Perhaps, if Mead had won, they may have picked up a lucky transfer like Ian Johnson.

University's first title brought with it a new transfer that summer and three returning juniors; they were again stocked and ready to rock the following year.

During Foot Locker that year, Ben went down to race and see how he stacked up against freshman on the west coast. Out of the 225 freshmen in the race Ben took 21st. There were two freshman from Washington State ahead of Ben, Chris Fayant of Mead (Jason Fayant's brother) who placed 15th, and Ben's teammate at Ferris, Andrew Ice, who won the freshman boy's race.

Whereas Isaac had finished tenth as a freshman at Foot Locker, Ben was a bit back of that.

Ben was not deterred by the race results. Isaac had run at state as a freshman, Ben had not, but that did not matter. There was still an offseason of training and a track season ahead of him. A parent of one of Ben's teammates remarked to Paul and Ann how they felt Ben looked a little blue in the face as he ran and how they could hear when he passed that it sounded like he was wheezing. Paul and Ann took Ben see a doctor who determined that he had athletically induced asthma. Ben was trying to do more with less oxygen. The quick answer to the problem was that Ben would use an inhaler before big workouts and races as a means of helping him catch his breath.

Ben was determined to mimic Isaac's working mindset. The freshman season had not gone as planned, but the offseason would be a place to plant, prepare, and put in the work for a future harvest. Wasting no time, Ben placed himself in a position to succeed by participating in the Thorpe run.

Thorpe is named for a road that the majority of the run consists of; Thorpe is the road you climb. Notable in this run is the short lived history of local GSL talent showing up on a semi-weekly basis to run the course during the offseason. In the days before GPS the rumor was that the run was 10 miles long.

The Thorpe run started at the Bloomsday Road Running World Headquarters in downtown Spokane. The run would eventually turn into a tempo run, and then into a full out race. It was a tough run, meant to build confidence and allow runners to see where they stacked up.

Showing up and competing, Ben willed himself to run alongside Ryan Craig, a Rogers athlete who would become one of the best in the state that track season. Ben was running alongside him, completing the course in 54 minutes. Ben was finishing within sight of Ryan, who would go on to run 9:05 in track that spring. As a freshman to hang with someone that fast is rather impressive and speaks to the grit and strength Ben brought with him to distance running.

However, Ben's freshman track season was not like Isaac's; Ben would not go on to districts in the two mile and finish 13th. Ben would not qualify for districts and run under ten minutes, Ben would be running 10:45 as his fastest.

Going into the summer, Ben trained and worked as a lifeguard, squeezing in runs in the morning and at night. With just another offseason of work, there would be better results in the future.

Running Through It All

As the summer season wound down, a local doctor in Ben's church had heard of Ben's breathing troubles with asthma. Upon further speculation from this ENT (ear, nose, and throat doctor) he concluded that Ben had a deviated septum. A deviated septum is nothing more than ill formed cartilage dividing the nose and the airway towards the lungs. If that passageway could be opened up then conceivably Ben would have more oxygen to take in and therefore run faster. To correct a deviated septum Ben would need surgery.

After an entire summer of running, training, and fighting to build confidence, it was decided that Ben would have the surgery in mid August. Near the eve of the season, Ben went in for his surgery.

The surgery went through without any problems. Splints and gauze were placed inside Ben's nose for a week while he laid at home trying to recover. Then the splints and gauze were removed. Ben returned home hoping for one more restful night's sleep before hitting the road in the morning.

Suddenly Ben awoke.

Ben initially thought his pillow was wet. Upon further investigation he realized it was soaked. Once Ben reached the light he saw his bloodied pillow. Blood was still coming out of his nose. Cupping his hands around his face he immediately went downstairs and into his parent's bedroom.

"Dad, Mom!" Ben said.

"Ben, what's going on? It is two in the morning," Paul said.

"Mom, Dad, I got a nosebleed," Ben coughed out.

The parent's bedside lamps flickered on and they immediately saw this was no simple nosebleed. Paul quickly arose and guided Ben to their bathroom and had him lie down on the ground by their tub.

Ann instinctively phoned the doctor from their church as if she had practiced this scenario before. She got through and explained the situation in a quick and calm, yet urgent, manner. The doctor told her to take Ben to the emergency room and he would be on his way.

Right as Ann finished hanging up with the doctor, Paul, who had perched himself on the tub right beside Ben in their bathroom, suddenly fainted. Paul fell forward and landed on top of Ben.

Ann instinctively jumped to the ready, pushed Paul aside, freeing Ben. Paul quickly came to but listened as Ann told him to stay there, that he had fainted, and that she would be running Ben down to the hospital.

Ben got into the car and saw his mom race through the empty streets of Spokane at two in the morning. Once more Ann raced her son towards the hospital.

Once at the hospital Ben was put under and placed in emergency surgery. The scar tissue from the surgery had broken open and Ben had been swallowing a trickle of blood throughout the night. During the surgery as they were trying to stuff gauze down his nose, Ben's body felt the gauze as a tickle on his nose and so he instinctively sneezed. Blood splattered everywhere. After the surgery they had to pump his stomach for blood; they pumped three pints (of blood). The average human body holds 10 pints of blood. Ben, as a five foot five, 125 pound sophomore distance runner, likely had less than 10 pints.

The next morning, Ben was again released from the hospital and Ann drove her son up the hill and back to home. However, they did not make it home before Ben asked his mom to pull over. He vomited a little more excess blood he had swallowed. He felt better but very tired. He was yet again lucky to be alive.

Thus started Ben's sophomore year in cross country. He had paid a dear price to compete, that nearly cost him his life.

Expectations that sophomore year were reset after the surgery. Anything would be improvement and everything would be a gift. Under such conditions Ben began to surprise teammates and himself. Not only would Ben make varsity, he would be the team's fifth man, scoring clinching points in dual meets and invitationals.

The team made it through regionals and had a chance to place high at state. Ben would be running in state his sophomore year, whereas Isaac had missed such an opportunity. Ben knew that running at state beat standing on the sidelines watching any day.

University was still the team to beat. Mead had improved, Ferris had improved, and Lewis & Clark tried to run the table as well. Two teams from the South Hill, one team from the far north and another in the Valley were all ready for their time to run.

The race started and University took off like a team confident that the second year would be just as impressive as the first. Senior transfer Ian Johnson of University held tight with leaders, senior Tom Becker of Mt. Spokane and Sean Knapp of Gig Harbor. Two more University teammates were in the front; University had three in the top ten. Mead, still rebuilding, had found their leader: Todd Fayant a senior and Chris Fayant a sophomore, brothers of Jason's Fayant, were leading their charge early. Ferris had two runners in the top twenty, senior Tyson Magney and sophomore Andrew Ice. Lewis & Clark only had one runner in the top twenty.

The racers stayed in their same positions throughout the race. Ben was in the middle of the pack coming through the first mile.

Through the two mile things only spread out, positions did not change, and then everyone made their final moves to the finish.

Ian Johnson leaned it out at the tape taking first place by mere inches. The team score would not be as close. University ran away with it scoring 48 points. Mead placed second with 116 points, Lewis & Clark would surprise in third, and Ferris placed fourth. It was all GSL and all Spokane standing on the podium.

After the race Ben looked for his name in the results but could not find it. A race marshal had deemed at some point that Ben had not stayed on the course and so disqualified him. Dejected with his efforts and the team result, Ben's first two years of cross country seemed to disappear, if not on paper, at least in terms of the view of anyone watching. Teammate Andrew Ice finished as the top sophomore in the state meet.

The Foot Locker Western Regional seemed the next place to try and get back to having a normal race. Another four weeks of work would be helpful since the first two weeks of the season did not exist for Ben.

At the Foot Locker Western Regional Ben ran in the Seeded Race as a sophomore wanting to see how he stacked up.

The only Washington runner to make it to Nationals that year came from the Tri-Cities and a 3A school, Adam Tenforde. Also making it to Nationals from the neighboring state of Oregon was Ian Dobson. Both Adam Tenforde and Ian Dobson would be teammates of Isaac's at Stanford. Both ran fast times and Ian Dobson would be a future Olympian, representing the USA in the 5,000 meter in the Beijing Olympics.

Ben did not see the front of the race develop. With a poor start Ben finished near the very back of the pack, taking 216th place overall. Yet none of the runners he went up against had their stomach pumped during the first week of the season. None of them had lost three pints of blood in late August.

The return to Spokane came, and with it a winter on the roads. Ben had lost out on precious time. He wanted to seize on the opportunity before him. The window of opportunity seemed to be shrinking and the air seemed to be taken from him. The boy who had a vice like grip, could not put a choke hold on the air and force it into and out of his lungs. Ben wanted to run free of his asthma, free of excuses, free of the expectations heaped upon him, by others and himself.

Early morning runs continued for Ben as they had always gone: in the dark and alone, with nothing but his thoughts for company. He left the house running down the hill and then up the hill towards the top of Regal Road. He approached 65th Street and made a right turn, gaining slight elevation as he went by the dark brick building of the Methodist church and the lone light that outlined the corner sign. Ben continued up till he followed the road that slanted towards his left and he went down South Waneta Road to the stop sign on the Palouse Highway. The stop sign was the turn around point.

He had run 1.5 miles out.

Back he turned and retraced his route toward home. Gravity pulled him home. Down Waneta, down 65th Street, a left turn down Regal to the base of the hill before the final 600 meters up Regal and to home. After reaching home he would go down to the bottom of the hill and then race back up it, completing three hill repeats.

Morning after morning, Ben awoke, silently left home, ran this run, and thought over what he wanted, how he was working, and what the results would be.

He ran this route in fog, he ran it in misty rain. He ran it in sleet, in snow, in wind. He ran it in frost. Every time he ran it, he ran it alone and he ran it in the dark; those were the constants while everything else changed.

Track season finally came and the mornings started to have more light to them.

At the beginning of the track season Ben's first race would be a two mile at

Ben Hawkins, middle,
leading Ian Johnson of University to the left

an invitational in Clarkston, Washington. In the race would be Ian Johnson, who had not only been on the state championship team at University High School, but he had been the individual state champion as well. Ian finished his cross country season with a 15th place showing in the Foot Locker Western Regional Seeded Race. Ben had fished near sixth from the bottom in that race. Those results did not deter Ben from believing that he could go out and shock the world, including Ian Johnson.

The race began and Ben, as a sophomore, shot to the front to try and hang with senior Ian Johnson. Around the curve and into the backstretch they went, with thirty five other athletes following, then around the next bend and into the homestretch.

As they approach the start line, the starter shouted the pace, "71, 72, 73, 74, 75."

Ben went through with Ian Johnson in 73, and again they continued into the curve and down another backstretch, again another curve, and again they went through the homestretch. The starter welcomed them with shouts of the pace.

"2:21, 2:22, 2:23, 2:24, 2:25" Ben and Ian, side by side, went through, leading the pack in 2:24. They were running around 9:40 pace. This would be a PR from Ben's freshman year by over a minute. This is the type of jump he expected and trained for. This was why he woke at five in the morning and went out in the cold and the dark.

Through the next two laps they would go and as they passed through the first mile of the two mile race Ben heard the starter shout out 4:50. Ben had just set his PR in the mile, in a two mile race.

That would be the highlight of the race.

From there on, Ben's pace would fall off, and he would fade from Ian Johnson and all those chasing him. A time back in the mid 10 minutes waited for him as he crossed the finish line in twentieth.

Isaac enjoyed huge improvements over the course of an offseason, and similarly Emily had gone from not making it to state in track to winning it in cross country. Ben was frustrated by the fact that his times improved by single digit seconds from season to season.

More practices, more morning runs, and similar results followed during the course of the season. Ben could go out with the leaders, hold the strong pace but could not sustain it for the last quarter or half of the race. Again, no qualifying times for districts, so Ben, as a sophomore ran in the JV All City meet.

At districts in 1999 Ben's sophomore teammate Andrew Ice did qualify for regionals. At regionals, Ice did the improbable and made it to state in the two mile, taking second to Ian Johnson by only three seconds, running 9:24.18.

The Greater Spokane League, which was already strong, had gotten stronger. The regional meet indicated the strength of the GSL. If the top eight finishers in each event were combined from the 800 meter, the mile, and the two mile then of those 24 finishers, only five were not from Spokane. This was perhaps the strongest the league would ever be, top to bottom.

At state, Ian Johnson would win the mile and two mile races, while fellow University High School teammate Kris Martin would win the 800 meter crown.

Barbero's boys had done well in the distances and there were a pair of pole vaulters finishing second and third to help deliver the team title in track to University High School. Second place was 24 points behind.

During the two mile at the state meet, Andrew Ice ran tough and finished third overall, running 9:17.73. He would be the top returning athlete next year, and he would only be a junior. Ben saw this all from the sidelines. He had seen runners rise before, and they had come from his own family, now it was a teammate. While it was Ben's turn to run with the baton, under the lights and before the crowds at postseason races, he stood on the sidelines, frustrated.

Moment of Truth

The summer came and with it work. Ben continued to lifeguard like he had the previous summer. He would wake, run, then bike to work, work, then bike home, run again and get ready for the next day. This was the typical work week for Ben. The days were long, spent in the sun, and it was hot. A dark tan came as a result of the hours he spent outside all day.

Ben heaped upon him pressure and expectations. Isaac's junior year was when he won state, when he won the Western Regional, and when he was in third for most of the race at Nationals.

Increased efforts should yield increased results.

For most of the season Ben ran as the number two man on the team, Andrew Ice was the clear front runner. Ben had gone from not being on varsity as a freshman, to on it and scoring for the team as a sophomore, and now was one of the top runners on the team. Improvement had been made.

There was no surgery to start off his junior season like in his sophomore year. There was no discovery of asthma like in his freshman year. Coach Hadway's Ferris team looked like it could take a step on the podium at state behind their number one runner and top returning athlete from the year before.

The week before regionals Ben came down with the flu. Vomit, diarrhea, and a complete loss of fluids came as a result for four days in late October, with no training during that time. The lack of running brought with it a lack of confidence.

With three days of running back under his legs, Ben toed the line with teammates on the famous Hangman Valley Golf Course; sight of Pre's last NCAA

Cross Country Championship, and sight of Isaac's sophomore year denial.

Many of Ben's 15 mile long-runs had taken place on Saturdays in the offseason that passed by the Hangman Valley Golf course. Ben had run into and out of that valley many times and he was running in it once more.

As the gun raised, 21 teams crouched, waiting for the starting shot. 17 of those teams would end their season that day and any individual not in the top 20 would also be watching state from the sidelines in the following week.

Bang!

And off they went.

The conditions were wet but not overly cold for that time of year. Barbero had coached University to two straight years of championships and wanted to make it three. Pat Tyson had caught hold of the ears of the youth of his school and as a result Mead ran with three sophomores, three seniors and one junior leading the way. Coach Hadway had an older team, with five juniors and two seniors; this team had been to state the two previous years.

Yet the race quickly shaped and developed with Ferris dropping back and out of contention. The only Ferris runner that seemed to show up to race that day was Andrew Ice. Although on paper at the beginning of the season he had been the favorite, he too got pushed aside by others hungrier and who had been left out of postseason races as sophomores.

Junior Michael Kiter from Shadle Park led from the beginning and ran away with a 17 second victory. Mead's Chris Fayant, a junior, took second. Ice from Ferris and also a junior would take fifth, nearly twenty seconds back of Fayant and forty seconds back of Kiter.

The team scores at the top were tight: Mead 100, Mt. Spokane 105, University 110. Had Mt. Spokane not split from Mead, then the result would have been lopsided in Mead's favor, scoring 48 instead of 100. The divide in the schools had hurt the Mead program, but Coach Tyson is Coach Tyson and he takes the best that all his athletes have to offer.

Ferris would finish a dismal 11th out of the 21 teams. Ben came in fourth for the team and 86th overall.

His junior season had ended.

A silent somber Ferris squad sat on the hill with their wet gear and wondered what had just happened. Looking on from a distance they watched as the awards ceremony began. The fourth place team that day was Lewis & Clark. Sacajawea Middle School has 98% of its student population go on to Lewis & Clark; only a small percentage switchover and go to Ferris High School. These were former teammates of Ben's, all of which he had beaten heading into high school; they too had passed him by.

Hangman Valley was supposed to be a home race. Ferris is the closest school to the Hangman Valley course. Almost always within the first week of practice, whether it is cross country or track, Coach Hadway has penciled in the Hangman Valley 15 mile loop. Ben had run by this course dozens and dozens of times throughout the course of each year. Yet coming out of the Valley on this late day in October, he would not be on one of the top four teams, nor one of the top twenty individuals.

The GSL had again dominated. Eight of the top ten finishers were from Spokane. Of those eight, seven of them came from different teams: Shadle Park (2), Mead, Rogers, Ferris, Mt. Spokane, University, and North Central.

Ben laid on the wet ground on the Hangman Valley Golf Course, looking up through the trees surrounding him and took stock of the situation.

He was not going to state.

The only time he had run at state he did not show up in the results due to a disqualification of some errant step he did not even remember taking. Now, as a junior, he had finished 86th out of 143 runners at regionals. He had finished in the latter half of the pack and now only had one more cross country season left. Three years of running, training, preparing, logging thousands of miles, doing hundreds of repeats, of fartleks, of morning runs and double days in the dark and the cold and what did he have to show for it? Who would ever see all he had worked for?

86th out of 143, clocking 17:45.

If running is only about finishing first then 99.9% of runners will feel discouraged. The winners of any race may well be part of that 99.9% if there was a larger pool of people to draw from. All those that had claimed Isaac's success were not there now to claim Ben; all except his parents and siblings. Few ever knew of the sacrifices Ben made to run. But his consecrated efforts would impact the lives of his younger sister Liz and younger brother Peter. Experiences at the top, like with Isaac or Emily, are what almost all kids strive after. The realities with running are that most will put forth great effort at a great cost, and never cross the finish line first.

Paul stood, surveying the situation and knowing that comparisons between children could not occur. Isaac was not Ben and Ben was not Isaac. Yet siblings know one another and act as barometers for each other's expectations. Anyone comparing themselves to Isaac in running, sibling or not, could feel fairly bad about themselves and 99% of the population in the country could if they tried. The standard Paul expected out of Ben or any of his children remained the same: best efforts. No matter the talent level, best efforts were what each child needed to give and what the younger siblings needed to see.

Paul knew that the absence of time was the current measure of success. The faster the time equated to the better the runner at that moment, but more time would be needed for Ben to see all that he had accomplished. He was running in one of the most competitive leagues in the country, at one of the most competitive times the league had ever known.

Ann stood there on the Hangman Valley course, looking different than the figure that had been caring for her children at the start each morning; feeding them as they came home from seminary. At home in those early hours, she had risen looking like a figure from the dead. With eyes half open and half asleep she gathered the eggs from the fridge, plugged in the electric griddle, mixed the pancake batter, and found the spatula in the back of the drawer. This daily sleepwalk maneuver had been done for years now.

Hair fresh from the bed, and standing in her nightgown, she cracked the eggs, poured the mix and let it cook as she slowly stepped and felt her way back to the pantry. Once there she pulled out the peanut butter, found the bread, then the fruit, and the paper bags and the plastic bags to put it all in.

Back she would go, flipping pancakes and putting together lunches, slowly becoming more alive with her movements and gradually picking up the pace. Her eyes began to open more behind her glasses. Once the kids were all off to elementary school, middle school, and high school she would finally be awake and already exhausted.

Eventually she would make her own meals, but not before preparing lunch and breakfast for her seven children. If they were going to excel in athletics or the classroom, they needed to start the day off with energy and that meant healthy breakfasts and lunches. Silently she went about her early morning work, and in the dark as well.

"I love you. Be good, work hard, have fun." Those words coupled with the meals would be her hill repeat. She would speak those words to her children, hoping they stuck. Perhaps more important than any word ever spoken to her children was the lesson Ann taught through her actions every morning.

Ann stood there, surveying her son's disappointment and the team's disappointment. Yet, there was not much to be disappointed about. They were workers, working at something they loved and wanted to win at, where had they lost? She could see that races came and went, but the work and the willingness to work within the athlete was the jewel.

Ben finally arose from the wet grass and grabbed his gear and made his way back toward home.

Isaac had his epiphany at the fry bin on 29th and Regal, Ben had his walking through the small parking lot at Hangman Valley Golf Course. Isaac's words welling within him were *This must work* while Ben's would be *I don't care what it takes, I am never feeling like this again.*

The teams that left regionals and went on to state in 1999 came out with different results. Mead went from being regional champ and expected title bearer to third place at state with 90 points. Mt. Spokane went from second at regionals to second at state, failing to pull out the victory with 82 points. In a late season surge, University walked out the winner at state by the narrowest of margins scoring 81 points. Had the race been run five times it likely would have yielded five different results.

Ben needed confidence after the implosion at regionals, and so, at Foot Locker Western Regional instead of running in the Seeded Race, Ben ran in the Junior Race, and finished 13th. After the race, Ben went along Muscle Beach with teammates and others from Spokane that made the trip.

Along Muscle Beach they walked by a pair of rings that hung in the air.

Ben got on them and did a few moves from his gymnastics days, then finished by holding the iron cross, a move that entails holding both arms straight out to one's side. It involves incredible strength only possessed by a few, and yet there Ben was, holding the iron cross after spending three years away from the sport. A picture was taken, and then he got off the rings. Others tried to mimic, but they were skinny runners lacking in the natural strength that Ben brought with him.

Off the beach they went, back to their bags, back to Spokane and the cold they knew awaited them.

Another dark lonely winter came with runs on the road.

Another track season came and went, and Ben did not make it on to regionals or state. His teammate Andrew Ice qualified for state in the two mile and improved on his time from last year by seven seconds running, 9:10. But he was beat by three other people who had improved by nearly thirty or forty seconds from the previous year and the winning time was 9:05.

The truth Ben had to face was that something had to change. The answers did not lie in just running more miles, and the answer did not entail relying upon the relationship to family members who had run at state and won. The truth was that Ben had to run these miles with high intensity. The quality of the mile had to be just as valuable as the mile itself. At this lowest of low points, Ben would decide to put forward one last year of effort.

Finishing Strong

Midway through the summer heading into his senior year, Ben calculated how many miles he had run that summer. The total was 460. If he wanted to get to 1,000 miles before the season started, he would have to run 540 miles. There were only six weeks before the summer ended and the season started. Ben had to decide whether he was willing to put himself through six weeks at 90 miles a week. Those would be 90 miles a week on six days of running due to religious observance of the Sabbath day.

Ben decided to give one last solid and sustained effort. There would be no excuses, no drawbacks, no issues, no hold ups emotional, physical or otherwise. Before and after his summer work as a lifeguard, Ben made time for quality running.

One of the few summer road races that local athletes of Spokane perpetually participate in is the Cherry Pickers Trot out in the Greenbluff area northeast of town. It is a four mile course that has a tremendous drop and rise in elevation in the last mile and a half. The course record is 19:05 run by Isaac Hawkins.

Ben entered the race and took second overall, finishing behind his teammate Andrew Ice in just over twenty minutes. Ben knew that the results of high intensity training were coming.

Coach Hadway's team held promise. They went through the season surprising teams. One of those teams they looked to defeat was Coach Tyson's team at Mead which stood poised to win another state title. Coach Hadway's teams at Ferris had never beaten Mead on Mead's home course. Year after year there were races run between the two teams and year after year that they ran on Mead's course Ferris had lost.

Ben's senior year they ran once more at Mead. The three teams running were Ferris, Mead, and Lewis & Clark.

Ben ran against the perennial power Mead, he ran against former teammates at Lewis & Clark, and he ran against the time he had left in his season.

The Whitworth course covers a low valley and ends uphill. The team looked in great position and needed to remain so going uphill. Andrew Ice ran away early and took the first spot, brothers Chris and Jesse Fayant from Mead were running second and third with Ben charging right behind them. Back and forth the runners from Mead and Ferris were staggered as they came across the tape. When it all totaled up, Ferris was the winner 27-28 over Mead.

They had done what no team Hadway had coached had done; they beat Mead on Mead's course. During Pat Tyson's coaching career at Mead High School he compiled a 145-8 dual meet record. Ben had been part of something that happened rarely.

Weeks later, Ferris would have the opportunity to run against Mead in an Invitational, where the scoring would be similar to state. The teams descended on the Bend, Oregon Invitational which showcased the best teams from Oregon and Washington. Ferris drove back from the meet the overall winner, besting Mead yet again.

Ben was running up near the front of the pack with the leaders and he was earning the results he had worked for that summer. Ben came to grips that an individual title was improbable, but he could do what neither Isaac nor Emily had done: win a state team championship. Ferris had not won since 1981 when Herm Caviness was coach and Jon Knight was their frontrunner.

This win also resurrected hopes for Ben of running at an Ivy League University. During the previous summer, prior to his 1,000 miles, Ben visited Columbia and Yale. He visited with the coaches at each University. The Yale coach even returned the favor, stopping by the family home in Spokane.

Ben decided to go with the early decision at Columbia based upon assurances from that coach who had said, "Don't worry, apply and I'll get you in." The early decision would effectively decide whether he would go to that university. Ben had enjoyed New York. Based upon the coach's assurances, Columbia looked like Ben's future. Columbia was not the powerhouse school of running that Stanford was at the time, but Ivy League schools assured opportunity that others did not. Competitive running would someday come to a close. Running could open a door like Yale or Columbia to someone who had the grades and the mind. Ben had both, he just needed the running piece to come together in a more complete way.

Morning runs had been invigorating. The taste of victory had been sweet, and the ultimate prize was coming closer. Everything was working out for Ben.

Part of Ben's morning run had involved lunges. While coming in from the run, Ben would do lunges for the entire length of the 200 foot long driveway. After a morning run in mid October Ben felt a tug on the inside of his right knee.

The lunges after his morning runs had been instrumental to his success that fall. His knee lift had been stronger and higher and the results were self-evident. The tug on his knee was something bad and Ben knew it.

Practices continued and so did the last few races of the season. He only favored his leg when he was alone. He did not want to make excuses.

He did not tell anybody about the injury.

The only person besides Ben who knew about his knee was a physical therapist, Bill Ham. Ben went to him on his own to get some work done. Ben knew that eventually a bill would find its way back to the house, but that was a month out and the same time as the state race.

The regional race came and it looked like University's reign at the top was coming to a close because they finished fourth with 116 points. Ferris finished third scoring 66 points, Mt. Spokane finished second scoring 63, and Mead was the winner with 57 points. It was a tight group in the top three, though all four teams would move on to state. The GSL title had been a three way tie due to each team having one loss to the other. Ferris had beaten Mead but lost in a dual meet to Mt. Spokane. Mt. Spokane had lost to Mead.

At regionals it was expected to be close.

Ben finished an uncharacteristic fifth for Ferris and came in 22nd overall. At the regional meet, the first 22 people to cross the line were all from Spokane. Never before, nor since, would the league be as strong as it was in that moment from the top to the bottom. Ben was in that top tier, competitive and cutthroat as it was. Had Ben lived in the Tri-Cities at the time he could have been the top runner from those towns. But he was wanting to be one of the best amongst the best.

State was a week out. Ben knew his knee was killing him, but he hoped he could make it one more week. He was so close. He needed to rebound and the team needed to rebound in order to win. Ben was fighting something else not so secretly: a chest cold. He would cough up the mucus and spit it out, but coupled with his asthma it made for difficult breathing. He did not want excuses, he just wanted to make it one more week. All Ben or anybody on the team simply needed to do was race as they had proved they could throughout the season. They had beaten Mead twice; they just needed to do so one more time.

Ben had been sick with the flu during last years run up to regionals and mentally collapsed because of it. He knew that road and did not want to go back down it. There would be no excuses.

Knee hurting and silent to the world, Ben lined up at state waiting for his moment to finally leave his mark on the stat column and hopefully atop the podium.

The race started and once more the teams disappeared from the view of the spectators and only the PA could bring to life their movements.

"It's Kiter of Shadle Park in the lead followed by the Fayants from Mead in second and third."

This was not welcome news for Ferris.

Into the first turn they came, Mead had runners up front, but surprisingly so too did University. Mt. Spokane's team was slightly farther back and so too was Ferris.

Away they went off to the distance of the silent outer rim, away from the view of the families and spectators of the teams who went to the fence near the two mile mark. The race began to spread out. For the second week in a row and only the second time all season, Ben was running fifth slot for Ferris.

With a knee on fire, he ran. With asthma, he ran. With years of seasons cut short, he continued on, fighting and trying not to hobble; he tried to keep form despite the pain.

Around the two mile and up towards the final hill and the final meters of the race he struggled on. He did not want to feel what he had felt at Hangman. He did not care how bad it hurt, he would not fade further in the race.

Running on one leg, Ben came down the homestretch and was finally counted at the state meet, finishing 62nd out of 150 runners.

He finished.

He did not know the results of the race, he just knew that the searing pain in his leg would eventually start to subside.

Mead had two runners in the top ten, University had two runners in the top ten, Ferris had one runner in the top ten. All total, seven of the top ten finishers came out of Spokane.

Nervous teams waited and wondered over what had happened. University, a team which had been all but written off due to various defeats over the season, looked like they might have done the improbable.

The announcer came on.

"Fifth to second place in the 4A Boys team competition are only separated by 10 points."

It was a close race. Who had won? Where did everyone's fifth runner come in? There were only questions.

The top five teams were announced as follows:

5th place, Ferris 117

4th place Kent Meridian 116

3rd place Mt. Spokane 113

2nd place University 107

1st place Mead 95

Ben had finished fifth for Ferris, whereas he had always finished second. Had he finished just one spot ahead of Ferris' typical number three runner, Dave Betts, then Ferris would have scored 90 points and walked out the winner that day.

Ben had given everything, but you can only go so far on one leg.

With Emily and Isaac having surged forward Ben felt he had been the opposite leg, being pushed backward. Silently he went back to his gear, back to the van, and back to a quiet ride to Spokane.

Shortly after state, Ben received word from Columbia that he did not receive early admission; the coaches promise came up short. Yale retreated from their offer. Ben's Ivy league future went dark.

It takes a certain resilience to try when nothing seems to go right. At Foot Locker Western Regional Ben would run after resting his leg and continuing to see a physical therapist. Ben would finish 68th out of the 216 in the Seeded Race. He would be the sixth runner from the state of Washington across the line that day. He would beat Jesse Fayant and Brandon Stum who had finished third and ninth at state only a month previous. He would beat everyone on Mead's team and everyone from University's team. He did not beat Michael Kiter who had won state and would finish 6th and therefore qualify for Nationals. Ben had put to rest some of his demons.

Spring brought with it one last chance in track to improve. The biggest race Ben would run was the Pasco Invite. Ben was slated to run the two mile. This would be the last big distance event before the 4X400 relays. The meet got behind schedule and so the race was run under the lights.

Ben would line up against Shadle Park's Michael Kiter, against Mead's Jesse Fayant and Chris Fayant, against Brandon Stum from University, against Mike Heidt, who was the 3A state cross country champion from Selah. In this race

Ben would have his chance to run the fastest time all season.

Through the first laps they went at a quick honest pace and Ben was there near the very front.

On the curve near the homestretch the families and coaches crept onto the track, advancing as their

© Peter Hawkins Personal Archives

athletes came around the bend to yell and cheer, then to recede back.

Paul stood on that corner with his son Peter who would start his freshman year of high school in only a few months. Together they kept the time and cheered as Ben raced. He went through the mile in 4:30, a PR, and he did not seem to be running out of steam.

Round and round they went and Ben was still near the top ten. Down the homestretch they came on the final turn of the final lap. Ben would finish 11th overall out of the 49 runners in the race, clocking his personal best 9:35.1.

Ben glowed in the accomplishment.

Ben demonstrated that greatness is not an accolade but an attribute.

Paul had to fight back tears, knowing that 9:35.1 meant just as much coming from Ben as everything Isaac or Emily had accomplished. In one race Ben had set two personal records. It was his finest track meet.

Ben would make it to districts but not on to regionals in the two mile. He graduated and went to Brigham Young University, ready and willing to walk on to their team, which is exactly what he did before following in his brother Isaac's footsteps and serving a two year mission for his church in Asuncion, Paraguay.

Following Ben's missionary service he completed a degree in Philosophy from Brigham Young University before going on to earn a Masters in Business Administration from Eastern Washington University. Ben lives with his wife Meredith and their three children in Spokane. Ben works alongside his older brother Isaac as they try to expand their father's business.

Sylvia Quinn: Captain of the Volunteers

In the mid 1990s Sylvia Quinn stood sporting her brown bobbed haircut, her glasses, and her usual running attire as she worked the finish line of Ferris High School's home cross country meet. The athletes funneled through the finish line and she made sure that the process continued smoothly.

At that time she was making sure that the junior varsity girls race finished without any blockages or mishaps. As the girls head coach stood there staring at a stopwatch and snapping off times towards those passing the finish line, Sylvia stood shouting orders to the finishers.

"Keep moving through the line! Put your hands on the shoulders of the person in front of you! Keep moving!" Sylvia said.

Sylvia's voice was louder than what people expected to hear coming from her five foot, two inch, 100 pound frame. Her commands were not stern, but they were obeyed. She kept her head and eyes moving back and forth making sure to track the runners all the way through the finish.

Off in the distance came a junior varsity girl athlete who suddenly went from her jogging race pace to a sprint finish. Clearly the girl had too much energy left and had failed to spread out her efforts evenly throughout the race. Racing towards the finish she worked her body into a dramatic frenzy and her face as well contorted. As this girl passed the finish line she flung herself down upon the ground.

Sylvia automatically walked over to where the girl was lying down. Other girls would be finishing after her shortly.

"Get UP!" Sylvia demanded.

The girl thought she was going to receive someone catering to her collapse at the line but instead she received some strong words from what appeared on the outside to be a little old lady in her sixties.

"Get UP! You are not hurt!" Sylvia said again. "You're holding up the line for those that follow!" Sylvia said.

The girl stopped flailing about on the grass. The tears stopped as well. She quickly stood on her own power and wore a look of disbelief on her face as she continued her way out of the finishing chute. Sylvia returned to her post at the finish line making sure that the path was clear for all those that were still in the race.

Helping others get up and go has been the story of Sylvia's life.

Born the oldest of twelve children on October 23, 1936 and growing up in a quiet, forgettable part of the southwestern corner of Louisiana, Sylvia acted as the unforgettable mother-figure to her eleven siblings. With French and Italian ancestry on her mother's side and French and English ancestors on her father's side, Sylvia grew up a true Ragin' Cajun in the hot humid tract of her grandparent's rice farm. Waiting idly by is not in her makeup. Life and circumstance demanded that Sylvia be ready each and every day.

Routines marked the time each day as Sylvia kept everyone and everything moving swiftly in their home. She prepared everything from breakfast, lunch and dinner, to the bathing of her siblings. There were spills, falls, scratches, cuts, and bruises that she attended to. Sylvia stood before each scrape recognizing that feeding into a fall meant more drama. She stood still and expected her younger siblings to rise any time they fell. Her looks of confidence instilled a calming effect. There were neighbors in the small community that took notice of little Sylvia's efforts.

At the age of ten, Sylvia had her first paying jobs: ironing dresses for a neighbor as well as cleaning her entire house. The quality of her work guaranteed a return trip each week. Money saved was money earned.

Between going to and from Catholic mass each week, Sylvia found ways to keep the younger siblings out of the house and spending up their energy. Constructing makeshift track events around their house and using sticks as batons, Sylvia divided her siblings into evenly matched relay teams. Running barefoot and trying to slice through the air and stay in the shade, rivaling siblings would sprint off. As they rounded the opposite side of the house they wore tough competitive looks on their faces. They ran without a watch to keep the time. Relays were sometime between lunch and dinner.

One young enterprising brother constructed a makeshift long jump pit and high jump bar.

At the end of each day it was Sylvia's job to wash the children and she did so, three at a time in the bathtub. Ultimately it came time to clean those feet that had mapped out the front and backyard. Scrub brush in hand and a mason jar with tide soap ready, Sylvia would tackle the ticklish and slippery feet of her siblings. Laughter and sloshing water abounded. Serving these children brought undying love on both sides, knitting the family member's hearts together in unity.

Sylvia started small and remained small throughout her life. She never reached a height of more than five feet two inches and weighed no more than 100 pounds. But for all that Sylvia is not, she still looms large in the eyes and hearts of her siblings and all who know her.

Iota means a very small or inconsiderable quantity. Iota is also the ninth and smallest letter of the Greek alphabet. The town of Iota, Louisiana lives up to the small name it serves. During Sylvia's youth there were a thousand people recorded on the census records. Iota's highest numbered street was five. Sylvia kept busy caring for her siblings and did not worry over the size of her town. Her responsibility loomed large in her heart.

Besides running around the house and taking care of the tasks that were demanded of her, the only other real running Sylvia did in her youth was the run to school each day. The high school was just under a mile away and often Sylvia prepared her siblings up until the last possible minute before she finally had to head off to school.

Sylvia enjoyed school and the limited opportunities that were afforded her at the time. She lived in the pre-title IX days of women's athletics and all the outmoded expectations that went with it. The only sport she or other young ladies participated in during her high school days was basketball. It was not full court basketball, it was only half court basketball. The reasoning was that a girl should not run up and down the court and get all sweaty. The position that fit

Sylvia's size and makeup was point guard. She could not shoot over anyone, but she could help direct the floor.

Sylvia worked, played, studied, and helped take care of the growing family. Life was lived in a state of preparation; preparing the children for the day, preparing breakfast, preparing lunches, helping to prepare dinner, preparing for bed and doing so twelve times over. Mass came and went each week with the Catholic Priest standing and hoping to plant seeds of faith into those few souls in that quiet, small part of the vineyard in Iota, Louisiana. Sermons on sacrificing, dedicating, and consecrating oneself were tossed from the pulpit each week. The words and spirit of those sermons sunk deep into Sylvia's heart. She lived what she heard and served everyone.

Quickly, Sylvia's youth ended, and her graduation from Iota High School brought with it an opportunity to continue her education at Southwestern Louisiana Institute, which is now a division of Louisiana State University. Sylvia's chosen career path was Research Bacteriology. Shortly after graduation, Sylvia moved to the big city in Houston, Texas. While in Houston, Sylvia ran into a young and handsome Air Force navigator stationed out of Houston, Texas named Patrick Quinn.

At the age of twenty-four and in the year 1960, Sylvia and Pat were married. The marriage brought with it quickly their first child, Molly, who was born on the Fort Worth base. Next came an assignment to move to the stationing base in Puerto Rico, two years went by and the second child Jane was born. A new stationing assignment came for Florida and so they moved once more, welcoming their last daughter, Brigid to the world. There would be one last move for the Quinn family as Pat finished up his last eight years of service in the Air Force, and so the family packed their bags and made the long trek from the Southeast to the Northwest. Pat was stationed at the Fairchild Air Force Base just outside of Spokane.

Pat was an Electronic Warfare Officer in the B-52 bombers during the Vietnam War and was gone from home six months at a time before he would return for 26 days. Sylvia had the three children to keep herself busy, but her mind would drift towards her husband's service and there would be only the news stories and updates on the war in Vietnam to comfort her.

Running Clock

One of Pat's navigator's on his plane was an ex-Air Force Academy distance runner. Pat had run a little in high school and enjoyed running with a friend and fellow soldier as a means of keeping his mind and body healthy. During a stressful war-time period when other soldiers spent their strength in other, less noble pursuits, Pat was training to keep his body and mind fit. Pat had a wife and kids to think of as he went out running and circling around the tracks on the bases with his navigator. Between flights and during down time, these two would run, talk and speak of their lives, past, present and future. In Guam or Thailand, these two would run about, never escaping the three H's as they called it: heat, hills, and humidity.

Returning home from six months of running, Pat knew he would need to keep up the pace that his navigator had set, and so he continued to train at the Air Force Base in Spokane. Sylvia, wanting to soak up every spare moment with her husband while he was alive and in town for twenty-six days, took their youngest daughter Brigid who was not in school yet, and went to the track at the Air Force Base. She sat in the infield, watching her husband run laps around that old black dirt track.

"You want to try this?" Pat asked as he rounded the corner towards the backstretch. He liked running with someone, and figured he would run with his wife.

Sylvia looked down at her white Keds, and then up at her husband.

"Ok," she said.

Sylvia thought to herself, *With running, all you do is run, how hard can that be?*

Brigid dawdled around the infield as her parents took off on the backstretch and around the first curve.

The first half of the lap came quickly and nothing was working. Sylvia's breathing was all a mess, and the pace was quick. Sylvia quickly fell off pace and semi walked, semi-jogged, trying to figure out this running thing that seemed so easy in her youth.

Finishing up his run, Pat turned to his wife who was now collecting Brigid from the infield.

"I just don't think you will ever be a runner," Pat said.

Looking down at her once white shoes, Sylvia then looked up at her husband, and with beads of sweat forming around her brow she piped up.

"Well, it's the shoes," Sylvia said.

Pat had a pair of running shoes he had purchased in Okinawa.

"Well, we can do something about that," Pat said.

The two went down to the old Kimmel Athletic store in Spokane to buy Sylvia her first pair of running shoes. It was the day before Pat would be heading back out to Vietnam. Sylvia's once white Keds were traded out for a pair of white leather Adidas running shoes with three black stripes on either side. The shoes were stiff and not breathable, but they were cherished by Sylvia. Her husband went off the next day with his shoes, and she was back in Spokane with her own.

Sylvia made a commitment to herself after her husband had left. *Before the six months ahead of me are up*, she thought, *I will run six hundred miles*. It did not seem like too big of a goal. Finally, she decided she would voice it aloud, and so she did, "I will run six hundred miles before six months are up."

Gradually Sylvia worked her way up to running six days a week.

Sylvia was running in a time right before the running boom was about to hit America. Bill Bowerman's book *Jogging* would ignite a running boom across America, selling over one million copies. Sylvia had not heard of Bill Bowerman and she had not read *Jogging*. She made a goal that she would be able to keep pace with her husband by the time he returned.

During the wintertime, Sylvia ran indoors because she had never seen anyone running outside in the winter. People had already stopped her while she was running on her own and asked her if she needed help. When she responded that she was fine, they asked why she was running. Older people out running was not a common occurrence.

The Air Force Base had three large basketball courts right next to each other that made up the gym. Sylvia took her daughter Brigid and placed her in the stands of the basketball court with a box of crayons and a few coloring books to keep her busy while she ran laps. Twenty-four laps equaled one mile.

Twenty-four laps became forty-eight, which became seventy-two, which became ninety-six, which became one-hundred and twenty. Short straight aways, and hard corners welcomed Sylvia at each turn.

She thought of her husband. She thought of her daughters. She thought of the war in Vietnam. She thought of her goal to run with her husband. She thought of life. She thought of death. And as all these thoughts came and went something soothing coursed through her stride.

Some days Sylvia would go longer on her runs and other days she would go shorter. She had no coach, no stopwatch, no one watching her, no feedback, nothing but an inner voice indicating what pace she should run and how far she should go. Sylvia ran off of feeling and did not mark the time, she only marked the distance she ran.

The winter months came: laps were run, coloring books were filled out, letters were sent off and letters were received. The days were ticking off like laps.

Sylvia finished her 600th mile, and the next day her husband would be back. The girls were excited to see their father, and Sylvia was excited to see her husband.

"Let's go for a run." Sylvia suggested.

"Ok." Pat said.

For five miles, Sylvia kept just off the pace her husband kept. He may have been stronger and faster, but she could keep with him and she did. Although the war separated them for a time, they were back together in their Adidas running shoes keeping the same pace.

Twenty-six more days of bliss were followed by six more months wondering, running, and taking care of the girls. Another twenty-six days of bliss were followed by another six months of worry.

In the winter of 1973 with peace talks stalling between the United States and Vietnam, Pat Quinn received orders for what would later be termed *Christmas Bombings*. Flying in the B-52 with his crew members, they would fly multiple missions over enemy territory, bombing away at targets below. During the massive offensive, there would be multiple planes shot down, with some surviving as prisoners of war, and others who were left to their final fate.

Back home, in an empty Air-Force gym, running around and around the same path was Sylvia Quinn. She knew that death would be had on both sides in the war. She did not want war, she wanted her husband home and she wanted to see him safe. Sylvia kept busy and found solace in the laps.

The end of the war finally came, Pat came back home, and the worry was over. Pat retired after over 20 years of service. With the end of the war, the Quinns decided to move into town and bought a home on the South Hill of Spokane. Pat traded out his runs with his navigator for runs with his wife who had always been his north star. By then Sylvia could keep pace with him no matter the distance.

Pat and Sylvia's running did not go unnoticed by others. The next door neighbor, the Smith's, saw Pat and Sylvia running to and from their house together. Dr. Smith saw them running while he stood lighting a cigarette. He was a physician and was struck by these two people, similar in age to himself, out and about exercising. His wonder was eventually substituted for admiration, and eventually he would toss away the cigarettes and lace up his own pair of running shoes with his wife and they too would go out for runs with the Quinns.

Pat and Sylvia were a pair added to the growing Spokane running community. It was a community that grew in its initial phases by single digits.

One of those leading the way in converting locals to the running scene was Dr. Rockwell. He was a one man operating crew, who took his love for fitness and running and published it in the local papers. He advertised for the fun runs of his day that he named *Heart Runs*. Knowing the benefits that exercise created, Dr. Rockwell tried to get people out running everyday. He even went around seeking out new leads of those he knew might be runners.

"Sylvia, you can run the five mile race." Dr. Rockwell said.

"I don't think I can run in a race." Sylvia said.

She knew Dr. Rockwell and appreciated his enthusiasm, but she had in her head the idea of racing and associated an all out effort. She could keep pace with her husband. She did not want to be left behind. She had never raced in her life.

"My secretary Mary will be in the race, so you won't be the only female out there." Dr. Rockwell pleaded.

Pat seeing the conversation, finally entered in. He used his same motivating tone from before.

"Yeah, I don't know that you can do it." Pat said.

"I'll try it." said Sylvia.

The mother of three, Sylvia Quinn, volunteered her efforts to help support the Heart Run and she showed up to toe the line with eighteen others in the race. Sylvia saw Dr. Rockwell's secretary Mary at the starting line looking even less excited. Mary had probably shown up due to her boss indicating she had to. The only other woman in the race was Jan Pappas, a student in the area who was originally from Lawrence, Kansas; the same Lawrence, Kansas that had housed the athletes Billy Mills and Jim Ryun as they competed collegiately for the University of Kansas. It may not have been a battle between Mills, Ryun, and Lindgren, but they had their neighbors, out and about trying to do their best with running.

Dr. Rockwell raised the gun, fired it, and then handed it over to his wife, along with the stopwatch. The race had begun.

Mary started the race walking and never ran a step, while Sylvia, Jan, and the rest took off on the five mile course. There were no aid stations, no water stations, none of the athletes had numbers and no one directed the route and turns. There had been brief instructions at the beginning and so Sylvia kept her eyes up on the men in front of her and tried to keep pace. Jan ran right beside Sylvia as they made their way through the course, running through Spokane neighborhoods on a Saturday morning. Since Sylvia had never had a stopwatch going while she ran, she wondered what pace she was running. As Jan and Sylvia passed the finish together at the same time, she kept her ears attuned to Dr. Rockwell spitting out the times.

"Forty minutes. Forty-oh-one, Forty-oh-two."

Sylvia had run five miles in forty minutes; she had averaged eight minute pace and she had been tied in the position for the top woman in the race. She had even beaten a few men and did not end up in last. Sylvia now considered herself a runner. She had gone from not running, to running, and from not racing, to racing.

Sylvia and Pat continued to run and continued to show up to local races put on by Dr. Rockwell, or any of the other local runners. Sylvia's neighbors were added as instant friends through the running. More and more people kept getting added to the her social circle through running.

Sylvia's first marathon was the Coeur d'Alene, Idaho marathon run on May 28, 1977, where Sylvia ended up being the first female finisher clocking 3:27:50. Her fastest marathon ever was clocked on the same course in 1983, where she ran 3:04:45. Again she was the first female finisher and she was forty-four years old at the time. In 1997, Sylvia, aged 60, won the USATF Masters 8k Cross

© Sylvia Quinn Personal Archive, Photographer Unknown

Sylvia & Pat Quinn

Country Championship race with a time of 38:14. Although she was late to the running scene, her effort was always right on time. Her running led to more than just fast times and good fitness, it lead to a widening circle of friends.

One of those people Sylvia got to know was a local runner, Don Kardong. Standing with him after the Turkey Trot fun run, run annually on Thanksgiving morning at Manito Park in Spokane, Sylvia listened as Don spoke about a fun run he envisioned now called Bloomsday. Don said he planned to run the race in the late spring of 1977. Pat and Sylvia put the race on their calendar and kept on running.

Had there not been enthusiasts like Dr. Rockwell with the Heart Runs, Ken Latting with the Heart Marathons, or Herm Caviness with the Spokane Summer Games, then there would not have been the built in audience of distance runners in the community. These early enthusiasts brought the older generations out to run. They were not young kids chasing after world records, state championships, or national titles. They were the common person doing the simple and uncommon: trying.

The older runners in the community showed up for these local races and tried to stay fit. Not many people thought there would be 1,200 people lining up for this new road race, Bloomsday. As it was, Sylvia Quinn lined up in the same race as Don Kardong and Frank Shorter. Sylvia was also there the following year when Bill Rodgers came to town. Sylvia Quinn has been in every Bloomsday Race since the beginning. She has not beaten any of the big names, but she has continued to run. She ran under an hour each time she competed at Bloomsday until she reached age 70.

In 2016 Sylvia finished Bloomsday, a 12k course, with a time of 1:10:16. She was 5,404th overall, averaging 9:25 per mile. Among perennial runners (those that have run in every Bloomsday since 1977, of which there are only 82 left) Sylvia finished tenth, only four spots, and two minutes and eight seconds, behind Don Kardong. Against 79 year olds running the race, Sylvia crushed it. Whereas the average 79 year-old walks 18:35 per mile, Sylvia is running 9:25. Sylvia finished second place amongst 38 people with the same age, being beaten by one man. Sylvia was the 2,079th runner in out of the 16,485 runners from Spokane. She finished 4,146th out of the 33,517 people from the state of Washington. Out of the 25,084 females in the race, Sylvia finished 1,744th. And Sylvia was the first finisher of 20 female runners aged 79 in the event. She was also just under eight minutes ahead of Bob Barbero, another perennial who has raced in every Bloomsday since 1977. Yet for all the statistics, they mean very little to Sylvia who has not kept track of any of the miles she has run except for two time periods in her life: that sixth month period when she wanted to run 600 miles and then in 1977 she had a goal of running 1,977 miles.

It is all about the spirit of running for Sylvia, and that is the only stat she holds on to, as undefinable and incalculable as it is.

Race Director

Sylvia and Pat kept showing up for Bloomsday and the local fun runs, and it was only a matter of time before Don Kardong and the volunteers at Bloomsday talked Sylvia into becoming the Race Director. She took over as Race Director in 1981; Bloomsday had only had one other Race Director before Sylvia and it was Doug Kelley. He had more or less operated the race from the trunk of his car.

Sylvia learned to be a Race Director much like how she learned to become a runner; simply by doing it. Leaning upon others, asking questions, and seeking out information, Sylvia learned about the permits needed, the advertising, the race figures and projections; the volunteers needed, the aid stations, and the finishing times that needed to be compiled for the next day's newspaper.

One of Sylvia's chief responsibilities was to raise the numbers of those involved in the race, and there was no better way to get people to turn out than to approach them on their turf, much like Dr. Rockwell had done to her. The approach was effective. Prior to Sylvia helping out as Race Director in 1981 there were only 11,962 finishers in the race; by the time she left her post in 1990 the number of competitors had swelled to 51,122.

Sylvia went to retirement homes, office buildings, schools, and anywhere people would listen to her and let her leave a flier with the information regarding the next Bloomsday Race. Her goal was to help increase overall participation, but she especially wanted to help raise the number of women participating in Bloomsday. In 1978 the race was made up of nearly three quarters of male runners as opposed to the just over one quarter female runners. By the time 1981 came around and Sylvia was Race Director, the number had improved to just over 38% female racers. Each year she was on the job the number of women increased and by 1986 the women participating finally outnumbered the men 50.7% to 49.3%. By the time Sylvia finally walked away from the Race Director position in 1990, the number of female participants had reached 54.3%.

"It's an event for some and a race for others," Sylvia said as her sales pitch. "This is the one sporting event you can be in and you don't have to qualify for and you can take your time. The course will be open for four to five hours and you can talk. You can be in a sporting event." Nearly sixty percent of the fifty thousand plus racers are from the Spokane area. Whereas other road races have come and gone, Bloomsday remains, due in large part to volunteers with the same spirit and approach as Sylvia Quinn.

Sylvia spoke to her former self and to the reluctant runner in each person. She spoke to what running had meant to her and what it could mean for anyone willing to try. Men and women who had never ran before started to train and started to believe they could be a part of something positive in the community and in their own lives. She came to the sport later in life and stood there, small but secure in her statements. Old habits changed and were replaced with the positive impact of running for anyone that listened to her. The worry of day to day affairs that floated in the air of each individual life could be placed aside and running would be there to help.

Sylvia Quinn volunteering at Junior Bloomsday

© Sylvia Quinn Personal Archive, Photographer Unknown

Approaching Elementary schools, Sylvia switched her sales pitch. She wanted the children to work for their keep and as such there was an awards program setup within the Fit for Bloomsday Training Program. There were different badges and certificates that students could earn by running certain times and distances. As PE teachers saw the completion of the times and distances the certificates were awarded publicly at school. Sylvia motivated the children and helped them train for Bloomsday. This one woman, no taller than five feet two inches said to her small audience, "If me, an old lady can do it, you can too." And the boys and girls would try to get out and beat Sylvia Quinn.

Marshaling her efforts from her living room floor with volunteers, Sylvia spoke to those that would line the streets. She coordinated an effort before the ease of chip timing; when the finishing chute was manned by dozens of volunteers collecting the bib numbers being torn off the bottom of the race numbers as people came through the finish. Wallie and Cathy Eggar manned the finishing chute. George Schwartz took control for the Medical Services. Most of their meetings were on Tuesdays each month as they discussed different aspects of the race ranging from entry forms to sponsors, to the race bibs. Those race numbers torn off were placed along a line of string that held the order of every racer that would be synced up with someone who had a clock clicking every racer passing through. By midnight Sylvia would take the times to the *Spokesman-Review* to be printed in the next day's newspaper. It was all a monumental effort and Sylvia Quinn was there to deliver the final message for those nine years that she was the Race Director.

After each race and each year, Sylvia would stand back with the volunteers and analyze how the race went. What went well? What needed to improve? What adjustments needed to be made for the following year?

During the same time that Sylvia worked as Race Director at Bloomsday, she also volunteered her talents to help at the Washington State cross country meet. Bob Barbero, another perennial of the Bloomsday Race, asked for Sylvia's aid as he helped to coordinate the state meet that was held at Hangman Valley Golf Course from 1983-1985. Sylvia would man the finishing chute as hundreds of athletes went through. She was there in the last year the race was held at Hangman Valley Golf Course and saw the reason for its change. A snowstorm had come through the day before the race and turned the course into a muddy, wet, slippery experience for everyone. Sylvia saw as one runner grabbed a hold of Barbero's jacket and ripped it from him as he fell to the ground at the finish. At the same time that Sylvia was helping the state's elite finish races, she was also volunteering her time at Ferris High School where she helped start the girls cross country team.

The very first girls cross country team at Ferris High School consisted of only five girls; one of those girls running was Molly Quinn, Sylvia's daughter. The first girls coach at Ferris High School was Pat Freeman, who had never run so much as across the street. Her advice to the girls as they left to run was not the most encouraging.

"Don't run too hard and don't get hurt."

The focus was not on what to do, but rather what not to do; the emphasis was on the negative not the positive.

Sylvia did not interject or cowboy the coaching position. She was a volunteer and as such she supported each coach that the girls team would have at Ferris over the years. Her approach was to simply offer more running for those girls that wanted to run a little longer on Saturdays and during the summers.

Being the only girls coach or volunteer out there with the athletes, Sylvia kept running with the girls as they left and returned to Ferris each day. As such, she encouraged the lead girls to run out to a point off in the distance and then sprint back to the very last girl in the group, and then jog with her for a few minutes before increasing the pace and repeating the process. The results were multifaceted.

The lead girls ended up running longer distances than the slower girls. The slower girls felt that they were appreciated and not neglected. The slower girls also got an opportunity to run with someone on the team, if only for short bits of time. Sylvia helped slower girls on the team. She encouraged them to see what fast girls did, and how they could mirror their efforts.

To keep the girls together Sylvia used her refrain, "If we don't all do the same workout everyday, we don't get better." The togetherness of the girls started, and everyone started doing the same work. Sylvia saw the teams come together and she was there for the only two championship girls teams that Ferris ever had in 1980 under Coach Dennis Driskill and 1991 under coach Wayne Gilman.

Sylvia volunteered and gave hours after school, hours in preparation for meets, hours spent watching others run and cheering them on and through the finishing chute.

Hours and seasons were spent by Sylvia volunteering during track practices. She saw Coach Herm Caviness, a master in his craft, shaping the lives of his young athletes. She saw his precision and attention to detail and recognized instantly why all his athletes admired him and worked for him; it was because he worked for them. Their success was his success. She saw that the numbers of track championships at the school was only an outgrowth of

Herm's desire to build boys into men. She wished that everyone could have a coach like Herm Caviness.

Sylvia tried to inspire those in her own family to take up running. Knowing that family members, including her father, had passed away from heart disease, Sylvia kept to her mantra of extolling the virtues of distance running. While visiting family down in Louisiana, Sylvia found a marathon and entered the race while on vacation. One of her younger siblings showed up to see her finish and remarked to someone nearby as Sylvia entered the finish chute exhausted, "Oh, she just does that for show."

Sylvia stood there, panting in the heat and humidity of the day and looked back at her sister whom she had cared for growing up.

"If I wanted to do something for show, believe me I wouldn't be doing this." She said.

Chasing Gunhild Swanson

Sylvia still volunteers, but spends most of her volunteer time at Hamblen Elementary School in Spokane where her grandchildren attend. She stands on the sidewalk with a washable marker to mark the hands of those little athletes

Gunhild Swanson, left; Sylvia Quinn, right

© Spokesman-Review, Photographer Dan Pelle

running around the property. The marks help the kids keep track of how many laps they have run.

As much as Sylvia helps others keep marks, she doesn't hold on to the times that she has run, nor does she care all that much about them. There are boxes full of the marathons and fun runs that she has participated in filled with medals she has won for her age group over the years. But she does not display any of the awards or the accomplishments.

She does not tout the fact that on the United States of America Track & Field Top 25 Age Graded-Performances she ranks 6th, 8th, and 19th all time. She is the only female athlete listed three times. Each of those marks came from different marathons run at the ripe old age of 78. She is truly in a league of her own.

For the 77 year old age group, Sylvia has the world record for the marathon running 4:24:27 at the Coeur d'Alene marathon on May 25, 2014. More of her times would be world records for her age the only problem is she has not run her times on official courses. An official course cannot have too much of a drop in elevation. In order for it to count as an official timing, the course can not be point-to-point, or an out and back course. There can be only so much of the course that can be repeated or overlapping. The two courses where most marathon records stand are in London or Berlin.

In the fall of 2015 Sylvia planned on running the Portland, Oregon Marathon which is an approved and recognized race by the record keepers. However, prior to the race, Sylvia suffered a terrible fall during her training run. Two and a half miles out she suffered the fall to her left side which she has always favored. Her foot caught the pavement at an odd angle and this five foot two inch, one hundred pound woman made out of determination, got back up and tried to shake it off, but she could not. The pain was excruciating.

Four days of rest ensued before Sylvia tried to go back out and run again. Once more the ice-pick stabbing like pain was too great and finally she decided to go in and see a doctor.

The x-ray revealed that Sylvia's legs were out of line and that there was severe internal bleeding. It was also noticed that there was little padding left in her lower back area due to the thousands of miles run over the course of her lifetime. The only positive result was that her hip was still in her socket.

Three months of physical therapy ensued. This was not the first time that Sylvia had been in to see a doctor. For nearly five or six years she had been hit with stress fracture after stress fracture, in multiple parts of her feet and legs. Finally a bone density scan by her endocrinologist revealed that Sylvia suffered from advanced osteoporosis. With supplements and help from her doctor, she has found the right balance of treatment that has allowed her to run. She is just more selective about the races she enters. She is grateful that she can return to her early morning runs with her early morning training partners.

Sylvia Quinn makes up just one of a group of seven women that arise and run during the weekdays. You could run with them, that is if you can catch the 4:45 start time and if you can locate which Starbucks they meet at on the South Hill of Spokane. It is typically a five mile loop and they typically talk with one another while they run. They run in every sort of weather even icy roads and rain. This crew has been running together for years.

One of those people that Sylvia runs with and is trying to chase down is Gunhild Swanson, ultra-marathoner and YouTube sensation. Gunhild is eight years younger than Sylvia and she captured the minds and hearts of people all over the world as she finished one of the most electrifying races in all of human history.

Gunhild's family has been well connected to the Spokane running scene. Her son Chris Morlan competed in the Olympic trials for the marathon in 1996. Chris was a graduate of Lewis & Clark High School and eventually returned to be their longtime boys coach. Chris' son Turlan, competed at Gonzaga Prep and qualified for the Foot Locker National Championship race in 2017. Their running has spanned the generations.

At the age of 70, Gunhild Swanson, a Spokane resident, entered into the Western States 100, a race that is arguably one of the toughest ultra-marathons in the world and is located along the Sierra Nevada Mountains in California. The race had never been completed by anyone, male or female over the age of 60 until Gunhild came along and did it. A decade passed and she decided she would try to be the first 70 year old to complete the course.

There are time constraints to completing the Western States 100, cutoffs that must be met or the runner will be pulled from the course. Gunhild would have to complete the 100 miles in less than thirty hours or her time would not be registered.

All was going well during the race that would include over 18,090 feet of total elevation gain. That is almost three and a half miles of climbing. The amount of climbing in the race equates to running up Mt. St. Helens before its top blew off, not once, but twice. Or it would be like running up Mt. Rainier in Washington and knowing you still had four thousand feet of climbing left once you made it to the peak, or it would be like running straight up Mt. Everest and being just shy of two thirds the way up that mountain. Gunhild was doing great, having run 80 miles already and had passed the last time check before the finish.

Gunhild was running with her grandson and looked up to see some runners off in the distance and so she went after them, believing them to be part of the race; unfortunately this mile and half error was not recognized until she approached the people and realized that she had gone off course with precious seconds and minutes slipping away. Backtracking, Gunhild recovered her steps without recovering the precious time lost.

30 hours is the magic number for any time to be recorded in the Western States 100 race. If someone tries to finish after that time they are pulled from the course and their time is not recognized. Gunhild, with all the might that her 70 year old frame could give after more than 80 straight miles of running, sunk her teeth in for the final 20 miles, and kept running.

Up and down she continued, over and around bends in the trail. Eventually she saw the finish in the distance and the hundreds of people who had shown up to support other runners in the race.

In this moment, Gunhild became everyone's runner.

As she entered the track, the PA announcer spoke as much for Gunhild's sake as for everyone watching.

"You have 75 seconds," he said.

Nervous looks were worn by fans lined along the interior and exterior of the track as they tried to out lean the people around them to get a look at this last runner.

"Gunhild Swanson from Spokane Valley, Washington" The PA announcer said.

Chatter began to go from one person to another as they quickly weighed the time verses the figure in the distance.

Whether there were doubters or believers lining the course, one thing was certain, they all cheered on as Gunhild made her way toward them.

Rounding the final curve heading into the home stretch the clock read 29:59:40. She had a little less than 100 meters in front of her and 20 seconds to do what had been considered impossible. More than 100 miles had already been run by her, but they were not on the official course and so they did not count and could now keep her from the official recorded time.

The PA announcer came on a second time and repeated his refrain.

"Gunhild Swanson from Spokane Valley, Washington!" He spoke to her as if helping her identify herself and what she represented after the delirium of the previous miles.

The roar of applause rose as Gunhild passed by people shouting and hoping she would make it in time. With eyes up on the clock and arms pumping, Gunhild kept pace heading for the finish line.

Left foot, right foot, left foot, right foot.

Gunhild went down the final steps of the straightaway with her grandson by her side and the echoes of the crowd reverberating around her. Observers stood watching sheer will pass by them in the form of seventy year-old woman wearing a neon green singlet.

For the final time the PA announcer stated his refrain.

"Gunhild Swanson from Spokane Valley, Washington!"

Under the finish line hung the official clock reading 29:59:54, and Gunhild crossed the finish line.

This grandma finished the race and accomplished what had not been accomplished by any male or female aged 70 years and older. Gunhild Swanson, who ran the Western States 100 (and for her it was 103 due to a wrong turn) finished under the allotted time. People with smartphones had recorded the event and instantly Gunhild had rock-star running status. People the world over watched her finish on YouTube and found themselves cheering as well for this old woman.

One of those watching the finish online was Sylvia Quinn. She too was excited and cheering for her friend. On the next Wednesday when Gunhild was back in town, Sylvia and her went out for their usual run together in isolation and without the notoriety accompanying them.

To the casual passerby it looked like just two older ladies out for a run, but it is more than that for the people who know them. They are an old hare and an old hound still running around.

Sylvia is still inspired by her friend and she is out there to run with her. Sylvia recognizes she had a nine year head start on Gunhild, but now it is Gunhild that leads the way. Sylvia knows as any runner worth their shoes, that the only way to run faster is to hang with the fastest people around. Sylvia continues to chase her friend around the roads of the South Hill of Spokane.

Before Joan Benoit won the first Olympic Marathon at the LA games in 1984, there was Kathy Switzer sneaking into the Boston Marathon and finishing the race. Today, Sylvia Quinn and Gunhild Swanson continue to run after those women from the past with the same spirit and love of running.

Sylvia recognizes the social life that running has given her over the years. Her friends are numerous and vary in ages. These are her people. They strive for their best. This timeless sport has tied her to timeless friends along life's different mile markers.

One of the strongest friends Sylvia has is not someone her age or someone from her family, but Jennifer (Smith) Anderson.

Jenny began running at Ferris High School in the early nineties and would become the nation's fastest high school female miler. Since her graduation, she has kept in contact with Sylvia almost daily. The two talk and run together to this day. Jenny is almost half the age of Sylvia, but that does not seem to matter too much to either of them; nor did it matter to Jenny when she made Sylvia one of her bridesmaids at her wedding.

This tireless woman continues to serve those around her. She continues to volunteer an hour or two after school, feeling that such time really is not all that much. Sylvia has lived a lifetime as a volunteer, giving the hour or two each day that she can to those around her. The effects of her efforts do not always

© Gary Wang

reach back to her, but every now and again they do. When the principal of Hamblen Elementary approached Sylvia in 2016 she said, "I remember seeing you volunteer when I was in school." Generations have passed by Sylvia Quinn, some have noticed her and others have not, but her actions have impacted untold thousands which is just fine with her.

Sylvia Quinn continues to train with one leg weaker than the other, with osteoporosis, with one leg that does not rise as high as the other, and with numbness coming from sciatic nerve damage down her one leg. She continues on one leg when others need two and does more with it than most people do with both their legs. She is incredible regardless of the age group she is placed in.

Through all her years of volunteering Sylvia has noticed a steep decline in children running around sixth or seventh grade. These kids are suddenly swept up and lost to a sea of smartphones, gadgets and games that take their attention, their time, and their ambition for anything that matters. Girls are often lost to the short sightedness of trying to act older and more sophisticated by mimicking all that they see in the media around them. Parents ignore the warning signs that something is amiss.

But Sylvia Quinn still serves anyone willing to try and she does so with a smile. She continues to serve in her Catholic Church, ironing the linens used on the altars during the service. She holds fast to that faith, that dedication, that sacrifice she learned in her youth. Sylvia will wear out long before she ever rusts out.

Liz Hawkins: Races Worth Running

All that Liz accomplished could have been thwarted by one simple decision before she ever ran a step in high school.

It was around the time that Isaac was finishing up his high school career, having won six state titles, and Emily was gearing up to win an individual title in the coming fall, that Liz was in seventh grade, just one year behind her older brother Ben. Liz was just like any other girl in middle school who was trying to find herself.

She found herself focusing not on grades, but on the expectations of attaining the attention of those around her. She was on the dance team and enjoying life. Her focus was not on her forthcoming future.

Being the sociable, lovable, extravert she was, Liz had people that wanted to hang out with her. If Liz was there, it was guaranteed that others would be laughing and enjoying themselves because Liz put them at ease. Her bubbly personality became contagious and infected all who associated with her.

During one Friday night Liz was invited to hang out with some of her newfound friends on the dance team. She went over to a girl's house with many members of the dance team, not knowing that this girl's parents were out of town. After awhile of talking about boys they thought were cute and different dance routines that they had practiced, the girl who played host wanted to get into her parent's liquor cabinet and start drinking.

At this all important station in life, Liz had to quickly decide which train she would hitch herself to. Decisions are like train tracks that lead to final destinations. Liz did not feel comfortable. She was not someone that needed stimulants in order to fit in. She knew that turning towards alcohol could lead

Liz Hawkins running at
Sacajawea Middle School in 7th grade

towards other decisions that would limit her future. In a move showing her integrity and a foresight beyond her years, Liz made her way to a phone and called home to her mother asking to be picked up immediately.

Ann quickly arrived and Liz tearfully got into the car explaining what had happened. Together they drove up the road leading out of Hangman Valley where this girl lived and went towards home. Ann was grateful for her daughter's integrity.

There are many races. Races of acceptance. Races of identity. But ultimately some of those races are spectated and cheered on by those with insecurity. Much of what is considered entertainment is a race to rationalize wrong for right. Too many youth race for something that has no value.

The best races of life are not brief. The best races of life demand a dedication and determination that sees beyond the immediate seconds that seem so difficult. The best races and the best training occurs when no one is watching.

Liz looked like Anne Hathaway, talked to people like Barbara Walters, and made those she spoke with feel like they were talking with Oprah. Rarely would she be left to herself at any event; school, church, or otherwise. People loved Liz and Liz loved people. She could make Ellen DeGeneres appear like an introvert.

Liz's alarming good looks could have arrested and intimidated people, but instead they were disarmed by her kind word and quick wit. Somehow, in some way, Liz would know something and link it to the people she met, or she would uncover a connection neither side had realized.

Liz was the same height as Ben but lacked the muscles. She lacked the competitive edge her sister Emily carried with her and she lacked the speed of

Isaac. But for all that was absent in Liz, she was present in so many more ways. She engaged in life and in the stories of life that everyone had.

© Peter Hawkins Personal Archive

Olympic Decathlete Dan O'brien; Liz Hawkins

While Isaac was at Nationals running for a title, Liz was walking around with Dan O'brien, the 1996 Olympic gold medalist in the decathlon. Dan was brought in by the meet promoters of Foot Locker. He was brought to be the face of the event. While young skinny, highly talented athletes scampered about, Liz spoke with Dan about his life and about what he had accomplished.

"Oh you went to Spokane Community College and then the University of Idaho in Moscow, I'm from Spokane." Liz said.

Continually she made such connections. Dan and Liz continued to talk back and forth while a national caliber race played out in Balboa Park.

© Peter Hawkins Personal Archive

Liz Hawkins; Gerry Lindgren

Dan did not know anyone at the event that he was paid to show up to, but he did not mind this nice young lady who was talking to him at the race and who was there that night as the final ceremonies were wrapping up. Being famous can put people off. Liz was not intimidated by the myth behind the man; she simply spoke to him and he spoke back. Conversation, for Liz, was as easy as putting one foot in front of the other. And she could do this with anyone.

If it was not Dan O'brien, then it was Gerry Lindgren.

Bloomsday had set up an event whereby Gerry came back to Spokane. At the event, who should want to talk to Liz but Gerry Lindgren. Anyone who has met, conversed, or spent time with Liz is not surprised by this.

Liz would just as soon speak to the best instead of try to compete with them athletically. And Liz did not just talk to the athletes and people of note and respect. Liz knew everything about everyone that was within her radar.

For one Thanksgiving, Paul and Ann had challenged their children to do something nice for someone before Christmas. Their children went about various tasks to help one another or others they knew. Liz found a girl on the bus that did not appear to have friends and made sure that she would have a friend going forward. That challenge, issued in Liz's youth, was one she would live up to the rest of her life. This was Liz the person.

Liz the athlete approached running knowing that what her siblings had achieved was outstanding. She saw the work Ben put into running each day and could smell it in the car to and from seminary as well as after practice. The scent of hard work and the fruits of it she was well acquainted with; yet she knew that she did not have the killer instinct needed in running. She worked at running, but she did not feel she had anything to prove to anyone by doing it.

Isaac, Emily, and Ben had all run the marathon together. Liz probably would have been welcome to run if she wanted to but that was the important part; she did not want to compete.

The only thing that kept her in the running was the fact that she did not find another sport or activity she enjoyed doing in her middle school years. She had turned out for volleyball but did not enjoy the yelling. She had gone to gymnastics and enjoyed the events but after splitting the balance beam she decided to walk away from the sport. Liz could shoot hoops, but why run back and forth on the court when there were boys in the stands to talk to.

Running was Liz's default option and so with it, she turned out for the Ferris girls cross country team. The days of Emily Hawkins, Jenny Smith, Kristen Parish, and Missy Blackshire had gone and with it any resemblance of a state contending or even qualifying team. The only staple of the program was volunteer Sylvia Quinn, who had been with the program since its inception. Sylvia approached Liz on the first day having heard she was a Hawkins. Before she could say anything Liz spoke.

"I know I'm a Hawkins, but don't go comparing me to Emily or any of my other siblings." Those were Liz's first words to Sylvia.

Despite her deadpan dead interest in the sport, Liz ran well enough to letter all four years and even ran on varsity for a few meets. But Liz's sights and aspirations to race never elevated themselves higher than the JV All-City race.

Liz showed up to run, to stay active, fit and trim, and because her parents would not allow her to just come home and sit around. Paul and Ann knew that the greatest harm that comes from decision making with high school aged students is in the two hours immediately following the end of the school day. It is the time that most kids are left to their own devices before parents come home from work. Liz, like all of Paul and Ann's children, had to do something and she had to actively pursue it. She may not have had the same talent as her older siblings, but her best efforts were expected. And so Liz took to running.

Keeping Form and Running Tall

Working jobs and running went hand in hand in the Hawkins household. It was no surprise that Liz's first job was as a hostess at a startup Italian restaurant called *Portobello's*. The surprise came four months after the opening of the restaurant when Liz went to deposit her check at the bank. The bank teller told Liz her check had bounced. Confused, she went home and told her father Paul what had happened. He took her to her work and instructed her to have them pay her out of the register the amount allotted to her on the check and he instructed her to quit immediately after she was paid. It was the only time he ever encouraged any of his children to quit. Liz did as instructed and had the manager pay her from the till. With cash in hand she went back to the car where Paul gave her a lesson on finances and predicted *Portobello's* would soon be out of business. His prediction came to pass in just over a week's time.

Using his real estate expertise he explained why *Portobello's* was a bad idea from the start. Its location, on the rear facing side of the Lincoln Heights shopping center implied failure. There has never been a shop to succeed in that allotted space. There is no great exposure or main street passing near it. Shops need great exposure to compete in the business world.

The real surprise with Liz's employment came with her second job.

McDonald's.

The Golden Arches.

The home of the Big Mac and Happy Meal.

This second job was an unwelcome one for Liz. Isaac the workhorse could work there, but not Liz. She did not want to have her pretty face associated with all the stereotypes that are thrown at McDonald's everyday. Working at a restaurant had its allures; getting tips, practicing and enhancing her social skills. Going from waiting tables to flipping burgers seemed a step backward.

Paul knowing that McDonald's had been good enough for two other people he cared deeply about, his wife and oldest son Isaac, told Liz that all he wanted her to do was apply.

Liz knew applying for the job likely meant she would get the job. This was in the days before Internet applications. Liz would have to physically go into the store, ask for an application, fill it out and return it, all in a matter of minutes. Based on her physical features and easy ability to bring joy to others she knew she would be hired. The only problem was she did not want to work there.

A battle of wills ensued.

Paul asked Ben to drive Liz to McDonald's to have her fill out the application. The trip was taken to the McDonald's, but Liz never left the car to fill out the application; at least not the first time.

Paul needed to reach his daughter and not the one that was currently sitting before him. He had to see the days ahead of her and help her disregard her prejudices about the people she thought she knew so well.

"What's the difference between you and the people that work at McDonald's?" He asked.

Liz sat on the nice leather couch in the family room of the house, thinking. She knew the answer but did not want to say it.

"You have some nicer clothes, a nicer place to call home, and perhaps some parents who have expectations for you that others never had and that's it. Our work allows you to have these nice things, but it doesn't allow you to look down on others or their honest hard work."

Liz knew her father was right. She just did not say it or anything for the moment. She knew one of those luxuries she had was a car that her teenage siblings had used in order to get them to and from school or work.

"Ben, take her back to McDonald's." Paul said.

Swallowing pride, Liz finally made it into McDonald's where the manager gave her an application and had her fill it out on the spot, after which a short interview occurred and Liz was immediately hired. She started that very next weekend.

Paul and Ann saw multiple benefits from having children working while running. The less time a child had, the more it forced them to use their time wisely. Better to have a child making money and saving it away, than to have a child wasting time with friends in other pursuits that had no profit-financially or otherwise. Working such jobs also provided an opportunity for each child to see firsthand the value of their education. Also, a tired child would not have the energy to make mistakes that other children might. And finally, working was another way to develop or reveal skills and character.

Liz expected to spend time on the grill making hamburgers but that never happened. Every time she showed up for work they either had her at the front register or working the drive through window. After a few weeks of this routine, Liz asked her manager why he never put her on the grill.

"Why would we hide your bright smile behind the grill? We need you up in the front," he said. Kind and true as his compliment was, he also showed business acumen. A kind beautiful face at McDonald's ensured loyalty and happy customers.

The well-placed word from her manager also gave Liz the confidence to own the position at the front counter or the drive through window.

A great desire to succeed welled within Liz. She would break free from stereotypes and expectations that shroud a place like McDonald's. Perhaps the best response to the documentary *SuperSize Me* should have been a film crew following the change that took place at the McDonald's Liz worked at on Regal Road.

Liz brought a light to those she worked with and served food. She inspired those about her to be their best on the job. Moving quickly to learn her task, then happily engaging with everyone, customers as well as co-workers, Liz's attitude melded loyalty with respect from her coworkers. The store quickly earned the award for being the fastest drive through in the city of Spokane (against all other McDonald's locations). One of the perks from her hard work was a gift card to the Valley Mall.

Fresh off her taste of success Liz set her sights on a new goal: Employee of the Month. This accolade was not going to be handed out to anyone. Respect and admiration are earned over time.

Month after month passed. Tray after tray she kept cleaning, all while offering quick, kind considerate service to anyone walking through the door. Liz took the extra step to help others in her job and she did it all with quickness.

Liz's McDonald's sat directly across from a youth soccer field. At the time of her employment, this McDonald's was the closest fast food location for over a mile. Saturday mornings as well as lunch times were slammed with customers. Liz was on the front line, the one taking the orders and pulling together the meals, all at a lightning pace and with a genuine smile. Quick efficient action followed every order and the people came back, again and again, after having a fast, positive experience.

Yet, as the months passed by, Liz still had not achieved the Employee of the Month. She looked for opportunities to help at work. She asked her coworkers and her manager what she could do to be better, faster, more efficient; how she could best serve them at work and make their job easier.

Liz began to be invested in her job, in her coworkers, and in the culture of success. She wanted to be the best at what she did. And suddenly it did not matter that she was working at McDonald's. Perhaps it was because she worked there that she wanted to earn admiration. She did not want it to be given to her. She recognized that her coworkers and manager did work hard. She witnessed that this was a day in, day out grind for them, but one that was worthy of accolades not assessments of, "Oh, well it's just McDonald's, anybody can get a job and work there." Liz was in the trenches with these people that she began to love.

Seeing customers that treated employees poorly endeared the employees to

Liz. These were her people and she would defy expectations.

Liz's moment of opportunity finally arrived. One of these people who looked at McDonald's and "its people" as something to be bossed about and looked upon without impunity came through as she typically did in the drive through. She was a regular customer that came in at least once a week. Every time she came she complained about something being wrong with her order or not served quite right. Typically she would order fries without salt on them as a means of ensuring that the fries were fresh and then she would ask for salt packets to sprinkle on the fries herself.

After being asked to pull forward for her large order so that other customers could be served behind her she refused. Since the customer is always right, adjustments were made on the fly. Everyone who worked at this McDonald's knew this customer once her voice reached their headsets.

On one particularly windy and wintery night in Spokane she wheeled her large dark SUV around the curve of the drive-through where the oversized menu reflected upon her. The window came down and she spouted out her order. Through the headsets connecting the employees to one another came the word, "We got her again."

As was typical, she gave her order while simultaneously giving orders and insults to her children in the car with her.

Tonight would not be a particularly heavy order, a drink and some fries, no salt, but the salt packets should be ready when she asked for them at the window.

The SUV rounded the corner to the first window. With the wind whipping and windows being slid open and down, the lady held out her ten-dollar bill. Liz reached out to grab it but the wind forced it from her hand.

As if she had practiced the move her entire life, Liz put her five foot eight inch, 125 pound frame through the tiny window and went after the wind blown money.

Touching her headset she explained what had happened and relayed to the boss that she would be coming through the front door quickly.

Liz returned back to the window after sprinting through the front and gave the woman her change back.

"Is there anything else I can do for you?" She asked.

The woman in the SUV was spellbound.

Although Liz worked for Employee of the Month she would never receive it. Liz demonstrated her ability to work hard amidst a team that needed some lift. In running, as in life, it is important to keep form no matter the race and to always run tall. Often those overlooked in running hover near the back of the pack. Just as Liz changed that McDonald's, she also challenged the notion that winners are always the ones who cross the line first.

The Greatest Race Never Seen

If people who knew the Hawkins family and had seen their children race were asked who ran the best race, they would undoubtedly point to Isaac or Emily and their individual state championship efforts or races. The last person they would think of as having the greatest race would be Liz.

During Liz's freshman year time trial she finished dead last on the team, right around the twenty-seven minute mark, averaging nine minute mile pace. From the time trial to the next race Liz improved by six minutes. Liz saw she was capable of improvement and continued to do so from race to race and season to season, but there would not be as big of jumps ever again.

Her teammates voted her "Most Improved" for not one, but two straight seasons. In racing terms she may have seemed more tortoise than hare, and as such she improved, slowly and steadily. She would take running and life at her own pace.

Liz enjoyed her identity as a Hawkins. The first three had all been runners and with it came a territory of instant appreciation and admiration for all of their hard work. At school, church, and wherever Liz went she had the confidence that came from being known as a Hawkins. At school she could see other students and classmates that had an identity crisis. Her work at McDonald's had helped her see into the windows and worlds of those passing by. What she came to see was a lack of vision, a lack of confidence, and a lack knowing oneself. She saw it in the halls at school and in the conversations she so easily started with those around her. People pretended to be something in front of others, or they mirrored what they saw in TV and movies, taking their cues from music videos or the latest in pop culture. They were chasing after some social craze.

Liz's senior year of cross country ended at the JV All City race. She wanted to go on to Foot Locker and run as a reward for her hard work.

Paul saw an opportunity.

"Liz you can go down to Foot Locker and I will pay for it so you can save your money for college next year, but I want you to run in the Seeded Girls Race." Paul said.

The Seeded Race at Foot Locker is reserved for the state champions and people placing atop the podium in their various states. Liz knew this as well as her father knew it.

"Dad, you know I'm not going to win that race, I'll get crushed." Liz said.

"You need to have a big race experience. Big ticks hang with big dogs." Paul said.

"I'll finish last." Liz said.

"Who cares?" Paul said.

He wanted his daughter to see beyond the race and to life after high school. The results of races are not as important as the realizations taken from them. Life would be difficult, but there needed to be the confidence to go into difficulty and realize that you could come out still placing one foot in front of the other.

"You need to give your best against the best." Paul said.

Liz stayed silent. Her father had been right before with McDonald's and this seemed to be another learning moment.

"Fine." Liz said.

And she continued to train for an entire month after the cross country season had officially ended. Liz wondered and worried over the race. She went out the door to train each day running the miles differently than she had in the past.

One of the last breakfasts Ann made for Liz before she went off to Foot Locker consisted of some eggs, toast, and a short conversation. Ann moved about, silently and slowly, yet again making breakfast at an early hour, and making lunches for her children.

"How do you feel about your race coming up?" Ann asked.

"I don't know. I'm afraid I'll come in last." Liz said, stirring her eggs on her plate.

Ann continued to slowly open brown paper bags and start to place in sandwiches.

"Well, you know someone has to come in last in every race that's run," Ann said.

Liz looked up from her plate towards her mother.

"If you end up last, just make sure to own it." Ann said.

Liz smiled, grabbed her lunch and went off to school with a little more perspective and hope.

It is one thing to be running in the front of the pack and fade, it is another thing to be in the back of the pack and fade. Liz knew this race at Foot Locker could be embarrassing instead of empowering. Teammates and friends of Liz's were running in their own class races, opting out of the Seeded Race for fear of looking bad in front of their peers. She had signed up for the Seeded Race and now had to give it her best against the best.

And so on the first Saturday in early December of 2001, Liz laced up her spikes and strode out in the Seeded Race. She replayed her mother's advice over and over again in her mind, *If you end up last, just make sure you own it.* The race started at 10:15 am.

And so this unknown girl with the brown ponytail and wearing the purple singlet and shorts kept striding out until the starting marshal had the girls head to the start line. The only people standing on the sideline and watching the girl wearing bib 3520 were her father Paul and her younger brother Peter who was a freshman and had yet to race.

The call from the starting marshal came and Liz lined up against the 131 fastest female runners on the west coast.

The gun was raised.

Liz stood there in the box with the ghosts of Isaac, Emily, and Ben beside her.

The gun fired and they were off with Liz charging hard with the rest of them.

The first mile of the Mt. Sac course is flat and dusty. Two small laps are made before heading up the first of three enormous hills. Inside the middle of that dust bowl stood Paul and Peter, looking for Liz.

They caught her, in the back of the pack but pushing hard. Around the first lap they went and onto the next. They would hit the first mile right before making the turn to head up the hill. Paul and Peter stood at the mile mark.

"5:44, 5:45, 5:46, 5:47"

Liz came through the first mile in 5:46. Liz had never ever run under six

minutes in her entire life and here she had gone fourteen seconds under the mark. Likely Liz had set a personal record in the 100, 200, 400, 800 meter, and the mile all in one go. She had gone out with the best and she indeed was giving it her best.

Around the corner she went and up the first hill, alone and away from the shouts of her two supporters. Back and forth along the switchbacks she climbed.

Paul and Peter waited at the bottom of the hill, waiting for Liz to arrive. Down the path she came. Paul took out his camera and started snapping pictures. This would be a moment to remember, just as valuable as any. Both Paul and Peter yelled, cheered, and encouraged Liz as if she were on world record pace. One could not have noticed from the way that Paul and Peter cheered that Liz was at the back of the pack instead of the front of it.

Away Liz continued onward and upward towards the next big hill. She was tired, her face beat red, and sweat poured out of her, but she went at the hill as best she could.

Up the hill she climbed about the same time as the leaders were coming off of the third hill and heading towards the finish. One of these young runners coming off the hill was Zoe Nelson, from Kalispell, Montana. Zoe was a freshman in high school and would qualify for Nationals that day. She would qualify each year of high school and then earn a scholarship to run at the University of Oregon.

While the future of women's distance running came off the mountain, a future wife, mother, and leader climbed the backside of Mt. Sac, clinging to a belief in her identity.

The trail of female athletes continued to come off the mountain and down onto the track for the finish. Liz would be the last off the mountain. Waiting at the track's edge were Paul and Peter, snapping pictures, yelling, and cheering themselves hoarse.

The announcer did not know that this was the last one.

"Looks like we have one more coming, let's bring her home." He said.

The few spectators still at the finish clapped but not as they had when the leaders came through; the only two doing that were Paul and Peter, who knew what this race meant to the person running it.

Liz came around the last bend, exhausted, sweating, and with her red face glowing. Liz crossed the line 132nd out of 132 runners and with a time of 25:30. On such a tough course, Liz had run with all the effort and zeal she could muster. She ran up those hills after having run the fastest mile of her life. She had run straight into oxygen debt and continued onward to the very end.

She earned her place.

She did what teammates and others had been too afraid to do: try. Under the brightest lights and on the biggest stage Liz had given everything. It was the widow's mite of racing, and it went unnoticed, ignored, and pitied by everyone but two people. It was one of the greatest races, never seen.

On the flight home from the race, Paul spoke to his daughter and tried to express all that he had seen and felt at Mt. Sac. Paul began to tear up and cry as he tried to put to words what her efforts had meant to him.

"You know, you ran a really good race and it wouldn't have been easy to have done it. What you did is not something your siblings would have been able to do. I am so proud of you and I love you." Paul choked out through tears.

Often those at the back of the pack are overlooked, ignored, or forgotten. In the spectrum of racing, however, they still cover the same distance. Each runner who lines up to race is vowing their best.

Liz would finish up her high school career and attend Brigham Young University-Idaho. She would join up with the intramural cross country team on those windy, cold fall mornings and enjoy the instant friends she made through the sport she had come to love.

Liz graduated with a degree in Family and Consumer Science and married her husband Brad Ashby. While Brad earned his law degree at Arizona State University, Liz completed a Masters in Educational Curriculum and Instruction Development. They have since moved to North Bend, Washington where they are raising their three children.

Peter Hawkins: Number 5

As the fifth child in a family of seven I had the unique opportunity to observe my future through the lives of my older siblings. I saw the freshman through senior experience in high school four times over. As I witnessed important events I tried to conceptualize what it all meant. At the time I could never really put into words what I felt. I merely kept within myself a message that I took from their experiences and I hoped would shape my own someday.

I saw the finish of the marathon that Isaac, Emily, Ben, and my Dad raced. I saw Isaac race at every race that my parents went to, which was almost all of them. I saw Emily race against Missy Blackshire in middle school. I saw Ben wrestle his competition, tying them into pretzels on the mat and I saw Ben tuck, twist, and turn himself through the air and other apparatuses in gymnastics meets. I saw my sister Liz talking and walking with Dan O'Brien as if they were long lost friends while Isaac was running at Nationals.

I witnessed my parents work. My mother's silent vigil to the counters as she cooked for all of us each morning is an image that sticks with me to this day. I saw my father's vice-like grip on a young college aged kid in that judo match; I saw his head turn towards Isaac, Ben and I, and then back to the man he choked out for victory. I saw that same look in his eyes as he watched all of his children compete.

These were all moments of will; moments where someone did not shrink against a significant struggle. For me it was all the same race: Isaac swimming down the home stretch in track his junior year to pull out the victory; Emily cresting the hill at state her senior year; Ben, coming through the mile at the

Pasco Invite and proving he would not fade; Liz, lining up at Foot Locker, knowing the result before the gun was raised yet racing with reckless abandon.

These were my heroes. Their stories became my own. I saw the world through races, through running, and through splits, and times.

Through all the races, all the times, all the highs and lows of the sport for each sibling, I stood as observer and cheerleader. These were not just my siblings, they were my friends. The thrill of victory and accomplishment I enjoyed, and the bitterness of being just short of it, I felt as well. With each moment, I logged away in memory and said to myself, *When it's my time I will* ... but again those final words elluded me.

I felt them but I could not put them into words.

© Peter Hawkins Personal Archive
Peter Hawkins; All City Race, 2nd Grade

Before it was ever my turn to run I would talk about running. As a kid I had a working knowledge and vocabulary for distance running that most people never know, nor will appreciate. During my tme in grade school there was show and tell each week. When it came time for me to get up I never showed anything. I always stood before my fellow classmates and told them what was happening with the Ferris cross country and track teams. They sat there with blank stares as I rattled off times, places, scores and standings, and tried to give a context to what it all meant.

One day a fellow student of mine brought a horse to school. It stood outside of the classroom on the front grass of Mullan Road Elementary. Students laughed, cheered, and wondered how fast the horse could go. When I got up after the horse had left, I spoke about how my brother was like a thoroughbred racehorse that was faster than anybody in town, the state, and the west coast.

It was the type of claim that a kid could make and then be patted on the head by his teachers about but it was true. The student following me talked about his blue Power Ranger. I was stuck between a horse and fantasy, yet what I was speaking about was full of more life and truth than either.

My first memories of cross country came as I peered through the chain link fence on the Sun Willows Golf Course in Pasco, Washington. I watched as Matt Davis in the neon lime green jersey of Mead High School run what appeared to be a solo race at state. Walking around that state championship course on a yearly basis I saw the Mead sweatshirt and the years added to the back of it signifying the number of championships they had won. I saw this sweatshirt over the years at regionals, I saw it at the dual meets, I saw it on the backs of parents and grandparents proud to show up and support their boys. I saw Pat Tyson with his hat on and his hordes of athletes, parents, and supporters that followed him everywhere. I even remember seeing Pat Tyson at our dining room table one night as my parents had invited him over as a means of getting to know him better.

Tyler Byers and I rode the same bus to and from school. His siblings would sit and talk to my siblings about anything and everything. I would see Tyler compete at various cross country and track meets.

My cousins attended University High School and joined the cross country and track teams simply because they had seen my brother Isaac run and thought they could do it too. I saw University's Bob Barbero, that Einstein look alike, instrument the first of a series of wins over Mead.

I saw Mike Hadway's spaghetti western like stare and toughness as he would warm up with his team, then race along the course shouting at his guys to keep pace and get the guy in front of them. He gave everything he had to those few who were willing to give everything to him.

I ran in Fit for Bloomsday, a program that never would have happened had Don Kardong not started Bloomsday. I saw Fit for Bloomsday championed by Sylvia Quinn. I saw Sylvia at meets with my sisters, but more often I saw her on the roads in front of my house training.

I first remember hearing Don Kardong's name when my mother told my brother Ben that he would take out Don's daughter since she had asked him to go to Lewis & Clark's Sadie Hawkins dance. My mother informed Ben that he was sure to show up on time, to be respectful, and make sure she had fun.

Rick Riley came to my awards banquet in cross country during my sophomore year and brought with him his team USA jacket he earned as a representative of our country. He spoke about the mileage and dedication he had and the results that followed, in simple, matter of fact terms. After listening to him, he made it seem like anyone could earn a spot on the USA team if they were willing to work for it.

Tracy Walters I saw sitting in the stands at track meets watching and cheering. I knew he coached Gerry, I knew he had gone to Tokyo and that he was one of the greatest coaches of all time, but he simply was a nice grandpa looking figure sitting in the stands booming his voice about as he cheered. I remember hearing his voice announce at the Mooberry relays which is a track fundraiser hosted at Rogers High School on a yearly basis.

Herm Caviness I saw at track meets in the pole vault pit, helping various athletes and representing various teams throughout the years. After Herm retired from Ferris he never retired from being a volunteer coach. Herm would even be the man I asked to perform my marriage ceremony to my wife.

Dave Fuller would coach up my competition in middle school at Chase, which is Sacajawea's rival, but then all those rivals became my teammates at Ferris as we rose up and tried to make our push to a state title.

I saw the very grandfather of modern distance running, the coach himself, Arthur Lydiard, as he came through Spokane on his tour of the United States in October of 2004. I sat in Lewis & Clark's theatre and listened as this 87 year old sage sat on the stage and spoke about how Americans were fat, lazy, and did not know how to train properly. He would die only two months later, but he spoke with a quiet intensity and assurance that I am sure resonated with his athletes Peter Snell, Murray Hallberg, and Barry Magee.

In my youth I seemed to think that every town had a legacy of running like Spokane. Only in the years after I left Spokane did I come to realize the unique blend of coaches and athletes that has made it a wonder to the world of distance running. It seemed like all roads to running led to Spokane, or at the very least, went through it. And so I began to run, following the path outlined before me, trying to keep my eyes up and my hopes alive.

Prior to my freshman year I took part in various sports in middle school. I ran cross country, I wrestled, I played basketball, and I ran track. I was the only student to participate in all four sports at Sacajawea, seventh or eighth grade and I was recognized with a plaque from the school signifying the achievement. I did not know that life could be any different than participating in sports. I thought everyone did it.

Little did I know that the basketball hoops on houses would serve as a marker for a forgotten time period in America. These abandoned hoops would represent a time when the youth of the country spent their efforts outdoors achieving, instead of inside on Xbox's and Wii's living virtual lives of achievement in their air conditioned, fridge like status.

I enjoyed all sports. I had more eye-hand coordination than any of my other siblings. I participated in Hoopfest, another Spokane gem, which boasts the largest three on three basketball tournament in the world. For a weekend in late June the streets of downtown Spokane are closed as makeshift basketball courts are erected and teams join together in a tournament for all ages and categories.

I was part of a team made up of members of my church so we only played Saturday, due to religious observance of the Sabbath day on Sunday. During that time playing basketball I scored from beyond the three point line, (but in Hoopfest the scoring is simply one point and two point shots). I scored 18 points in our first game of the day. That was nine three point shots (two points in the Hoopfest system) that went in. It was a great start and there were still two more games to play that day.

In seventh grade I made the varsity basketball team, a feat none of my other

© Peter Hawkins Personal Archive

Peter Hawkins; All City Race, 8th Grade

siblings had accomplished. I believed I might have a career in basketball ahead of me. Yet, I saw limited playing time, mostly students that had played with each other or against each other in AAU games were the ones playing in the varsity games. I had raw skills and talent, but there was not a coach that wanted to spend time explaining how I fit into his system.

By the time my eighth grade year came around I was put on junior varsity for basketball, even though I ran the lines faster than anyone on the team. I could hustle, but that did not translate to playing time. I was shorter than anyone on the team, and again had not been involved in AAU sports.

Wrestling was fun while I was winning but when I started to lose, it lost its savor. And so, the one sport I had loved and watched others achieve in became my own as I entered high school.

With my brother Ben's graduation from high school and my sister Liz entering her senior year, I started my freshman year. I was excited to finally have my chance to run in the meets. I was grateful that I could now write my own chapter and be in the race instead of merely watching it. I quickly discovered that watching and cheering for someone in a race was far easier than being the one in it.

Throughout the course of my freshman year I ran on the varsity squad for a few races, but got bumped off a couple of times. It was frustrating for me to not run on varsity the entire season. My assumption was that I needed to simply show up and race, and then I would win. The reality was that in running you earn every step.

However, I should have taken heart looking at the state meet results my freshman year. Ferris took third. Mt. Spokane took second and Mead won yet another title. The hope lied in the fact that the first three runners in for Ferris that day were a freshman, Ben Poffenroth, and two sophomores, Mike Quackenbush and Justin Houck. The top of our team was young, and it was good.

At Foot Locker my freshman year, I took 11th place in the freshman race. They had two heats of the freshman race, and so overall I was the 22nd fastest freshman on the west coast. The only other athlete to beat me from Washington in my race was Laef Barnes of Mead High School, he placed second.

I was encouraged by what could happen and approached winter training as a badge of honor. I wanted to improve and knew that in order to do so I would need to train like my siblings had done. My father had an analogy to running revolving around finances. Each mile in the offseason was like a deposit into the bank; when the end of the season came, all of the previous hard work that had been saved could now be cashed out. I started to put money in the bank.

Throughout the offseason I trained and when track came around I thought I would be on varsity, but again, I had only a few races that I ran on varsity. For my freshman year of track I hoped to make it to districts and run in it like Isaac had done as a freshman, but that did not happen. I ended up running in the JV All City Race. Comparisons were unfriendly to make, but being a sibling, you could not help make comparisons. Brothers and sisters efforts became a measuring stick for oneself. Another problem with comparisons is the over-simplistic analysis that comes from comparisons.

Isaac had finished 10th in his freshman race at Foot Locker and Ben had finished 21st. I had finished 11th in my heat of the freshman race but 22nd overall. Unfortunately as a kid I shaped my views in terms of absolutes. Like any fourteen or fifteen year old I wanted to win. I did not want to work hard and lose. To me, success was only winning, and winning at the very top. I did not have a grasp for what losing really meant. All I knew was that I did not want to lose.

The track season came and went quickly. For a race or two I would run varsity, typically the two mile because no one wanted to spend eight laps running around the track. Then I would be in a JV meet running in the mile. I learned a lot about myself, I learned about my teammates, and what leadership could be or a lack of leadership could mean for a team.

My personal records in track that freshman year were 4:52 in the mile and 10:25 in the two mile. Again I made comparisons. I was faster than Ben in the mile at my age and in the two mile, but I was still well back of Isaac. I felt like I was running between two packs. I was stuck in no man's land. I had not seen this story before, and did not know where it went.

Ferris' distance team was young and I was fighting against some young athletes that were very competitive and very strong. The sophomores above me and my own freshman class that ran varsity would all go on to run Division I in cross country and track. I did not know that was the future of my team, all I knew was that I was on a talented team.

The offseason came and I welcomed the opportunity to work and improve. With two seniors gone, I knew that I would have a great opportunity to run on varsity and score points for the team. The summer came and with it the opportunity to put more money in the bank. I had not gone to districts and I had not gone to state. I wanted to achieve those goals in my sophomore year.

Falling Behind

I did make varsity my sophomore year. I was excited to wear the varsity uniform and be part of the varsity squad as a sophomore. Our team was still young; there were only three seniors on varsity, Cody Kunz, Ian Chestnutt, and Chris Lewis followed by two juniors, Mike Quackenbush and Justin Houck, and two sophomores, Ben Poffenroth and myself. Yet, over the course of the season I had my spot on varsity challenged by two teammates, fellow sophomores Brendan Chestnutt and Greg Kleweno. There was also a freshman on the team that looked promising in Robert Cosby. Our team was fairly young and fairly talented.

As the cross country season approached the end there was a district championship race that was held on the far north side of Spokane. On the same day of the varsity race they held the JV and Freshman All-City Races. This usually does not occur. Typically the JV and Freshman All-City Races are held by themselves. I was running in the varsity race and had my worst race of the season at the worst possible moment. I finished near the very back of the pack and was passed by Mead's seventh runner that day as I ran towards the finish. Had I gone with that Mead runner and fought to pass him in the last four hundred meters I would have run fast enough to go on to regionals.

I did not realize the consequences of the race until after passing through the finishing chute. The consequences of giving up had not caught up to me. I gave mediocre effort and was still on a great young team.

As I made my way to my warm-up gear and training shoes I heard that my time was beat by two of my teammates. Brendan Chestnutt beat it by four seconds and Greg Kleweno had beat it by two. Brendan would be on varsity.

Reality struck.

I went from being on varsity, to being the second alternate on the team heading to regionals and state.

I was angry at myself, angry at my performance, and angry at how I had let a moment go so carelessly. I had seen past races of others and seen their mistakes in their sophomore year. For another week I showed up with some zeal in my legs and heart, but realized the only way I would get into the race was if two of our varsity squad went down with either injury or illness.

At regionals, one of the varsity squad, Mike Quackenbush, was nursing a sore calf and so it was decided that he sit out the race. Suddenly, Greg Kleweno was in the race and now I was the first alternate. No other teammate was ill or injured and so I would watch from the sidelines, another regional race.

I watched as not only Brendan Chestnutt, but Greg Kleweno were now racing on the varsity squad. At regionals the one that did not beat the other would be kicked off of varsity going into state. Brendan had a poor showing at regionals and so Greg Kleweno would be the unlikely seventh man heading into the state race.

I replayed over and over in my mind what had happened. Had I finished stronger by just four seconds, I would have been on varsity and had I finished just two seconds faster, I would have been back on varsity with a chance to stay on the team. I had heard of the sophomore blues, but now I was the one singing them.

Again, I made my way back to Sun Willows Golf Course to watch the state meet. I had the sinking realization that half of my high school racing was almost over. I could not go back and rewrite those first two years. I had only two more years to go, and I felt like I had not even started.

I watched as Mead again won, being led by a sophomore Laef Barnes who finished third overall. Laef's teammates Evan Garber and Geoff Greer finished fourth and fifth overall. The Mead machine was back. Six of the top ten individual finishers were from Spokane. Eisenhower High School from Yakima took second as a team and Ferris came in third.

 Walking back to the car from the state meet, I thought over how two years had gone by and I had not competed in state. Ben had competed in his sophomore year. Isaac had competed in his freshman year. I was the first Hawkins boy to not compete at state in either my freshman or sophomore years. Comparisons were clouding my judgement, but I felt like I could not escape them. Again, unfair comparisons continued to be connected in my mind.

I could not help but think of how Laef Barnes of Mead, whom I had raced against in Foot Locker nearly a year previous, now took third overall at state. Mead won and it looked like Laef was the star on the rise. Not only was the state meet over, it looked like the future had already been written.

It all seemed like a script I had seen before. Mead has the top individual runner and the top team, and Ferris as a team cannot pull out the victory. For a second straight year, Ferris took third at state. All I could see was a reinforcement of negativity. I had not believed in fate before, but now I started to act defeated.

At Foot Locker my sophomore year, I decided to enter the Seeded Race. If I was held out of state, I would not be held out of Foot Locker. However, I finished 208th out of 236. I was not having an Isaac like experience.

In the Seeded Race at Foot Locker that year Galen Rupp would be in the race and as a junior he would go on to qualify for Nationals. Little did I know he would be the running sensation of his generation in America.

Rumors sprung up about Galen's altitude tent he slept in and his coach Alberto Salazar in high school. Little did we know that he would go on to be a silver medalist in the 10,000 meter race in the 2012 London Olympics.

The winter came and with it some motivation to try. I wanted instant results in a sport that requires years of effort before ultimate payoffs.

The track season came and went as quickly as any season before. I improved in track, running 4:42 in the mile and 10:05 in the two mile. I made it to districts in the two mile, but did not qualify for regionals.

I sat at the regional meet and watched as a trio of Mead runners, lead by Evan Garber, finished in the top three slots of the two mile and the mile race. I watched as my own teammate and classmate Ben Poffenroth ran in the 800 meter and the mile and qualified for state.

At state the Mead trio was broken up in the mile and two mile but they still all placed in the top five slots of the mile and the two mile, with Garber winning the two mile. The season came to a close and I felt like there was still a lot of ground to cover between where I thought I was and where I knew I could be. I felt my future in running had been foreclosed. I knew what state winning times sounded like and I knew where my own times were, and I knew that it would take a miracle coupled with hard work to have any chance of achieving my dreams.

Enduring Doubts

Prior to the start of my junior year in 2003, I went to a training camp up in Glacier National Park with Ferris' team. It was a fun experience, one that I had participated in each year prior to the start of the cross country season. I loved the runs and the trails, but every time I went out to run, thoughts of disappointment filled my mind. I was not seeing why there was still hope, I was starting to lock the door on my future before it had ever really opened.

My biggest fear, like any athlete, was failure.

I knew that I needed to push the pace in order to win, but I had not done the work necessary to succeed. In the time when I absolutely needed to buckle down and train, I was effectively walking away. I did not want to confront the fact that running demands best efforts consistently. I could push the pace for the beginning of runs but I could not sustain any pace for the duration of a run. I was not pulling away from my teammates, I was barely holding on to the pace they were pushing.

Since I was a Hawkins, and it was summer, I worked. I had a job at my uncle's candy store in the mall. I would sit and think over where I was with the running as customers came and went and I manned the till. I would run, work, and think over how this next season would play out.

Instead of facing the facts and deciding to train with my teammates that were all invested, some for their final season, I decided to start running on my own. The practices I put myself through were not difficult. The pace slowed, the doubts mounted with every step, and I started to come to a standstill.

At work, I considered the analogy my father had made of running being miles in the bank. I knew I had not put enough in the bank to have a big pay day coming my way. I knew by the end of the season I would be running in the red. My mileage dropped, my confidence was abandoned, and my running became hollow. I was a shell out there putting in a few miles each day.

After a lackluster practice by myself, I decided that I would likely quit. Why go through another season of disappointment when I could just quit and save myself the pain?

My father approached me after one of these lackluster efforts, while I walked down the driveway towards the house. He could see that I was hardly sweating.

"How are you going to compete if you're not out there working hard?" he asked.

"I'm done. I quit." I said.

My father was caught off guard. He had not expected me to quit. None of his kids had quit at anything. Here I was, a kid that had sat alongside him on countless road trips to and from races, who had briefed and debriefed races on Isaac, Emily, Ben and Liz, and now I was approaching the age of an adult and saying I did not want anything to do with it.

My Dad was stunned by what I had said and stood there blinking at me.

"Oh really, well, explain that to your brother," he said.

Dad then pulled out his cell phone and dialed up Isaac who was down at Stanford, training in preparation for his team's training camp at the time.

"Hey Ike, Dad here, Peter your brother has decided that he wants to quit running but I told him he would have to explain to you why he's quitting," Dad said.

With that he handed the phone over to me.

Here I was, standing in the driveway after a five mile run that I had hardly sweated through, and now with my brother on the other end of the line, and my father staring at me, I finally started to sweat.

"Pete, what's going on?" Isaac asked.

Here I was, on the phone, separated by distance, separated by time, but feeling so close to failure. I was confronting my great inspiration to the sport, who had conquered and persevered, and I could only shrink.

"I'm not going to win, and I'm not in great shape, and it's hard, and I can't do it." I said. "I don't care anymore."

I did what any good quitter does: they lie.

I voiced the inner thoughts of rationalization that had been running around in my head more than I had been running around in practice that summer. I was trying to talk myself out of trying. I had exercised my doubts more than I had exercised my faith in the future.

The biggest lie I told to myself was that I did not care. After I said that line to Isaac, that I had been feeding myself for months, I began to cry.

I did care.

Every quitter cares deeply.

The problem with quitting is not in caring, it is in caring about all the elements outside of your control that do not matter.

"Well, tell me where this all started. What has your training been like? What's got you feeling this way?" Isaac asked.

My Dad simply stared at me as I stood there, crying, and trying to find my way through this moment. If I were to go out a quitter, my Dad would let me feel everything that went with it. My Dad listened through the silence and heard bits and pieces of Isaac on the other side.

"I don't know." I said. Another lie.

I knew exactly when this negativity had started. It had lingered and festered over a season, since I had not made it to state in my sophomore year and I had been crushed at Foot Locker in my sophomore year. I had resigned myself to the fact that distance running is not simply about wanting something. There was a very real price to pay for success, and I was not willing to pay for it at that moment.

"Come on, talk to me." Isaac said.

I was trying to shrink, and my father and brother were wanting me to stand. I stood there, trying to clip my own wings, and there was my father and brother, trying to give me the wind to go beneath them.

"I go into practice and I get beat by Houck, Quackenbush, Poffenroth, Chestnutt, and even now a guy younger than me Cosby is starting to beat me." I said.

This was the first true statement I had uttered aloud in the whole conversation. I did not like the feeling that I was losing. I did not think I could live up to the comparisons. I thought the weight of the family name was too much.

"Pete, this happens, not just to you, but this happens to everyone." Isaac said. "I am down here on Stanford's team, and it's like you trying to make it on your team. You are working, you are trying, and then you got guys on your team that work or that are talented, or that are talented and work and you're thinking to yourself, *How do I survive this?*" Isaac said.

Isaac struggled.

Isaac, the one who had seemingly won everything in high school, was struggling.

What I was feeling, others had felt, and not only people at the back of the pack; it happened to people at the very front. My brother Isaac, whom I had hardly ever see lose a race, was in the fight of his life on Stanford's squad. While I, as a sophomore in 2002, was feeling sorry for myself at state, Isaac stood on the sidelines watching as his college team had four finishers in the top ten at Nationals. Four of the finishers were all juniors. Their fifth man that day was a sophomore by the name of Ryan Hall who would eventually compete in the marathon at the Beijing and London Olympics. Not a single runner on Isaac's varsity squad at Stanford that day would graduate. Isaac was running against Foot Locker finalists in every practice; Isaac was running against other Isaac's, more talented Isaac's, and he was getting his clock cleaned.

"There are two options Pete. You can walk away, or you can hold on and fight it out to the very end. And while you fight it out you adapt, you change, you figure out what works and you abandon what doesn't. You have to navigate the options and realities. While you are out there running you should be thinking over every reason why something should be working out instead of every reason why it shouldn't. If you approach running and life like that, what can't you do?" Isaac said.

As true as his statements were, I was not wanting to give up the fight of defeat I had already won in myself. Quitting was the only victory I felt I had in my win column and I was certain of it. Why trade the certainty of quitting for the uncertainty of another season in my junior year?

"Life is difficult Pete. Running is difficult. You have to take care of the details. What is your mileage at for this week?" Isaac asked.

"I don't know." I said. I knew exactly how far I had run. "40 miles," I said. It was a Friday night and since I did not run Sunday, likely I would only get 50-55 miles in for the week.

It was the last week in July. I should have been investing everything and running double that amount. I wanted to win but I was not willing to work for it.

"Well, you will need to up the mileage and you will need to talk to yourself better while you are out there. All you have to do is put yourself in a position to be in the race. If you don't do that, then you'll never have a shot at winning anything." Isaac said.

The conversation continued. Truth was being told to me in every line. I had my brother who was on one of the nation's best teams ever, giving me sound advice on running, on adversity, on work, and on life. I had my own hero, telling me the fight was not over and that I could still do it. I could win something if I put myself in a position to be there.

Yet, I still wanted to compare. I still wanted to validate myself and my decision making. I wanted to be the exception. The rules did not apply to me.

The phone conversation ended and tearfully I turned to my father and told him I would not quit. I told him I would give it one more season and one more try.

I finally closed my Dad's cell phone and he looked at me as I handed it back to him.

"Life is competition. You think running is hard, try being a father. You think it is difficult getting beat in a race, trying getting beat in the business world. We do this running not to win championships, we do it because it gives us a skill set for life and you will need this skill set. If you quit now you will quit everyday for the rest of your life." He said.

"Because if you quit now and adopt that attitude of a quitter then you will only go until something becomes difficult, and the moment something gets hard, you will walk away," he said, still looking at me. He was trying to stamp out my defeatist attitude. He wanted to shine some light of truth in my dark outlook.

We were all on the line in that moment. Isaac as a brother. Paul as a father. This was not a moment for any of us to walk away from.

"Life is difficult. Relationships are difficult. Work is difficult. You need to learn how to embrace adversity, not run away from it." He said. Then after a pause, he continued, "Now let's talk about your training."

My father outlined a training program to build up a base in only four weeks before the season started. I would run at each practice and try to push the pace at least twice a week, and the other times, I would at the very least run with the top guys. Also, for the final four weeks of the summer, my Saturdays would be different. After my early morning run of 15 miles I would then get on a bike and ride out to the state line between Washington and Idaho from my house. My Dad accompanied me on the rides out and back to the state line. Those bike rides were a 60 mile experience round trip each Saturday.

My father knew I could not run all the miles I had failed to accomplish in the summer up to that point because that would lead to injury. The most important thing I could do was elevate my heart-rate and build some confidence. So I ran, I biked, and I put myself in a position to at least be on varsity for my junior year of high school.

I had improved over the course of my freshman and sophomore years by running conversational pace in the offseason for most of my runs. Occasionally I would push the pace, but the level of intensity required to really accelerate my progression had rarely surfaced.

I thought that somehow since I had shown up to races in the past and seen how the great ones did it that somehow I would step on the course and magically be in front, pain free and crushing it.

I did not realize that in order to crush it you have to be crushed, and then rested, rebuilt and then crushed again. Running was a process, not an event. Simply running miles did not equate to wins. Quality miles equaled quality races. As simple and monotonous as running is, the miracle of the sport lies in the minutia. It is purposeful practice in every run, intense or rested, that through the course of seasons and years can create someone into a great athlete.

The season started and I made varsity, but I was not running where I thought

I should be. There was a great disconnect in my mind; I thought I should be winning, yet I knew I had not worked for it. I would embrace ultimate victory or ultimate defeat. I did not like the feeling of floundering, of being just off the mark, of running in the darkness and the unknown.

I still thought that in my junior year I could win it all and miraculously make up ground on my teammates. I would take off in practices and in races at the start with my teammates but I had no base or endurance to draw upon. Once they separated from me in workouts or races my doubts from before seemed reinforced. I was a hot or cold runner: all or nothing. My mentality, as well as my training, had not set me up for success or consistency of any kind.

At various points in the season I would be the fifth man, then the sixth, and near the end of the season I was the seventh man. Most of the season I spent running the end of races in the seventh slot, coming through the chute, shaking my head and fulfilling the doubts I had carried with me since the starting line.

Trailing Forevermore

The lowest point of my season and my experience in running came only four weeks before the state meet in 2003.

Ferris traveled to the Jim Danner Invite down in Oregon for a high quality meet. At the race would be Central Catholic High School, where Galen Rupp ran, along with Mead High School and Ferris. All were great schools and all had great talent on their teams. Alberto Salazar, the famed University of Oregon graduate who was a three time New York City Marathon winner, a Boston Marathon winner, and an Olympic marathoner, was coaching Galen Rupp at the time at Central Catholic. Pat Tyson, the heart of distance running had Mead in top shape again and looked poised to rattle off another nine straight state titles. Then there was Coach Hadway, the strawberry blond haired, pale boy from Rogers of Puyallup High School. He had run on great teams, but had been unrecognized because they were not Division I at the time. He had trained with Kardong, he had run with the best and trained some of the best individual athletes, male and female in the country, yet his team had never won state.

All of these coaches and their athletes showed up to race in this Nike sponsored meet. The race took place at the Tualatin-Hills Park & Recreation Complex. The race would wind through some early turns, disappearing on a wood chip path through a forested area before returning back to the park area and the finish.

I knew that after this race there would be another dual meet, regionals, and then finally state. I had four meets to get it right, when everything had been going wrong.

After warming up with the team and striding out, it came time to take off the warm-ups and get into the box of the starting line.

As the starting marshal raised the gun into the air, I crouched and thought over the moment and the opportunity before me.

The gun fired.

I shot towards the front.

Through the first two hundred meters it was a sprint, then the next two hundred was still ahead of race pace, then four hundred meters more I was running, finally at race pace, but by that half mile mark I was clearly in oxygen debt.

At this point, Houck passed me, then Quackenbush, followed by Poffenroth, Chestnutt, Cosby and Kleweno. I was the seventh man and I was not done fading.

Off into the woods everyone disappeared and I ran, lost not in a dream but a nightmare. I could not breathe. I could not escape. I had thought about quitting before the season started and now I wanted to quit the race. The pace was pathetic. I was tempted to just walk off the course outlined before me.

The ghosts of Isaac, Emily, Ben, and Liz all went on with those in the race, and I was clearly out of it. I realized that I would be trailing these people, my family and any others who had charged at greatness, forevermore.

I realized I could not escape them even if I did walk off the course.

I kept on the course, I came out of the woods, and eventually crossed the finish line in last place. Had the JV come and raced I would have been off of varsity.

My father watched me come out of the finishing chute and still claimed me as his own. He loved all of his kids and he loved watching them compete. However, even he realized at that moment that what had just happened was not competition, but the sign of something clearly wrong.

"I don't want to go to Foot Locker." I said. "If the season ends like this, I will quit. I want to quit right now, but I won't. I will see it out, but this was awful."

My father tried to keep me going.

"Pete, you can't go out and try to win the race. You haven't done the work to win the race. You need to run where you think you can realistically run, and then shoot for just beyond that. Don't look so far ahead. Don't look to Foot Locker or state. Just look to the next race. Where do you think you can realistically run?" Dad said.

"I think I can be the fifth man." I said.

"Well, today you were seventh and Kleweno was sixth, so maybe shoot for Kleweno. If you block out everyone else and you are right there with Kleweno and it's just you two out there running, do you think you can beat him?" Dad asked.

He was trying to make something so big be something so small. Instead of 5,000 meters it became the five feet between me and Kleweno; that was all I had to manage.

"Alright, I will aim for Kleweno." I said. We went from my warm-up gear over to the awards ceremony.

I watched with my teammates as Mead won the meet, Rupp had won individually, and Ferris took third overall.

Hadway then came to me, Cosby, and Kleweno and said, "You three are driving with me back to Spokane."

In the car we climbed and sat in the backseat of my Dad's car as he drove and Hadway sat shotgun looking back at us and telling us, "One of you three has to step up."

Cosby, Kleweno, and I all looked at each other and off into the distance. The sun was setting in the west and we were in a car heading east, right into the darkness.

"If one of you three can come through for the team, we can win state. I know you are all upset with your season and with the way the meet went today, but I have looked at the numbers and the results and I believe we can still do it." Hadway said. His eyes held certainty. Since 1986 he fought for his team to win and for 16 years the closest they had come was second place. He wanted to win as much as anyone.

Hadway knew what he was talking about. Mead only had two runners in the top ten, Ferris also had two runners in the top ten. We were matched up evenly all except for our fifth man. Had our team plugged in our fifth runner in a reliable position, then we could have edged out Mead and Central Catholic that day.

"I know you all want to be number one on the team, but you can't go out like a bat out of hell in the first part of the race and then die," Hadway said, looking at me. "You have to go out and hang with Chestnutt. If one of you will do that, then we can win the state title. Mead is not invincible."

Hadway was speaking as much to himself as he was to his athletes. Hadway had great teams in the past, but they had lost to Mead. Even when he had Isaac, Paul Harkins and Dave Schruth going 1,2,5, they still took second. When Ben was a senior and the team had beaten Mead twice during the season, they had fallen right at state. There had never been a solid fifth runner coupled with the solid four runners before him.

I stared out at the darkening sky.

"Don't give up. We have three weeks until state. Today was not state. We had a great opportunity to see where Mead is at and what we need to do to win. We can do it." Hadway said. He had not given up hope. He could see the win and wanted it just as badly as the three of us sitting in the back seat.

Into the darkness we drove back to Spokane, not getting in until two in the morning. Hadway kept talking and tried to tend to the fragile minds of teenage racers sitting in the back seat.

Positive Statements

Throughout the fall I had done my morning runs and ran hill repeats before going off to seminary. While running my hill repeats in the morning I had envisioned myself on the state course, cresting the hill in victory. Since the Jim Danner race and the conversation with my father, I shifted that vision to me cresting the hill and chasing after my teammate Brendan Chestnutt in front of me. For the next three weeks, I would be chasing him, passing by my teammates Cosby and Kleweno as I reached the top of the hill.

It was easier to pass the ghosts I ran against in the morning than the teammates in the flesh.

At the next dual meet at Finch Arboretum it was raining. The course consists of hill running. There is not a flat section on the course at all. It is a race of climbs and falls, a course Dr. Seuss would have drawn.

In the race I did not charge to the front but tried to hang with Chestnutt as long as possible, but once he separated and I started to float backward, I did not let Cosby or Kleweno fly by me. When they came up to pass me, I hung with them.

I did what I needed to do the whole time; cling to what I knew I could do and build from it.

I did not get lost in the race and I did not get swept out the back of the pack. I held on to Cosby and Kleweno, keeping them in my sights. I responded and held close to the five yards I said I would die on because I knew I could at least stay there.

The dual meet ended and I finished seventh, but it was not a bad finish. I had some confidence.

Next up was regionals, up in Deer Park. It would be a cold race, the coldest race I would ever run in as the temperature was in the low teens or single digits. I made the trek north, knowing that I would not be kicked off varsity, knowing that I would be going on to state, and knowing that with something to hold on to I could piece together something and perhaps come through and be the fifth man.

As the race got underway I got out to a bad start. My teammates all took off very well, but I did not. I had to work my way up. I did not panic, although the feeling was uncomfortable. I eventually saw in the distance Kleweno and Cosby. I was moving up and making my way through the competitors in front of me for the first time all season. As the race came to a close, rather quickly, I remember I had come to within five seconds of Rob, who was the sixth runner that day, and I felt I still had some speed left in my legs.

I had done something I had not done all season; I had passed people during the second half of the race. Here, one race before state I had done something different, I had passed people late and told myself I could do it.

All season long I had gone out, tried to hold an impossible pace and then struggled to hold on as people had passed me. In reality, my entire running career had followed that pattern: go out hard, die, hold on and hope not too many people passed me. I ran this way because that was how I was introduced to running. Matt Davis jumped to the lead at Mead. My brother Isaac was always in the lead. The books on Pre echoed how he was up front. Gerry also shot to the front and stayed there. I had refused to look at racing differently.

Surprisingly Eisenhower took first at regionals that day, the first time that a non Spokane school had won the regional race for almost twenty years. Ferris had taken second place, Mead was third, and Mt. Spokane was fourth. Although Mead took third, their top two runners had finished first and second overall.

The race had been bitterly cold. Perhaps it was an off day for everyone. With the state race in Pasco, the temperature was usually no lower than the thirties and could reach as high as the mid fifties.

The day before the state race we drove to Pasco and previewed the course. On the morning before I went to school that morning, my mother stood in the kitchen cooking some eggs and french toast. She stood, tired as ever, and slowly moved about the kitchen preparing lunches for her three remaining children.

As she finished flipping the french toast and while she went to get the lunches ready, she spoke to me.

"Peter, you just need to do your best from the very beginning to the very end. If you do that, that's all that anyone can ask of themselves." She said.

The woman who had taught the lesson, over and over again, to vote for yourself, was doing so one more time, but just with different words. With her words in my mind, I took my lunch and went to school.

After being released from my classes early in the day, the team met up in Hadway's wood shop, and then went out to his green Astro van. We were on our way to state. Before I knew it the miles had passed and we were on the state course.

I remember being on the other side of the fence for the first time. I would not be a spectator but a competitor. I was finally on the other side of the fence and running along the rolling fairways with my team.

I finally saw the mile mark, I saw the outer rim leading towards the two mile, I saw the final charge along the backside before the rise up the hill and down to the finish. I was struck by how quickly the finish came up and how soon after you crested the hill that you came into the finish.

All the previous years of watching, waiting, and filing away the phrase, *When it's my turn I will …* had now come. I was a day away from state.

That night, our team ate pizza since all the local pasta places were slammed with athletes waiting to carbo-load. We ordered out Papa John's Pizza and ate from our hotel. My teammates watched a movie together while I sat in the room with coach Hadway and coach Fuller watching a western. The evening came to a close and we all finally went to bed, trying not to think too hard about the race the next day.

Everything went quickly the day of state. The light morning jog came quickly, the breakfast, the handing out of the race bibs, the pinning the bibs on our jerseys, the final checkout of the hotel, and the drive to the meet all passed by rather fast. As fast as everything went we still did not make it over to the course until nearly midday.

Our team placed our campout in isolation, above the first hill and off in the distance from everyone. We laid about on the grass, each athlete doing what made them most comfortable. Some were listening to music, others were trying to sleep, some nervously pulled at the grass around them.

The 4A classification always ran the last races of the day and so we waited. A gun would fire and then a sea of jerseys and athletes would surge by, and we would stare, then go back to our own reverie, trying to contain the thoughts that were racing in our own minds.

Finally it came time to warm up and we bolted from the course and made our way under the overpass and towards a park. We stretched, did strides, and stretched some more. It was a warm day in comparison to the week prior. As I stretched, I remember Hadway coming to each athlete and telling them they could do it. He came to me.

"You can do this. We can win today. Do your best." He said.

It came time to run back to our bags and fish out our singlets and spikes.

Quickly we changed our spikes, quickly we changed into our singlets, and then put our warm up tops back on and began to stride out. I felt loose, I felt excited, and surprisingly calm.

I was going to finally run in the state meet. Lining up after our team circled up above the first hill and outlined a game plan from our captains, I felt grateful. I believed we could win state, and I believed I could have a good race. After a fairly disappointing season I still had one moment to redeem the time I had wasted.

I just needed to do my very best from the beginning to the very end.

Our team's spot at the start was not favorable. We were on the far left side of the starting line. The start leads directly into a hill only forty meters away, and then the course rises, plateaus and turns to the left. If our team had a slow start, we would be sandwiched behind teams.

The gun was raised and shot.

Relaxed and loose I went out with my team's leaders. I saw my teammate Cosby shoot out towards the front. I kept calm and made it up the first hill and towards the left. Luckily, we had not been boxed in. The teams to our right, had also recognized the fate of getting stuck and so they luckily veered more towards the right, thus keeping our team from getting boxed in.

Through that first mile we climbed gradually upward. A small pack was starting to separate as we veered left again and made our way towards the first mile marker. I could see the jerseys in front of me and I could make a quick count: Houck, Quackenbush, Poffenroth, and Chestnutt, then me. I was in Ferris' fifth spot.

Start of State Championship
Left to right - Peter Hawkins; Ben Poffenroth; Rob Cosby;
Brendan Chestnut; Justin Houck; Mike Quackenbush; Greg Kleweno

I did not focus in on the Mead athletes or Eisenhower at that moment. I saw where I was, I saw how the race was developing, and I saw that there were two packs opening up: the lead pack and the chase pack. I was stuck between the two groups being threaded out.

As I approached the 180 degree turn just after the mile mark, a wall of noise crashed about from either side. Amidst the noise I said to myself, *If I'm going to have any chance in this race I have to go with that lead group and I have to go now.*

The race was being played out in real time and I needed to react, not think. In that instant, I saw Mike Hartnov from Mt. Spokane pass me. I knew that Mike was a good runner and that he would be running up towards the front of the pack all season and so I blocked out everyone else in the race and decided that I would just focus in on his back and stay as close to him as possible. Mike began to pass people and I went with him. For only the second time all season I began to pass people after the first mile. Out towards the lonely quiet corner of the race we ran, Mike passing people and me sticking with him.

As we came towards the two mile and in front of the wall of noise, I saw Mike make a strong move; I could not make that strong of a move. The man I needed and had held to was now out of reach.

I went back to trying to figure out where I was and I saw Chestnutt in the distance; we were making our way towards the final turn up the hill. I knew the finish was close.

At this moment, I heard from someone in the crowd, "Go Mead, get that Ferris runner!"

I quickly looked over my shoulder as we ran up the hill and saw not one but two Mead runners behind me.

The morning runs from before came back to me as almost instinct. I started to climb the hill and as I did I said to myself, thinking of those Mead athletes:

Not today!

There was no way that anyone from Mead was going to pass me in the last 100 meters. I had faded in races before, I had faded in seasons before, but on this day, at state, at this moment, I knew that nothing wearing neon green would pass me in the last 100 meters.

I gave everything I had and bolted toward the finish with my head shaking and arms pumping. Before I knew it, the race was over. I ran into the runner in front of me and did not mean to shove them but I looked back over my shoulder and saw that indeed no Mead runner had passed me.

As I came to grips with what had just happened I looked to my right and saw jumping in the air Steve Kiesel, former teammate of Mike Hadway's, who was coaching at Rogers High School at the time. He shouted at me, "Peter, you did it."

I knew I had beaten the two Mead guys behind me, but I did not know which numbers they were for Mead. For all I knew they could be Mead's sixth and seventh runners, in which case Mead's fifth was ahead of me and likely we had lost the state title.

Out of the finishing chute I went and immediately became bear hugged by my father who was crying and trying to speak. Then out of nowhere came Coach Hadway, hugging me as well. He too was crying and trying to compose himself. The phrase he repeated over and over again was, "I think we got it."

Then my younger brother Tommy, with his chubby rosy cheeks came around with my younger brother Paul Jr. He looked up at me through his glasses with pure joy in his eyes.

"I think you guys won Pete! Paul said you beat the Mead guys that were right behind you; did you hear me cheering for you?" Tommy said, all earnest and excited.

I knew I had raced well. I knew that it was my best race of the season by far; yet I still was not sure if we had pulled it out. No one was sure. All that was known for sure was that Mead, Ferris, and Eisenhower each had a pair of runners in the top ten. Besides that, the remaining jerseys had been lost in the sea of runners.

Off we went to switch footwear and to get into our warm ups, then we made our way to the awards stand.

Eisenhower had won regionals the week before and they had done so with a runaway victory of almost twenty five points. Mead, you could never count out.

Back in my warm ups and with my team we went to the awards ceremony. On our way I saw Cosby with eyes red and moist. He was having a tough time. He had gone out hard and ran immediately into oxygen debt and felt he might have cost the team the victory. He was going through his own sophomore blues. He had finished seventh for us and felt terrible about his performance.

As a team we waited behind the podium and listened to the announcer as he began to rattle off the names of schools in reverse order.

"In 16th place Capital with 374 points, in 15th place Ballard with 328 points," He said. There was general applause and then there was the waiting.

"In fourth place, from Spokane, Washington," we waited, "Mt. Spokane High School with 140 points." We had not placed fourth. For the past two years we had placed third.

"In third place, from Spokane, Washington," we waited, "Mead High School with 115 points." Mead took to the podium. Their three straight years as state champions had come to a close. It was now between Eisenhower and Ferris.

Everyone had been so caught up with watching for Mead's neon green that perhaps we should have been focused on Eisenhower's blue and red. Could we have won it?

As Mead made their way off the podium we waited for that PA announcer.

"In second place, from Yakima-" cheers erupted from Ferris athletes, families and coaches.

We had won.

Eisenhower took second, edging out Mead by two points with a score of 113. Eisenhower walked up sullen from the reality that a week ago they had run away from Ferris and Mead, but now they were second place.

As Eisenhower's team walked up the podium a news reporter came over to my team and sought me out.

"What made the difference today Peter?" he asked.

I did not know what to say. Three weeks ago, I had planned on walking away from the sport and now I was on the winning team, clinching it as the fifth man and I was being interviewed for the first time in my life.

"I've not had a lot of good races this season," I said. I paused, knowing that was the truth; I had not raced well. "I needed it today," I said, "and I'll take it."

With that Eisenhower was now coming off the podium and we made our way up. The PA voice welcomed us atop the podium as we looked out over the crowd. "Your champions, from Spokane, Washington, The Saxons of Joel. E. Ferris High School scoring 91 points."

The two Mead runners coming up behind me on the hill were Mead's third and fourth place runners. Ferris had their first five in before Mead had their third.

Pictures and smiles came easily as we stood there, happy and exulting in a new experience for our team. It had been 22 years since Ferris had a team title and it was Coach Hadway's first.

We came down from the podium and off towards the pond. I did not know that it had become a tradition to throw the coach into the pond near the two mile mark, but the team went and we threw in Hadway. After he got thrown in, he came out and found me, wanting to toss me in. I did not go willingly but the water, cold as it was, was sweet.

In the midst of finding dry clothes my father came up beside me and said, "I guess we might be going to Foot Locker this year."

"I guess we are." I said.

After the win, I realized how lucky I was to be part of the team. Without Justin Houck, Mike Quackenbush, Ben Poffenroth, Brendan Chestnutt, Robert Cosby, Greg Kleweno and our JV squad, I would have never been able to be a part of a state team title. They all did their part throughout the season and on that day to give their very best.

We could have just as easily lost that day. I could have just as easily faded to seventh and walked off the course vowing to never return. I recognized, later, that Eisenhower's fourth runner from regionals had finished seventh for his team at state. The stats could have all been different at state and we may well have lost yet again.

As it was, we did win and with it came a confidence I had not known previously. I had found a way to be in the race late and I had held on.

The door on what could be seemed to burst open. Training truly became a place of belief for perhaps the first time ever.

At Foot Locker, I ran in the Seeded Race and finished 123rd overall. It was an improvement from the previous year by almost 90 spots. Evan Garber from Mead, who had won the individual title at state, went on to run at Foot Locker Nationals. Also qualifying was Galen Rupp of Central Catholic.

Winter time finally came. My brother Isaac came home for the winter break. His team had finished up their cross country season winning the national title again scoring 24 points and cutting their previous year's point total nearly in half. Ryan Hall lead the charge and came up short to Colorado's Dathan Ritzenhein for the individual title. Stanford had four runners in the top six individual slots; their fifth runner was 12th overall and their sixth runner was 13th. Before a majority of teams had their first runner in Stanford had their seventh runner coming in 33rd. None of the athletes on Stanford's team were foreign born recruits; they did not stack their team full of Kenyans and Ethiopians. Had Stanford evenly distributed their talented roster over two teams, their two teams likely would have finished first and second in the country that year. As it was, Isaac was on the second team at Stanford and did not compete at Nationals.

Isaac had not made the varsity squad his last year at Stanford. He still had an outdoor season ahead of him and he would be trying to give it his best. After serving a two-year mission for his church in the Philippines, Isaac had returned to Stanford and came back taller and heavier. Only by his senior year was he able to bring his weight down and have his training at its peak.

During the last season of his senior year, I was in the middle of my junior year. That winter break I trained with Isaac and enjoyed the opportunity to shift intensity and to speak with someone who had climbed up to one of the highest points in high school athletics.

I came to recognize that the way I thought and felt about my older siblings was likely the way my two younger brothers felt as well. I sought out opportunities to spend time with them while my last two years of high school came to a close.

My training intensity increased but it was coupled with a belief that I could improve, that I could run with people, and that the future held everything for me.

Although the Thorpe run had faded from popularity within the GSL during the offseason, I still showed up on my own, running and racing the course once a week. The lowest time I ever ran on the course was 50:45. I did not know how good of a time it was, all I knew was that I was running faster and pushing myself harder than ever before.

Along with my increased intensity in training came another job. I continued working at my uncle's candy store, and had picked up a job at Pizza Hut. They did not have me taking orders or delivering pizzas, I was the one making them. With less time, I had to make better use of the time I had. Every task had to be completed quickly and it had to be done in order. The added work was not a burden, if anything, it made me a better, more focused, more disciplined person.

With my focus set I entered my first race in track at the Banana Belt Relays in Clarkston, Washington. Coach Hadway had me signed up to run the two mile with Mike Quackenbush and Ben Poffenroth. I warmed up for the race, excited for the opportunity to see what hard work and positivity could do.

I started off the race conservative, not shooting to the front, but rather waiting for Mike Quackenbush to take the lead. He had finished eighth at the state meet that previous fall. I knew he was one of the fastest runners in the state and expected him to run like it. However, it seemed that we were going slow through the first two laps. I felt great and it did not feel like we were moving that hard.

I did not listen to the splits being yelled out as we ran by each lap. I focused on how I felt and decided to pick up the pace.

I ended up taking the lead starting the third lap and did not let go of it. I started to even build up a lead. I almost forgot that I was racing. I just kept my eyes up and pushed myself like when I was on the Thorpe run all by myself.

Finally there was the gunshot signifying the leader was entering the final lap and that leader at the time was me. I came back to thinking, instead of reacting, and thought, *I might win this thing*. As this thought came through my mind,

Mike Quackenbush had come from behind by ten meters and started to kick past me with 200 meters to go.

I tried to respond, but thought to myself, *I hope we break ten minutes.* I had half expected that Quackenbush would come back. As I crossed the finish line I finally listened to the person shouting out times.

"9:29"

I could hardly believe it.

In my first race of the season I had improved my personal record by over 36 seconds from the previous year. Although I had run an incredible time, my legs still felt fresh, as if I was getting ready for a workout.

Less than a week later, I would run my first mile of the season. A similar experience occurred. I went out conservative and then felt the pace was too slow and so I went and held the lead till there was 300 meters left and then Houck and Quackenbush both passed me. I ended up running across the finish line hearing "4:30." I had improved again, this time by 12 seconds.

The only problem I see, looking back over my racing, was my inability to not look at time. I focused too much on time and what the numbers meant. I should have ran off of how I felt, and I should have continued to start a little slower and then time my late race move.

I simply could not shake the race mentality I had seen growing up; go out hard and hold the competitor's feet to the fire till the tape. These first two races would be the fastest times I would record in the two mile and mile that year. Even though over the course of the season my mileage would drop, my times did not.

I made it to districts in the mile and two mile and raced in both, but I only qualified for regionals in the two mile.

At regionals the pace went out slow. I stayed with the leaders who happened to all be top 10 finishers at state in cross country. I did not recognize the huge jump I had made. I had gone from finishing 52nd overall in the state meet, 33rd in the team scoring, and made a leap past 40 some odd guys in front of me in a single off-season.

The slow pace continued and I remember running right beside Evan Garber, who had run at Nationals that fall. Through the first mile we went, then through a mile and a half and I was still with the leaders. The last two laps of the race were where the race was really run. When it came time to make a move, I did not and when they left I ran without confidence the last two laps and so I failed to make it to state.

I left the regional race grateful for the opportunity and grateful for the future I still had before me.

Nike Team Nationals

Heading south from the heart of Spokane's downtown there follows a steep rise in elevation, creating what is commonly referred to as the *South Hill*. This hill, if outlined would create a "C" shape, dividing itself from the Valley below it. One of my favorite workouts during the offseason of my senior year involved running around that "C" shaped ridge known to those in Spokane as the *Bluff Trails*. Most people know of a bluff as a form of deceit or posturing, but a bluff also refers to a steep incline or cliffs edge. I had gone from one bluff to another.

Once a week I would run 1,000 meter hill repeats on the bluff. Climbing those steep inclines would make me tough and exact my every effort. I would run five repeats as hard as I could and my rest and recovery was only the jog to the bottom of the hill. My run to the bluffs, the repeats, and return trip totaled around 12 miles of running.

I had done the workout during the fall of my junior year and it was the first time I had ever run it. I figured the run would be great. I ran to the trails, did the workout, and then ran back home. I was running lots of miles and the middle part demanded great intensity. One of those I dragged along with me on this run was my younger brother Paul who would be a freshman.

Isaac and Ben did not overlap in high school because they were separated in school by four years. The same was true of Ben and me. My senior year and Paul's freshman year overlapped.

I took Paul and gave him a taste of what to expect that season. To his credit he went and ran those repeats as best he could. On the way to and from the trail I was usually the only one talking and most of the time I was talking about this new race coming up, Nike Team Nationals.

Nike had seen an opportunity to enter into competition with Foot Locker for the hearts and loyalties of young distance runners by devising a way in which actual high school teams could race for a national title. Instead of Foot Locker being a championship race made out of regions and those regions creating makeshift All-Star teams out of the area, there would be the actual teams from across the country competing with each other for the national team title.

Nike Team Nationals became the title of the event and the fall of 2004 would be the first race. This race still exists today but goes under the title Nike Cross Nationals. During the first few years a team of high school sports writers and individuals at Nike would identify the top two teams in each region. Then there would be a few at large bids from areas of the country they thought held exceptional depth. Since that time, they have switched to regional qualifying meets where teams have to be in the top of their region before moving on to Nationals.

I was excited because Ferris had only graduated two seniors and our team felt like we were going to repeat with ease. My thoughts, as well as my teammates thoughts, were on winning the national title.

The season started off with our time trial to determine who was on varsity and to see where everyone was at. I ended up winning the time trial. On paper, I should have only been the third highest returner, but I had won the race.

The first big race of the season was the Stanford Invitational but the team as a whole ran terrible. It was a big race that we were leading through the first mile, but as we went up the big hill, the pack of five of us in the top ten fell apart. We all went into oxygen debt and bombed out finishing seventh at the meet. That was one awful race for all of us, but we returned to Spokane and got back to our winning ways.

The season continued and I would be near the front of races. Our team was talented and did not seem to follow any sort of order from race to race. There were times in the season when I was the number one runner, and there were times in the season when I was the number five runner. It was not just like that for me, it was like that for everyone on the team. The results were always the same, we won, but the way we did it was different. It was a pack of five that ran from our first guy to our fifth covering a span of 20 seconds. Every four seconds there was someone from our team passing by.

As the season drew near its end, our team went back down to the Jim Danner Invitational. A year previous I had nearly walked off the course and out of the sport all together. The race started off and for only the fourth time in my racing career I took off a little slow and began to pass people as I made my way through the first mile. Just after the first mile I had continued to pass people until I found that I was in the lead.

I kept the lead from the first mile to the last 800 meters of the race. Here I was, again simply reacting, not thinking. But as the end came into the clear and the crowds came back into view, I started to think, and with it people started to pass me, two of them being my teammates. I ended up finishing thirteenth overall running 15:42 for 5000 meters. Here I had gone from being last in the race a year previous, to nearly winning it all. My biggest enemy in running and racing was myself.

The last dual meet of the season I won and set the course record out at Nine Mile, near Riverside State Park. My confidence was high; maybe I could win an individual title. Ferris won the GSL title going undefeated in league meets; the only close meet being against Mead, at Mead's course. Pat Tyson always knew how to prepare his guys.

Going into the regional race I carried the successes from earlier in the season. The regional race was held at Carmichael Middle School in Richland. Through the first mile I came in second place, trying to chase down Robbie Barany from Eisenhower. He too was a senior and he had been part of the second place team from a year previous. He was one of the favorites to win it all and I chased him up the first hill, but I was passed by twelve runners; I did not fade forever but held my position till the very end. I ended up 13th that day, 29 seconds back from the winner, Robbie Barany.

For only the second time that season, we lost as a team. Eisenhower again won regionals and this time by seven points. Ferris took second scoring 67, and Mead was third scoring 72.

State was upon us and we wanted to repeat. We knew we could, we just could not have a collapse like we had at Stanford. We had not raced against Eisenhower all year and they were motivated to get some revenge for how last season ended up for them. We were not keying for a rematch at regionals, our eyes were on state and the opportunity to go to Nationals.

A week later, at state, our team ran great. I did not have my best race, but I held on and finished fifth for the team again. Our team won easily scoring 46 points. Mead took second with 92 and Eisenhower finished third with 104. I finished 23rd overall and was the only member of the top five of our team not to make it to the prestigious BorderClash meet following state. It is a race involving the best runners from Washington State, facing off with the best high school runners from Oregon in a unique team race hosted by Nike at their headquarters. The runners get free gear, free food, and they get to meet some great Nike sponsored athletes, all while running around the Nike World Headquarters.

Our top five guys at state were within 20 seconds of each other. Ben Poffenroth finished fifth overall crossing the line in 15:40, I came through 18 spots and 20 seconds later. Had I run my absolute best, I could have been near the top five in the state. As it was I had an off day and was still near the top twenty and part of the best team. Time has put into perspective what I accomplished as an athlete with my team.

As the team that won the state meet, we were invited to Nike Team Nationals. Mead also received an at large invite to the first ever team championship race. The race was held at a horse race track in Portland, Oregon.

We were flown down, put up in a hotel, and given free Nike gear. It was a high school athletes dream. Heading into the race, the highest I saw our team ranked or predicted was fifth, someone said they had us ranked third in the country.

We were excited to run, but the wet weather and extremely muddy conditions were something we had not ever trained on, or raced in. Nike spared no expense to fly in these high school teams and give free gear, but I always thought they should have done a better job to make a course that would yield fast times. I always thought they should have used the Jim Danner course which was friendly to the athletes as well as the spectators.

In the end, our team ran poorly, finishing 13th in the country that day.

© Peter Hawkins Personal Archives

Our 20 second spread turned into 1:02 on that muddy course. After the race we watched as it was announced that Mead, going under the name Tyson's Army, had finished third overall. Mead's team, which we had beaten by half their point total at state, now stood on the national awards stand. This is the only race I wish our team could have rerun, knowing that we could have been national champions.

The winner was York High School, going under the name Kroy that day.

York's coach, Joe Newman, is a legend in his own right; he and Pat Tyson are likely the two greatest high school cross country coaches of all time.

The only way that Nike could construct the meet was to have all the high school teams become club teams so as to not interfere with each state's high school by-laws. Our team was named the South Side Farm Team, in respect to Stanford's Farm Team. Ferris was on the south side of Spokane and so we went by that name.

When the season ended I continued to train and prepare for my last track season. I also took a trip to Montana State University and decided I would run for the Bobcats in college, and so I signed with them and had a half-ride scholarship at a Division I school. It was no Stanford, but I had started to come to grips with that.

The track season my senior year I only improved in the mile. I ran 4:18, improving by 12 seconds from the previous year, but my two mile time did not improve; I ran 9:34 at the Shoreline Invitational, but I did not run any faster.

At districts I failed to qualify in the mile to regionals and I made it in the two mile. But a late season cold ended any chance of making it to state. My high school career was over and my freshman year in college, and then a two year mission in Lisbon, Portugal were on the horizon.

After my mission I transferred to Brigham Young University where I earned a Bachelors in English. I went on to earn a Masters in Teaching from the University of Arkansas before returning to the Northwest. I now teach high school English and look forward to coaching a cross country team someday. My wife and I live with our two sons, Charles and Thomas, in Richland, Washington.

Paul Gordon Hawkins Jr: Yielding Seeds of Time

When Isaac ran at the state meet his freshman year of high school and Mead's Matt Davis was cruising to victory, Paul stood on the sidelines cheering on as a four-year-old. He did not know what the times meant. He only knew that he was expected to cheer for family and hope for the best. His mind was not absorbed with running, it was absorbed with learning.

Whereas his older brother Peter felt at ease playing or watching basketball, baseball, football, or doing anything athletic, Paul felt at ease with a book in his hand. Words opened up worlds to him. Watching a best of seven series in the NBA, NHL, or MLB held nothing in comparison to a best of seven series from J.K. Rowling in *Harry Potter*, or C.S. Lewis' *The Chronicles of Narnia*.

Instead of using his eyes to chase the tight spirals of college quarterbacks on Saturday and NFL quarterbacks on Sunday, Paul was more likely to chase that elusive golden snitch Harry sought. Championship rings from the NFL held nothing in comparison to following Frodo and Sam as they made their way to Mt. Doom in *The Lord of the Rings*. The more he read, the more he enjoyed stepping into an author's eyes, and seeing the world they had created. The sports world of the moment held little for Paul, because it failed to capture his attention.

One of the most profound moments in Paul's young life did not come in observing a race. It all happened in the basement of his family's house while Paul's mother Ann read to his older brother Peter at a young age. Paul watched as his mother read and Peter tried to puzzle out the meaning of words on the page. He saw her pointing to the words as she read from the children's book *Are You My Mother?* At a young age, Paul recognized a correlation. His mother could sift through words quicker because she knew their symbols on the page and could recite them from memory. *The more words you have, the clearer and quicker your thinking is,* he thought. *The reason why Peter is not as good at reading is because he does not know as many of the symbols on the page.* Thus began a love of learning for Paul.

School was the starting point for Paul's great academic adventures, but it was nothing compared to the education Paul gave himself. There was only so much a teacher could give him each day or over the course of a year. He saw that teachers had to manage multiplication tables while managing the multiple problems a student or two could create in a classroom. There seemed to be those students that got it and those that did not. Good students were reinforced with words of affirmation about their abilities from the teacher, while the difficult students were reinforced with words aimed at their inabilities to comprehend and their shortcomings. The top and bottom performers in each of these classes continued on with their educations and they did so with the compounding effects of rising to, or falling short of, expectations.

Paul recognized he was one of the gifted students, who had positive reinforcements in both the classroom and at home. He did not have to study for spelling tests because of how much he read. Spelling tests and multiplication tables were not enough for him. He wanted to know the world and more importantly, why the world worked as it did.

When Paul's older brother Ben was 11, he wanted to tackle the monumental task of running an entire 26.2 mile marathon. When Paul approached that very same age, he wanted to tackle the language and concepts in the 700 plus page behemoth of economics called *Security Analysis* written by Benjamin Graham and David Dodd of Columbia University.

Paul had seen his father combing his way through the book and decided that if it was good enough for his Dad, it was good enough for him since they carried the same name. *Like father like son* he had heard, and decided he would try out that old adage.

It was a game of vocabulary. The more words you know, the more concepts you understand, and the more you could unlock and map out the mysteries of the world around you. Reading unlocked visions of the past or predicted patterns leading towards future speculation. Words and concepts were just unexplored trails. If he did not understand the words or concepts, he could look them up. He read and re-read those parts that did not make sense to him. Paul worked on his mental endurance. He worked past the point of logical fatigue and figured out why the world turned as it did, with people in control and others controlled by them.

One of the early stories Paul puzzled over was from a book of Aesop's Fables regarding the *Tortoise and the Hare*. Obviously the Hare had the advantage and the Tortoise the disadvantage. Paul wondered how the Tortoise could ever be considered a favorite, seeing the obvious talent and speed of the Hare. Yet, Paul learned that there would be advantages that the Tortoise had that the Hare would never know. The deliberate commitment to each step brought with it a resilience that the Hare could never appreciate since his flight of foot came so easily.

At school Paul could easily apply the lessons of the Tortoise and the Hare. As most students gave effort based off of initial success or failure, Paul decided he would need to measure out meticulous efforts whether he knew the concepts or not. The Hares of the world were not always the ones to win in business or in scientific discovery. Edison's discovery of the light bulb had brought with it the quip that, "I have not failed, I have just found out 10,000 ways that a light bulb won't work." The illumination of life came not through successes but through setbacks.

Failure brought with it connotations that stymied confidence and for many, instead of endearing further effort, it ended it. Failure to endure was the worst loss. The failure to deal with uncertainty ends innovation.

In his off time from figuring out the financial world, Paul would stare up at the moon at night, reliving the words and explanations of his teachers from the previous day. His elementary school class had just learned about the phases of the moon. During this time Paul's family had received a telescope from their grandfather. The learning from books and from school could be seen in the world all around him. The moon's waxing and waning he witnessed at night. He saw that all the world around him was in movement. He ran his mind over what he read and compared it to the real life world around him. Out of the chaos of big movements in science, astrology, history, and economics, Paul looked for order.

Night after night, he would stay up late with his flashlight and read. He devoured books and thought deeply over their implications. But thinking did not exempt Paul from the physical demands and expectations of his parents to work.

At the age of five, Paul helped build a rock wall with his older brothers and sisters in the front and back yards. Parents Ann and Paul had seen houses from the east coast that had rock walls and decided they would put one on their property out in the country. It would be a great way for their children to work during the summer and to keep them out of the house. Paul would be the youngest one to work on the project the first time they built the wall.

Crate after crate came in with pallets full of volcanic rock. Paul's mind wondered at how magma from volcanoes could spew out and dry up as such porous rocks. With his tiny hands and glasses slipping on his small nose, Paul grabbed what rocks he could and helped build up a three foot wall that circulated just over 600 feet around the property.

Seven years would go by before the wall was renovated once more by the children. The rock had settled into the earth and had summarily sunk just over a foot. The sunken rock acted as the foundation upon which the next layer of rock would be cemented. Paul, then twelve years old, came out from behind his books and went back at the work with glasses that now had bifocals due to his deteriorating eyesight. He was an old soul at a young age.

Paul Hawkins Jr, middle with glasses

He brought with his efforts to the rock wall, an understanding of what he had read in history. He had learned the word ziggurat and came to see it as the pinnacle of building making in Mesopotamia. There was also the great wall of China, the distribution of labor and specialization. He saw low skill labor, but also an opportunity to save some money as his parents were paying the boys for their work. Ben was the leader, mixing the cement and giving orders, Peter the first foreman, while Paul saw himself and Tom as grunt laborers. Tom now was the youngest worker.

While working with his brothers, Paul thought of the words of Herodotus, the great father of history who said, "Of all men's miseries, the bitterest is this: to know so much and have control over nothing." Paul did not dictate how the rock wall was built, he merely obeyed the orders of those above him and recognized that history had spoken truth to him.

Paul also helped plant over 30 trees around the house, as well as the multiple lilac bushes and rose bushes that faced the street. When there was work to be done, the oldest to the youngest were all expected to help. Paul often heard the refrain from his mother or father as they were all out working in the yard, "The family that works together stays together."

It seemed to Paul that the family did most everything together. Isaac took up running and so did Emily, Ben, Liz, and Peter. When Isaac involved himself in ASB as a classroom representative at school, the rest would wait for their opportunity to run for student office. Emily became the school Secretary at Mullan Road Elementary. Ben was the Sergeant at Arms, Liz the Treasurer, Peter would also be Treasurer at Mullan Road and then ASB President at Ferris. Paul decided to follow in his family's footsteps and became the Treasurer at Mullan Road and then the ASB President at Sacajawea Middle School. From the mother that had hardly won anything, came a group of children that hardly seemed to lose anything they entered into.

When there was not a cross country or track meet to attend and support a sibling at, Paul spent Saturdays in the flower beds, picking weeds, or mowing a lawn, and cleaning out a garage. Once the outside work was complete then there was always work inside the house. Toilets were scrubbed, floors were swept, carpets and rugs were vacuumed, windows were washed and bedrooms were all cleaned out. Once those tasks were completed, Paul could dive back into his books.

Paul learned to do his own laundry around the same time he was first building the rock wall. Ann trained him like she trained all her children, so that each individual monitored their own lives and kept track of their own clothes. A house that gradually sunk into a messy state over the course of the week would then be put back into order in a single day with all hands on deck.

Paul read about nature versus nurture, and wondered over whether we create the world around us or whether the world creates us.

Reading, studying, and pondering life were not the only endeavors Paul pursued. Sports at school held an access to a different kind of knowledge and confidence. He quickly saw that the eye and hand coordination he developed from playing baseball, basketball, and football with his older brother Peter in the yard brought with it an instant access to friends and social standing. Paul was not the last one picked for a team, but often was one of the first kids picked. Sports created friendships. Being able to produce a touchdown because of faster foot speed brought with it the desire for other kids in the school yard to be associated with that person.

During recess and before school Paul enjoyed pickup games of basketball and football. He studied the tendencies of those he played against and he preferred playing defense in basketball and being cornerback in football. He had to read the floor and the field, predicting tendencies and snapping at an opportunity presented to him. He had to anticipate the moments in a play developing before him that could shift the game in his team's favor.

Observant as he was, Paul saw that Ben's gymnastics had transformed his body. Paul also wanted to gain strength and so he signed up for gymnastics. He would stretch his body as well as his mind moving about the spectrum of sports.

As middle school started Paul participated in cross country, wrestling, basketball, and track. He would balance the athletics with his academics and continue to read a great depth and breadth of material.

Standing on the side of the chain link fence at the state meet, watching his brother Peter and the Ferris team pull out a miraculous race, Paul finally sunk his teeth into the sport of distance running. With all the data he collected he made his analysis. He was not likely to be tall, considering he was just over five feet as an eighth grader. Basketball would not be an option or football. Wrestling was fun, but he did not have a winning record at it. Tennis was something that he thoroughly enjoyed and something at which he was extremely talented, yet he was short and the taller athletes would ultimately have the advantage with their serves and the angles they could use.

At the All City race in track Paul's eighth grade year he ran a 5:01 in the mile. He had the fastest time of any of his siblings in eighth grade. He had finished third in the race and was only outkicked by two athletes he saw had physical maturity on their side. Paul decided to be a distance runner by his own choosing and logic.

Getting On Board

Prior to entering the world of high school athletics, Paul would go for runs with his father Paul Sr. in the early morning darkness as his brother Peter sat through seminary classes at the local church. Paul, like his older brother Peter who had run early in the morning with their father, would cover anywhere from 4-8 miles before the start of school. Paul's base brought with it strength that others did not have and it brought confidence that he could win.

Paul saw from training runs with his older brother that a spot on the varsity squad would require all the effort he could muster.

During the course of the season Paul ran as one of the top JV runners and he was the top freshman on Ferris' team. He earned a spot as an alternate at state and would be one spot away from being at alternate at Nike Team Nationals. Not many freshmen have the opportunity to run at or witness national competition like Nike Team Nationals.

Paul could see the disappointment in his brother and his teammates eyes as they walked off the course with a 13th place team finish. He also took a look at the stat sheet and saw four seniors set to graduate and leave the team. He knew of several sophomores on the team that he would compete against in the years to come that were just as hungry for success. It could have been easy for others to say that the success of the team would end with the passing of the seniors, but Paul's analysis showed otherwise. He saw teammates showing up to practice and saw a determination in their eyes to do more than those who had gone before.

In Paul's freshman year of track he improved his mile time from 5:01 to 4:52. The improvement came, but not to the level he would have expected based upon his training. Summer came and so did more training.

Paul knew that success had brought with it more athletes wanting to be part of a winning team, a team that would win state and have an opportunity to run on the national level. While most high school athletes play basketball, football or soccer, they never get the opportunity to perform on the national scale. Spokane's distance running allowed high school athletes that very opportunity and so the team that used to have 12 running at Ferris soon doubled and with it came depth. The men Coach Hadway cut out of wood were continuing to follow the format and outline of his previous models.

Paul's sophomore year was the first time he ran on varsity. That season he consistently ran as the sixth man on the team, but he knew that any bad race or poor performance and he could be pushed off the varsity squad. The team was deep and it was lead by senior Rob Cosby. Following Rob there were four juniors: Steve Olsen, David Hickerson, Cameron Quackenbush and Pat Maloney. Paul was the lone sophomore and youngest on the team. Following

Left to right - Paul Hawkins Jr, Cameron Quackenbush, Steve Olsen, Robert Cosby, David Hickerson, Joe Roberts, Pat Maloney

Paul there was one more senior, Joey Roberts. Ferris stood in a position to do what many thought was impossible: win state again.

At the 2005 regional meet during Paul's sophomore year Mead won the team title with Ferris placing second 40-54. Mead had their five runners in the top 15 slots and Ferris had their top five in the top 16 slots. It was a close meet, with two teams battling it out.

At state one week later, Ferris flipped the script and won their third straight state title scoring 57 points compared to Mead's 73. The next big race was Nike Team Nationals. Again, Mead and Ferris would be selected and would represent the Northwest Region at the race. Once more, Mead would outperform Ferris at Nationals, finishing fourth running under the name Mead XC Club while Ferris under the name Spokane XC Club would finish tenth as a team.

That spring, Paul raced and improved in the mile again, but only running 4:48. His two mile improved to 10:03. He ran at districts but failed to make it on to regionals. Based on the 2006 track results it appeared Mead would win state in cross country during the fall. Mead had six runners at the regional race in the two mile and four runners in the regional race at the mile, whereas Ferris only had one runner in the mile and two mile.

High to Low

Paul's junior year he would be the only junior on the varsity squad; everyone else was a senior. Coach Hadway relied upon the routines of running that had yielded success with his past teams. As such, half mile repeats at Cannon Hill Park and quarter mile repeats along Corbon Park Straights in Spokane became staples. There were obviously rest and recovery runs interspersed, but back to these parks and intervals his athletes went.

On a team full of seniors, there were several juniors who wanted their opportunity to race varsity. The team knew that another state championship hung in the balance and an opportunity to run at Nike Cross Nationals.

One of those trying to bump Paul off of varsity was fellow junior Tom Everett. Tom had succeeded in running a faster time in a JV race than Paul had run in a varsity race right as the season was nearing its end.

At a race out at an area called Seven Mile, Paul would be running the JV race while Everett would be running the varsity race. The advantage was clearly to Everett who had faster competition in his race, who, if he hung with, would lead him to a faster time.

Paul was at a distinct disadvantage; he would be the top runner in a JV race, yet he had no one to chase. This would be the last opportunity to make a change to the varsity squad. Running on varsity meant running at regionals, state, and Nationals; running on JV meant seeing it all from the sidelines.

Remembering back to Aesop's Fable, Paul took hope in the fact that the tortoise could purposefully place each step and come out the victor.

With the JV race coming first, Paul warmed up. He put on his spikes, took off his warm-ups, strode out and stayed loose and ready. He waited for the starting pistol to sound.

Bang.

Off Paul went, taking each step as if it were the last he would take that season. Living and dying for each second, each turn, each breath, he wound his way through the hills and trails, running a solo effort. The clock would tell the tale.

Throwing himself at the finish line with one last lunge to the tape, Paul crossed the line of the hilly 5K as if he were out-leaning a ghost.

16:52.

Paul had won the race and walked back to his warm up gear. He cooled down as the varsity boys were warming up. His season was in the balance.

Watching from the sidelines, Paul waited as the varsity race had started and he kept his eyes firmly on that seventh spot. He knew that this race could be calculated in the number of meters run, the average split time for a mile, the average split time per thousand meters; it could be looked at by grade level; there could be the bell curve that comes in every endeavor. The only question coming back to Paul was had he done enough to climb up and push against the curve?

Everett started out with the pack, then faded from fifth position, to sixth, and then was passed and now running in seventh slot.

Wanting his team to do well, but wanting to be on that team Paul cheered and waited, looking between his stopwatch and the course.

Down the final curve towards the finish they all came and Paul stood right at the finish line. In came the seniors: David Hickerson, Cameron Quackenbush,

Steve Olsen, Pat Maloney, Nick LaPlante, Jeff Devlin, and finally rounding the curve came Everett with arms raised high, face contorted and legs churning towards the finish.

Through the line Paul's eyes tracked Everett and stopped his stopwatch as he crossed the finish line. He did not want to look at the time.

16:53.

Paul was back on varsity and on to regionals, state, and Nationals. The efforts of that day were impressive, but little did he know the impact it would have on his future school of choice.

The end of the 2006 season came and with it, another regional race. Once more, Ferris would take second at regionals to Mead, but this time by a single point: 42-41. Once more Ferris had five runners in the top 16 and Mead had five in the top 15. Yet again, history would repeat itself and at state, Ferris would flip the script once more and win 51-72. Again Nike Cross Nationals came into view and with it the opportunity to do what no Ferris team had ever done before: win Nationals.

However, at Nike Cross Nationals Ferris finished third and Mead placed fifth.

Paul's junior year of track brought with it improvement yet again, but with minimal returns, running 9:53 for two miles. He made it to districts but failed to qualify for regionals. All of those seniors on Ferris' team left and Paul would be the lone returner for Ferris' squad.

An offseason of work came and with it the opportunity to prepare for one last season and one last opportunity to move on to state and hopefully Nike Cross Nationals. Paul was part of a state championship team his freshman, sophomore, and junior seasons, a feat that none of his brothers had accomplished. Paul ran in the state meet in cross country as a sophomore and a junior in high school, another accomplishment that none of his brothers had done. Paul ran on a team at Nationals for two straight years, again a first.

Paul's senior season, however, would not be a Cinderella story.

Heading into his senior year Paul picked up work at Quiznos. He had one last season to give it his all. From mid July to late August Paul put together five straight weeks of 90 miles running, followed up by one week at 100 miles. He ran, then worked an eight hour shift on his feet and then ran some more.

Paul was a captain on the varsity team and he had the challenge of trying to figure out how to motivate his teammates. He turned to something he had read from Winston Churchill in his famous speech *Blood, Toil, Tears and Sweat*. He would start the practices with words to inspire:

> *I have nothing to offer but blood, toil, tears and sweat...We have before us many, many, many, long months of struggle and of suffering...You ask, what is our aim? I can answer in one word: Victory. Victory at all costs--victory in spite of all terror-- Victory however long and hard the road may be, for without victory there is no survival.*

Paul wanted Churchill's words to be their own as they approached practice. He knew that it was cross country running after all and not a real war they were engaged in. However, he also knew that expectations are as important to the future education of a first or second grade student as they will ever be as an adult. Cultivating that ability to believe and work should be treated with the same sincerity of battling a war. It is a war against oneself; against weakness and doubt, laziness and procrastination. Societies and economies flourished or floundered based upon confidence.

Paul knew that Ferris' team was young and he knew that Mead's team was hungry. He knew that defeat likely lay before them, but he needed to inspire. Like that tortoise with his distinct disadvantage, he went forward anyway.

Paul showed up to practice and brought with him his youngest brother Tom, who was a freshman. He wanted Tom and others to see that although Ferris would have setbacks, that their best races still were in front of them. He was trying to give a perspective to those who had not had one previously. He was trying to give a vision of what could be for those young athletes on the team. And he was trying to show the work it would take to get there.

All Paul could offer was his work, his words, and the effort that others could see each day. Something must have stuck with Paul's efforts and words because two years later the team would be back at Nationals where they would have Ferris' highest finish ever: second place in the country.

Throughout the course of the season Paul finished first or second in races to his teammate Adam Thorne who was a sophomore at the time. After one particular race where Paul fought hard to the finish, his youngest brother Tom came up and bear hugged him. He had seen someone give his all and walk the talk he had preached all summer.

"Paul, that was awesome." Tom said.

Tom knew that these moments of excellence after races did not come every day, and so when they did they needed to be recognized. He wanted to let his older brother know how much he meant to him. Paul could win

© Emily Ward Hawkins

the hearts of his teammates as well as his younger brother.

The season continued on and Paul jockeyed back and forth, fighting to lead his team and perhaps pull off the impossible.

At regionals in 2007, however, Paul finished third for the team, having an uncharacteristically bad race; finishing 35th overall. On a team of three seniors and four sophomores, Paul did not make it on to state his senior year and the team did not go on either. The only individual to qualify was sophomore Adam Thorne. Mead won the region that year and went on to win at state.

Ferris did not make it to the Nike Cross Nationals for the first time in the history of the event. North Central would be the only team from Spokane represented at the event in 2007 and they would place sixth in their first showing on the national stage.

Although the door to Paul's season closed another door opened academically. The University of Chicago, known as the country's most premier program in economic thought, accepted Paul for the following fall term.

Paul had sat through a class during his sophomore year in which he heard various presentations from fellow AP classmates about universities in the world. One of his fellow students spoke about the University of Chicago and said that it was preeminent amongst all schools regarding economic thought. Paul remembered the presentation. During the spring of Paul's junior year he went back to watch his siblings Isaac and Ben run in the Boston Marathon. Before and after the marathon, Paul went with Paul Sr. and toured various universities back east. Paul suggested stopping in Chicago on their way back to Spokane, as means of trying to figure out if the coach would be interested in him.

After touring the school and visiting with the coach, Paul said he would continue to keep him updated with his training and times. The coach was impressed to hear of Paul's siblings and their running efforts which had lead them all to different universities. The coach was also impressed with Paul running at Nike Cross Nationals as a sophomore and junior. Had Paul not earned his spot back on varsity at the end of his junior year cross country season, perhaps that door to the University of Chicago would have remained closed.

Every second counts.

With the excitement of being admitted to his dream university, Paul returned to winter training and one last opportunity to race in track. He came to the conclusion that his previous training had mirrored much of the same formula that his brothers and sisters had used which relied upon a large amount of miles. Paul recognized that not all miles were created equal. Time was relative and so was effort. In an attempt to give everything one last try, Paul went out on runs going no slower than six minute pace. Everything increased in intensity and with it Paul's confidence.

The week before Paul's first race of the season he completed a particularly difficult workout. He ran 30 quarter mile repeats on the track with his teammate Adam Thorne. Paul averaged 69.7 seconds for the entire 30 quarters. He felt great. The first few had been in the 73 second range, then during the heart of the workout he had been around 71-69 and then the last few he had finished in 67 seconds.

In Paul's first track race of the season he jogged through the first three laps and then raced the last lap and PR'd running 4:43 in the easiest race he had ever run. Paul stepped off the track knowing that he had not pushed the pace at all and that a huge PR awaited him as the season progressed. The only problem was that following his race Paul's ankle had started to bother him. Eventually it came to the point where he had his foot x-rayed and it was determined he had a stress fracture in his foot. He had run so hard so often that his bone had broken. Paul's senior year of track was ended before it ever really began.

For all the disappointment, Paul realized that specialization in distance running proved useful. Paul ran for the University of Chicago his freshman year before heading off to a two year church mission to Hong Kong, China.

Following Paul's mission he returned to the University of Chicago where he earned a degree in Economics. He then completed a Masters in Accounting while he earned his Law Degree from the University of Idaho. Paul is finishing up a Masters in Law at the University of Florida and he plans on returning to Spokane with his wife Melanie when he graduates. Paul plans on working at an accounting firm in Spokane following his graduation.

Tom Hawkins: The First Shall be Last and the Last Shall be First

Tommy stood in the outfield of the family's makeshift baseball field in the front yard, during the late spring of 2000. He was eight years old but walking and talking like someone much older.

Standing at home plate was Brad Ashby, a boy who had come to try and date Liz Hawkins and win over her brothers who were divided between two makeshift teams. The game was close and the count was full when Tommy decided to make his move from out in left field. With his baseball mitt cupped around his mouth he made his presence known.

"Hey Brad!" Tommy taunted from the outfield.

Ben was winding up for the pitch.

"Your girlfriend is in the outfield…" Tommy said.

The pitch was on its way.

"And she's naked!" Tommy said.

Brad with a sudden smile on his face swung and hit nothing but air. Strike three. It was the end of the inning and Tommy trotted from the outfield to home plate tossing his mitt at Brad.

"My turn to hit." Tom said with a grin.

The youngest child has to survive and sometimes their wits are their greatest ally. Tommy was not nearly as bookish as Paul and did not know all of the technical language that he seemed to soak up, but he had the street smarts necessary to accomplish whatever he needed.

Tommy had the lot of growing up the last and youngest of a family of great and competitive distance runners. What was left to accomplish? Siblings had

run in almost every slot and position on the teams at Ferris. They had a national caliber individual, they had a pair of individual state champions, they had team state champions; they had finished third in the country as a team. What was left for Tom, class of 2011? How would he turn the tables on all that had been accomplished and rewrite the record books?

Markings of time shifted.

Isaac was the lead example in everything for the Hawkins children. He was the first to do anything and he steamrolled ahead setting a pace that others could not match. Tommy was the caboose and the last to do everything.

Paul and Ann looked at the first day of school for Isaac with awe. Their oldest was off on a new adventure and they were navigating the schedule, the homework, and the routines with their son. The same was true of the first day of middle school, high school, and college for their oldest. Then it was time for the first marriage, followed by their first grandchild. These firsts became moments to define life.

There is not as much fervor or excitement for the last spot as their is for the first. If the life of the family moved like a runner, then with each life event pushing farther and farther into the future, Tom felt like he was that trailing leg or arm being pushed backward into the past.

While Isaac started high school and did so running, Thomas Andrew Hawkins had just come into the world, kicking, screaming, and surrounded by six siblings. From the beginning Tommy would be behind, starting smaller, weaker, and in the last spot.

Forever Tommy would hear how he was the baby of the family, the last one, the one that had everything. Yet for all that Tommy had, he wanted to have the admiration of those who had gone before. His siblings stood head and shoulders above him and he wanted to have a place and a story just as unique as theirs.

Whereas everyone was brought to watch Isaac participate, Tommy was left the lone one to pass through his events. He was the last to go to grade school, the last to move on to middle school and he would be the last to walk across the stage at high school. Whereas everyone showed up for the first, the last brought with it distance and circumstance that kept family members away.

Prior to ever entering high school or running competitively, Tommy had to decide which sport he wanted to do. He had heard all about Ferris' accomplishments and he had heard about all the morning runs and double days that the older siblings had done his entire life.

In an effort to distinguish himself from his siblings, Tommy took to football due in large part to his size growing up. He was a big kid for his age during elementary and middle school. Battling asthma as he did, Tommy would sometimes have to be admitted to the hospital due to his inability to catch his breath. Inhalers, breathing treatments, and steroids were used as a means of trying to build up Tommy's lungs. With the treatments came a side effect of a very hungry appetite. Tommy ate and grew thicker more than he grew vertically for a time.

Sensitive to his weight, but recognizing it as a strength, Tommy decided he would use his mass on the football field where he would play offense and defense as a tackle. Throughout middle school he played football on a very competitive team. Paul Sorensen was Tommy's coach. Sorensen played safety for Washington State University's football team in the late 70s and early 80s before eventually being drafted by the Cincinnati Bengals where he played for one season and then played for the San Francisco 49ers for a season.

Sorensen had his own son Cody that was Tommy's age and who was going through school at Sacajawea. Like with any endeavor, a good coach can make a world of difference. This team of young athletes that Tommy was a part of went on to win Ferris' only state title in football in 2010 during Tommy's junior year of high school.

But for an untimely tackle in middle school, Tommy may have found himself on that state championship team in high school. As a play in practice was winding up Tommy went for a tackle on a fumble and ended up getting his arm twisted. He was injured and did not play in the following game, the last of the season. The play shook up Tommy and made him reconsider the sport.

It was also during this time that Tommy saw his brother Paul's team at Ferris having success running off to Nationals and winning state titles. And as was tradition, Tommy started running before seminary with his Dad. The weight started to disappear.

The moment Tommy dedicated himself to running came as the family took part in the Ragnar Relay race covering some 200 miles with twelve athletes. Taking turns running throughout the night and during the day, Tommy saw his teammates and family members participating at various stages of the race.

At one key interchange in the race Tommy came down the hill to tag the next runner. Tommy came running through with a smile on his face and with laughter pouring out of him. Everyone wondered why he was laughing, but after he tagged the other runner he didn't stop running.

He went straight to the porta-potty.

Coming out of the porta-potty some time later, Tommy informed everyone that he wasn't sure if he was going to make it in time.

In that moment, Tommy saw all that had come from running for his siblings. There was the camaraderie, there was the fitness, and the confidence that came from doing something daily that was difficult. These were his people, this was his tribe, and he would be a runner. He was shedding weight and growing taller. His name, like his waistline, became shortened and he went by Tom.

Tom's freshman year would be Paul's senior year, and so he came and went to practices with the team captain, listening to his speeches about how to train and what would need to be sacrificed in order to achieve.

Tom tried to get on varsity but did not make it as a freshman. He ran JV throughout the season and competed at the Freshman All-City race.

Track came and Tom would run a 5:13 mile and a 11:06 two mile. He had improved in running. His previous best mile was around 6:30 prior to coming into high school. The end of the freshman year brought with it the end of Tom's first full year of running.

In 2008 Ferris' team improved dramatically as Tom transitioned from his freshman to sophomore year. The team made it back to state after winning the regional race with 55 points as compared to Eisenhower's 62 and Mead's 73. The team went from a year of obscurity to back in contention for the title, and even the favorite heading into the state race. However, at state, Mead would walk out the winner and Ferris would take third. In the 3A classification at state North Central won placing four runners in the top five individual slots and their fifth runner placed 11th overall. North Central's team score that day was 24. This team would go on to win the National Championship at Nike Cross Nationals. Tom stood on the sidelines watching all these runners accomplishing feats he dreamed to be part of someday.

Back home Tom went to work, having not run in state in either his freshman or sophomore year, just like his brother Peter. Tommy's sophomore year of track brought with it improvements in the mile and two mile, but not by large margins.

In the third GSL meet of the track season, Ferris faced off against Mead and Gonzaga Prep. Tom would run in the JV mile race and win it with a time of 4:54, out-leaning his fellow teammate and classmate Keith Fechner by one second. Tom won the race, but wanted to be in the varsity race.

In the two mile Tom would again PR, lowering his previous season best of 11:06 to 10:40, chopping off twenty-six seconds. Yet, Tom was again disappointed, comparing himself against the efforts of his siblings.

Into the summer Tom went, training and hoping to finally race on Ferris' varsity squad. The team was on the upswing, having left state with disappointment the previous year and with a talented senior class they approached a promising future.

The cross country season started off at the Highlander Invitational, where Tom ran the 2.5 mile course with his grade level. His 14:34 would put him as the eighth man on the team that day. Varsity was so close, and with it a spot on a team with state championship hopes and National Title dreams, having seen North Central win the year before.

Tom would only come as close as eighth that season, as he would later compete in the Tracy Walters Invitational, where 10 competitors are allowed to run on each team. Tom would finish tenth on Ferris' team that beat North Central that day.

Ferris would go on to win the regional meet and the state meet in 2009. Both Ferris and North Central would go back to Nike Cross Nationals. Tom would watch as teammates and classmates raced their best. On the jumbotron at the event, Tom watched as Ferris' team clung to second place. He wanted his team to pull it out, he wanted them to win.

© Peter Hawkins Personal Archives

Ferris placed second at Nationals in 2009.

North Central placed seventh.

A Cold Snowy Race in Reno

The season ended and Tom heard through his teammate Travis Thorne that there was a local meet they could race in and qualify for a national race in Reno, Nevada. They could run under the local running club *Spokane Mercury*. At a race at Planters Ferry Park, Tom had an opportunity to qualify for the USATF National Junior Olympic Cross Country Championships.

He needed to finish in the top five spots in order to have a chance to be on Spokane's team. It was no Nike Cross Nationals, it was no Foot Locker Nationals, but it was a race with an opportunity and a goal in mind. His teammates had gone off to race at Nike Cross Nationals and finished second in the country; Tom was lining up for an opportunity to race one last time himself.

I warmed up with Tom, having come to Spokane on break from school for the winter. We warmed up knowing what was at stake, but we kept it light and fun.

Heading to the start on that gray windy day, Tom lined up one last time, knowing the end was coming. My Dad and I stood there, watching and cheering as this tall young boy had the look of a tall young man before us.

The marshal called them to the line and Tom shot off. He was aware of the training he had put in and he was aware of the lack of results that had come, and he went after it once more.

The field began to spread out as they wrapped around the big loops.

I could not help it; I ran and yelled and cheered.

This could be Tom's moment and I would try and cheer him to victory.

For portions of up to a hundred or two hundred meters I ran alongside Tom, in my running gear, yelling at him to hang with the guy in front of him.

"Tom, you got this. You hang with this guy and you can do it!"

Away they went, and a young runner behind Tom took courage at knowing he was one spot away from a trip to Reno. Tom was passed.

My heart sank.

Off they disappeared.

I wondered to myself as I watched, *Why couldn't Tom have his day?* I waited to see them come back from the outer rim of the course, counting off the positions of runners that had not changed.

Tom was only five meters off the number five runner who had passed him half a mile earlier. His eyes were up on number five's back.

There was still fight in Tom's eyes.

I charged toward Tom on the course as he came around the curve with less than three quarters of a mile left.

"Tom, this is it, this is your spot!" I shouted.

All total, there were less than a hundred people in the race and watching all combined. I cheered and shouted at Tom as if my voice were competing with thousands to be heard.

Tom started to make his move.

"Yes! Tom! Go!" I shouted, flagging my arms towards the finish.

Tom moved past the runner in front of him and charged slightly uphill towards the finish.

"Hold on Tom!" I shouted.

Tom kept pace with eyes fixed on the finish.

He would not be passed on that day, earning the fifth and last spot to Reno.

At the race in Reno, Nevada on December 12, 2009, the weather was cold, windy and snow had fallen. Paul Sr. watched as his youngest boy tried to warm up in the cold windy weather. He knew that the weather would affect Tom's ability to breathe. He just hoped his son could find a way to make it through the next several minutes and gut it out as he had the previous week.

The race started and 150 runners from various club teams and individual organizations took off. Tom went with them, but the wind continued to whip about icy cold temperatures.

With his six foot two inch frame, Tom moved about with his pink arms and legs exposed to the elements. He was giving everything he had but the wind was taking his air and he struggled through the snow. Once more, the field ran past him, but Tom continued onward.

Finally crossing the finish line, Tom continued his slow trudge through the finish chute to see his father on the other side.

The snow had iced over the laces on Tom's spikes. Tom's hands were so cold he could not grip his shoe laces. So Paul Sr. stooped down, took off his gloves, and helped remove Tom's shoes. He could hear Tom wheezing, and knew they needed to get him indoors and in a place where he could breathe.

Paul Sr. was as proud of Tom in that moment as he was of any of his children.

Awards Banquet

Tom was part Ferris' most successful team in its history, taking second place in the country; only six points away from a national team championship. But Tom sure did not feel like a near national champion sitting in the back of the Ferris cafeteria during the end of the season awards banquet.

I went to the event with Tom. He picked a place in the back of the cafeteria to sit. He was tired, embarrassed, and hurt from the effort of the season. Here he was, sitting next to me, his brother Peter who had helped Ferris win its first title in over twenty years during my junior year, while he stood on the sidelines watching and cheering. Now, in his own junior year, Tom saw that he again was not on varsity, not at state, and he was not at Nationals. He was the only boy in the family to not run on varsity his junior year and the only one not to run at state in the first three years of high school.

To add to Tom's misery there was a phrase circulating on the team about Tom: Tommy the Turtle. Hurt by those he wanted to be embraced by, Tom walked up to the awards table as some on his team snickered.

Tom stood there as Coach Hadway spoke of Tom's efforts during the season.

Even from the back row where I sat, I could see Tom did not want to stand up there. He was shifting about, standing as if he were on live coals with bare feet.

The moment passed and Tom came back to sit beside me in the very back of the room.

Tom hunched over with hands on his knees and started to shake a bit. I went to ask him if he was ok and then he silently bolted out the side exit in the back, unseen by anyone except for my parents, myself, and the coach and athlete in the front.

The awards banquet continued without anyone noticing or looking back.

My parents both turned to me and silently asked what had happened.

"I don't know." I said.

My Dad and I went out into the hall to try and find Tom.

We found him. His tall frame was hunched over as he sat beside a locker crying ugly tears. His eyes were red and his breathing erratic; his chest and body heaving.

"Tom, what's going on?" Dad asked.

Tom just kept crying.

When Tom finally got composure over himself he looked up at us and spoke.

"I'm just not any good at this." Tom said.

I saw myself my junior year, wanting to quit and afraid of failure. I saw in him all that he had faced and the shame he felt at not being able to live up to expectations he had.

I tried to pump him up. I tried to do my best Isaac impression and help him up and give him the words and the encouragement needed to keep fighting. He had been knocked down and had the wind knocked out of him by some of his teammates, but I knew that the fight needed to continue onward.

Tom was the last in the family, but he did not want to be the last in the thoughts and esteem of those around him.

"Tom you can do it. You can beat these guys. We just need to get you out there with some higher intensity on your training runs. I will be back in Spokane this summer and we can really get you ready for your senior season." I said.

"Tom you can do it. Just calm down a bit and breath. Ok. You are on one of the best teams in the country, there is no shame in that. We have to make it through this awards banquet and then we have to figure out how to handle this situation we are in." Dad said.

Tom slowed his breathing down, wiped the tears from his face, bit his lip and finally started to compose himself. After ten minutes in the hall Tom walked back into the awards banquet as silently as he had left it. Silently he sat and stared up at his coach and his team talking about accomplishments, about heart, about effort, about breaking boundaries and redefining success; and silently Tom sat brewing with all these emotions within himself.

The awards banquet ended and Tom and I jumped into the back of the old red beat-up truck and headed home. Tom's eyes were still red from the tears. I tried to encourage him, to keep his eyes up and keep chasing down his teammates in front of him. On our way home he just sat in silence, looking out at the road illuminated by the one working headlight.

That spring Tom participated in track but his times did not improve. His mile time was worse from the previous year by a second and his two mile time regressed by sixteen seconds. Something was not right, and no one knew the answer.

Tom showed up to practice, he showed up to races and ran the first half tough but the last half he just seemed out of sorts. The culprit and cause of his poor performance was likely his asthma. Tom stood at almost six foot two inches tall and weighed 160 pounds. It is a lot of weight to carry around the track while also being asthmatic.

Tom's junior year ended and he went back to training for one final year.

True to my word, I was back in town. I came back home without work. Tom had since started his own employment.

Although Tom was the youngest child, he was still expected to work. Tom sought out employment like everyone else. For all the applications he put in he never received any interviews. He went week in and week out to various places of employment and tried to land that first job. No one had anything to offer. The housing crisis had come and dropped and it was hard for anyone to get a job, let alone a high school student.

Tom decided he would start his own business. He would do any sort of yard work or handyman repair work he could find. To get his name out there Tom printed his own fliers with the home phone number and then placed them in the mailboxes around the South Hill. Where others of his siblings stood at the command of bosses, Tom would make his own business and be his own boss.

Tom waited.

The phone started to ring and business started to trickle in at first. Tom's work spoke for itself. Those who gambled on the boy with the flier were impressed. They gave Tom not only more work but also more references. Tom ended up spending as much time in his Carhartt's and steel toed work boots as he did in his running shorts and trainers. If Tom was not running, he was running to and from jobs working for various individuals on the South Hill.

The money that initially trickled started to pour.

Tom had saved up ten thousand dollars over the course of his time working from his junior to his senior year, enough to nearly pay for all four years of tuition at Brigham Young University-Idaho.

I showed up at the start of summer in 2010 and worked alongside Tom. We would split different jobs we thought we could do individually and sometimes we would team up and split the money on an effort.

During the mornings and evenings we ran together.

There is one run in particular that sticks out to me from my time running with Tom. It was early summer and we went running up Brown's Mountain from our house. It is a 10 mile run. When we were almost eighty percent up the mountain Tom started to say he did not feel good.

I knew he did not feel good, because I did not feel good. It was almost 4 in the afternoon in July and the temperature was in the high 90s. Nobody feels good running up the mountain in that heat but I was there jabbering away about how this would make him tough and help him run on varsity his senior season. He made it to the top of the mountain but had to walk at one point. I simply chalked it up to dehydration.

As we came down off the mountain, Tom told me again that he was not feeling good at all. He stopped and told me to go and get the car and come back to him. I asked him if he was dehydrated, he just told me he did not feel good and that he thought maybe he was dehydrated.

Off I ran home and then I jumped in the car and picked him up. We got him home and we got him fluids, but I was not sure what it was that had kept Tom from accelerating like I knew he could.

The summer wore on and Coach Hadway took his Ferris team to their cross country camp. Tom was a captain of the team his senior year. At camp they ran up a trail called the Run to the Sun. It is a run that is literally all uphill. Seven and a half miles of climbing.

Tom started out with the team and pushed the pace hard and continued to climb as teammates his same age and younger than him passed by. Travis Thorne, Adam's younger brother and friend of Tom would lead the charge up the mountain. Dave Thorne, Adam's and Travis' father, was also on the trail and running up with Tom. The Thornes had run with the Hawkins in the Ragnar relay.

Paul Sr. was at camp to help out as a parent volunteer. Part of his duties included using the four wheeler to pick up the struggling younger runners and carry other runners off the mountain that could not make it. He came from behind and saw Tom struggling, wheezing, and willing himself up the mountain.

"Tom do you want a ride?" He asked.

Tom looked over at his father with a death stare and shook his head.

He was going to earn this moment as well as any spot on the team that would be his. Siblings of his had climbed this mountain and left their best and he would do so as well; even if none of them would ever see it. And so Tom went, one step in front of the other to the very top.

Tom ran on varsity at the beginning of the season running in a dual meet with Shadle Park and Central Valley. Tom took 18th overall in the race and was Ferris' fifth runner that day. Yet, as the season progressed he would be bumped from varsity and run at the Nike Pre Nationals meet that year in the Junior and Senior JV race. He had one of his finest races and happiest moments finishing 20th overall in the Junior/Senior JV race running 18:05. Tom was so excited he even pumped his fist as he passed through the finish line.

At the Tracy Walters Invitational that season he finished well back of where he had been running earlier in the season.

Paul Sr., trying to help Tommy figure out what was going on, asked him how he felt during the race.

"My heart felt weird out there," Tom said.

"Well you were pushing the pace and that's what it will feel like when you do that," Paul Sr. said.

Tom's senior season would be a season of firsts. For the first time in 21 years a team not from Spokane won the 4A state meet. Eisenhower won, Lewis & Clark placed second and Ferris took fourth. Tom was not on varsity at the end of the season. He watched from the sidelines as the individual winner that day was Kenji Bierig from Lewis & Clark. Tom knew Kenji from their days spent at Sacajawea Middle School. North Central would go on to win the 3A title and go on to compete at Nike Cross Nationals and finish sixth in the country.

During Tom's senior year at Ferris High School he had one last culminating project in his English class that was supposed to speak to everything he had learned growing up. Tom took this last assignment seriously. With his words typed on paper and a class full of his peers watching, Tom stood up in the front of the classroom.

His project was a poem. He dedicated it to his family. Here are his words:

> *As I slip on my shoes to run, I ask myself, why do I run?*
> *Is it for the satisfaction of me or for my family?*
> *I come from a family of great runners*
> *Tradition and legacy run deep in my family*
> *Running is the foundation on which our family's*
> *   reputation stands on*
> *To fall short of that is not acceptable*
> *I feel I have to run for the pure growing process that comes*
> *   from putting in the work*
> *Like my Dad always said, putting in miles everyday is like*

> *putting money in the bank*
> *One day you will be able to cash in on all the training and*
>   *preparation and work you do*
> *That day hasn't come yet, but I have faith that one day it*
>   *will pay off--*
> *That I will be able to cash in on my labors and reap the reward*
> *Every day offers the opportunity for a new run*
> *As I go out I contemplate the challenge that lies ahead*
> *I seek out this run for emotional gain*
>   *and psychological strength*
> *I run to reach goals*
> *I run to improve*
> *I run to be free*
> *I'll run out of anger*
> *I'll run out of dedication*
> *I run for the reward*
> *I'll run so that I can process previous events from the day*
> *I'll run for pure enjoyment*
> *And I'll run with friends who seek after the same goal:*
>   *progression and improvement*
> *While running thoughts forever race*
> *I think of the past, present, and future*
> *I think of friends, family, and school*
> *I think about what is to come in the future*
> *And I think about what it is that I need to do for the week on*
>   *my ever growing list of things to do*

Tom cried as he read. He put into words the message he had carried around in his heart his whole life. A stunned silent class watched as Tom then sat down, trying to regain his composure. The next student then stood and began their presentation. Eventually the class ended and Tom's senior year came to a close. He graduated and was on his way towards his future.

The summer of 2011 brought with it Paul Jr's return from two years in Hong

Kong, China where he had served as a missionary.

Tom had seen his brothers leave home. Isaac left when Tom was five, Ben left when he was nine, Peter left when he was thirteen, Paul left when he was fifteen. He had heard their tales and adventures; read about the faraway lands and wondered what it would be like for him. Tom waited for his opportunity to be placed in some far away land, with people to meet and stories to tell.

Tom knew that after his mission he would return to school, major in construction management and continue with his self-employed schedule building houses for people. He needed a truck, some gear, and a crew to work with. He saw a future wife and kids of his own to play with. Tom would love them just as he had loved his nieces and nephews.

During the summer Tom worked as a lifeguard but nearly walked away from the job. He completed the lifeguard training course but came home one day, struck by a video recording of a drowning. In the real life video none of the lifeguards present had seen the child drowning because they were not actively scanning the pool. For several tense seconds the child struggled and then several minutes floated limply until the child was discovered.

Tom thought about quitting, recognizing the value of life and wanting to live up to the task before him each day.

But he continued as a lifeguard throughout the entire summer.

The last time I saw my brother Tom was when he stood in his bedroom and gave me a hug; knowing that I was heading off to Arkansas and graduate school. We hugged and I saw this tall, dark, handsome young man before me who was strong and happy. Everything in the future seemed ready for him.

Unknown Mile Markers

On the morning of Saturday September 3, 2011, Tom went out on a bike ride with his father, Paul Sr. They road to the top of Mt. Spokane and then back to the bottom of the mountain. After the ride on the beautiful clear day, Tom and Paul Sr. went to eat at Five Guys Burgers and Fries. At lunch, Paul Sr. spoke to his last son, knowing that he would leave in two short days for school and that he was only a day away from submitting mission papers.

"You know I love you Tom." Paul Sr. said.

"Yeah I know." Tom said and then added, "You know you're going to miss me."

"Yeah, I will. You are a good kid and you have worked so hard and I am so proud of you." Paul Sr. said.

After the lunch they went home. Tom dropped off Paul Sr. and then went to do some last minute shopping for school supplies. He was planning on packing everything that day and had his clothes all clean and in piles in the basement.

Liz was in town, visiting with her husband and kids knowing that it would be Tom's last weekend before heading away to school. Isaac was in town and getting ready to head up the hill to visit the family with his wife and kids. Ben also living in town was on his way up to visit Tom for one last time. Paul Jr. was in town and had taken a car to Hastings to try and find any foreign film in Cantonese that he could use as a means of continuing to practice his language development. The only two siblings not in town were Emily in California and myself.

As Tom returned from the store, he was heading south on Regal and rounded the corner by the Moran Prairie Cemetery. He was less than a mile away from home. As he came out of the curve, the car began to drift across the left lane and came up the curb and slowed in front of a fence on the corner.

The first person on the scene was Paul Jr. who recognized the car and saw Tom inside hunched over the steering wheel.

The owner of the house came out and went quickly over to the car.

"Do you know what's going on?" He asked.

"Oh no, that's my brother." Paul Jr. said.

They both tried tapping on the window to wake up Tom but his head leaned against the window and he was unresponsive.

The neighbor called 911 while Paul Jr. called home to his father.

"Tom's been in some sort of accident but the car is fine, Tom is just not moving or responding." Paul Jr. said.

Racing up the hill Paul Sr. came.

Then Liz and Ann came up the hill, then Ben.

They watched as the fire department and paramedics finally arrived. The window on the driver's side of the car was punched out and Tom was pulled from the car with the engine still running.

Tom was not breathing.

Immediately the first responders tried doing CPR. It was quickly decided that Tom should be placed in the back of the ambulance and rushed downtown to Sacred Heart Hospital's Emergency Room.

Paul Jr. and Ben took the car Tom had been in back to the house, then they both went in their own cars down towards the hospital.

As the ambulance was heading down through the intersection of Southeast Boulevard and 29th avenue, Isaac and his wife saw the ambulance, as well as his parents trailing it with worried looks on their faces. Confused by why his parents were trailing an ambulance Isaac asked his wife if she had seen what he had.

Isaac quickly called his father.

"Hey, what's going on, we just saw you go through the light trailing the ambulance?" Isaac said.

"Tom's in the back of the ambulance. He is not breathing and we are taking him to the hospital to see what's going on." Paul Sr. said.

Isaac made the U-turn and started to also head down towards the hospital.

It was around this time that my sister Liz called me up and explained to me that Tom was being rushed to the hospital. I was on a highway road between Oklahoma and Arkansas, trying to get ready for my first year of Law School. I made various calls to extended family and left mostly messages since it was Labor Day weekend. All of my siblings were spreading the word to family and friends as to what was happening.

One of those calls went out to Dave Thorne, Adam Thorne's father and family friend who was a doctor. Dave had just gotten home from the hospital at the end of his shift when he got a call from Ben who explained what little he knew about the situation.

Dave went down to the hospital.

The family in town all stood in the hospital, just outside of the emergency room where there was a team of responders working and pumping on Tom's chest, trying to get his heart pumping. They used the defibrillator to try and shock his heart back into pumping.

Dave went into the emergency room and saw an X-Ray of Tom's chest posted. From the moment he saw it he realized that Tom had an oversized heart. Dave saw the team working away and explained how he knew the boy.

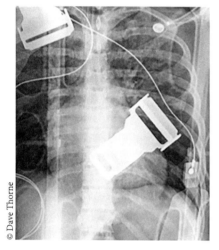

© Dave Thorne

Knowing Tom, Dave explained that there was not any drug use or abuses; that there was nothing in his history that would indicate why his heart was not pumping.

Dave Thorne walked out of the room and stood around Tom's family and had to explain that he was not going to live. Even if they continued to try to revive him and even if they did revive him, the Tom they all knew would not be the same Tom, due to the lack of oxygen circulating to his brain.

Walking back into the emergency room they went, Paul Sr., Ann, Isaac, Ben, Liz, and Paul Jr. Tom laid lifeless. In one moment, all that had been written and outlined about running, training, and time was redefined. The message changed for the Hawkins family.

I received the second phone call from my sister Liz and pulled over to the side of the road.

"Tom died." Liz said through tears.

She continued to speak, but I did not hear anything more. I sat in my car near unknown mile markers, and wept.

It takes a great deal of heart to run, and a healthy heart can help you do most anything. No one knows how long Tom had his oversized heart. Cardiomyopathy is the technical term. Tom had a heart that did not function as others did and due to that, he struggled.

Tom ran with his life in his hands with every effort, wanting to push himself beyond what he felt.

A week after his death, a funeral was held at his local chapel where several hundred people from the community packed inside of the church on 63rd and Regal. They had seen him on the roads, they had hired him to clean up their yards, and they loved that sideways smile he wore. All of Tom's siblings stood at the pulpit and spoke of what they knew of the youngest. Finally his parents stood and spoke about their son.

Tom was laid to rest at the Moran Prairie Cemetery. And those still living in his family, now trail him, hoping their efforts are as enduring as his were.

Tom's story is every runner's story. It is the story of someone on the road or trail that has a message in their heart which they cling to no matter the results.

Jon Knight representing team USA at a race in Milan, Italy in 1982

Jon Knight: Coming Full Circle

Jon Knight hurt as he toed the line for the district cross country meet in the late fall of 1981. Wearing his Ferris uniform with its red and white colors Jon thought back to a workout from the week before. He had run 6 X 1 mile repeats on the Hangman Valley road and his legs were still aching from the effort. He was trying to do something he had not done before: win the state meet. As a sophomore he had finished fourth, as a junior he had finished second, and now as a senior he was trying to finish first. But running was not the first thing on his mind.

For the past two weeks Jon had weighed the news in his own mind regarding his father's brain tumor. A surgery had been scheduled for his father on the day of the district championship. The extent and seriousness of the tumor was going to be known after the surgery.

Time was passing by. The leaves had all but changed colors and were falling from the trees. The cold air hung about as everyone crouched at the starting line.

Jon tried to breathe.

He still had to take the steps in front of him.

Physical demands and mental meaning make up the essence of sport as well as the movements of life. Jon had to confront the pain and find something positive. This would be the lesson of those final weeks of his senior year, as well as the lesson he would impart to those athletes he would eventually coach.

Jon and his team qualified to state.

He was tired, physically and emotionally.

After the race Jon went with his mother to the hospital. It was there that he learned that his father's brain tumor was cancerous and terminal. The doctor told the family that Jon's father could expect to live for only a year. Jon's father made it a year and a half. Jon mirrored the movements and toughness his father demonstrated in his own life.

At the state cross country meet his senior year, Jon again finished second place overall. Ferris, as a team, won the state meet for the second straight year with Herm Caviness as the coach. Jon knew as an athlete the sacrifice it took to win and the disappointment of finishing just outside the individual achievements he worked so hard to attain.

Since that time, Jon is now on the other side of the races; watching, cheering, encouraging, and coaching his athletes at North Central High School. North Central won 11 consecutive state titles from 2006-2016, a state record. Jon's teams have qualified for Nike Cross Nationals eight times and they won their qualifying race for Nationals seven times. Not once have his teams finished outside the top ten at Nationals. And as one of the winningest coaches in GSL and Washington State cross country history, Jon Knight knows that there is more to life than running.

Jon came from a long line of tough people on both his father and mothers side; this included tough women. The story goes that Jon's maternal great-great-grandmother chopped down her own barn during one particularly tough winter; she was 90 years old at the time she did it. She had run out of firewood and went out to solve the problem herself. Jon's paternal great-great grandparents were also cousins to the great Civil War General and future President Ulysses S. Grant.

Jon's great-great-grandparents on his mother's side of the family originally lived in Minnesota. After the Civil War they decided to load up their wagon and head west. They ended up settling in Deer Park, Washington, just north of Spokane. On Jon's father's side of the family his grandfather grew up on a homestead in Fort Benton, Montana. He eventually moved to Spokane and attended North Central High School in the late 1920s. For all of Jon's connections to Spokane, he would start his life in Santa Monica, California. His parents had gone down to California in the 1950s seeking work. In 1963 Jon Knight was born and lived his first two years in Santa Monica before the family moved back up to Spokane.

Before Jon ever knew about chasing a rabbit in a race, he was off with his dogs running in the fields of the South Hill. He ran up near Browns Mountain with his dogs following his every footstep. He enjoyed the fun of running. It was something he was good at and he knew it.

In the early 1970s Jon's first taste of competitive distance running started at Camp Reed, hosted by Tracy Walters. At the camp Jon entered the 600 meter race. He ran hard and finished third. He was only a second grader at the time and he had no idea who Tracy Walters was, but he enjoyed the experience. Don Kardong may have even been at the camp. This was before Jon would know their names and their impact on the sport of distance running.

Jon enjoyed the effort based rewards of running and so he continued to run. He ran to and from school at Adams Elementary, but did not think anything of it. His family grew up on the South Hill of Spokane but that was back when Freya street was still a dirt road. The South Hill still had vasts amount of hay fields. Before Jon ran off to school he helped his father earn a little extra money by tipping hay bales. Jon and his brother would tip the bales of hay over just in front of their fathers truck so that he could reach down and grab the wires more easily. The hay fields were located over where Chase Middle School would eventually be built. The vast expanse of the Palouse was an area for Jon to explore.

Alongside Jon in his adventures in the woods was his father. Together they would go into the woods with a chainsaw, cut down trees, and split wood.

These were the moments that brought Jon peace: being in the woods with his Dad, up in the mountains, in the wheat fields, or out on a run by himself. Operating a chainsaw required complete focus to the task at hand and the awesome power that went with using those tools.

The use of the wood was not some quaint experience but a necessary commodity. Jon grew up knowing that his family was poor. As he saw his classmates show up to the start of the school year wearing new brand name clothes, he quickly realized that the patterns of his shirts and the stitching on his pants were not anything that anyone would recognize from a storefront window.

Small Jon sprouted into his taller figure. The clothes and patterns his mother had ready always needed adjustments as each season passed. And so, breaking stereotypes that all those kids who go to Ferris were rich, Jon went to school, trying not to draw too much attention to himself. He felt an anger and a little ostracism as he went to and from school. He had friends, but he also knew of other kids that would try and pick on him because of where he came from. Running was an outlet for Jon, a place where he could put his pain and anger and receive some positive attention. He needed someone like Pat Tyson to help him realize where he had his strengths.

Jon would actually cross paths with Pat Tyson in 1979. As a fifteen year old Jon first met Pat while at Clear Lake Cross Country Camp (now known as White Pass); one of the earliest running camps in the country. Pat was a camp counselor and young coach over middle school athletes. Jon rode the mini-bus to and from runs at the camp and saw this young coach starting to refine his craft. Over the years Jon would eventually compete against Pat and always try to win like he did.

Jon was also heavily influenced by his father. Jon's Dad was an avid Scouter. In 1976 he organized and led 25 kids on a bike trip across the United States during one summer. Jon was part of the troop making their way across the country. They road from Spokane, Washington to Washington DC. A trip of nearly 2,500 miles. All along the way Jon was there listening to his father and watching as he guided and directed the endeavor, making sure that everyone survived. The enthusiasm for high adventure continued throughout Jon's youth and he eventually earned his Eagle Scout award.

Jon knew that his father did not make any money from being a Scoutmaster, but he recognized his passion and dedication towards making boys into men.

Initially Jon did not turn out for cross country. Jon's father loved football and played during his high school days at West Valley in Spokane. Jon decided that he would turn out for the sport. He sat mostly on the bench but could beat everyone on the team at the end of practice when the football coach had everyone run a half mile. Recognizing that others around him were getting larger and putting on weight, Jon saw that his body and skills were in the distances. His eighth grade year in track proved he had speed, because he won the city championship in the 800 meter. Herm Caviness even paid those young athletes at Sacajawea a visit, trying to encourage them to turn out for cross country in the fall. But Jon wanted to be like his father. No one in his family had ever been a distance runner.

The day after the football season ended, however, Jon went out for a seven mile run along the Jamison and Ben Burr roads that tie into the Palouse Highway. Later that winter, Herm helped Jon enter into an indoor meet at the Kibbie Dome in Moscow, Idaho. Jon would run a half mile race in 2:05.

Herm knew talent and toughness when he saw it.

Also watching that race unfold was none other than Len Long, Jon's future assistant at North Central.

Jon knew of Len Long, a former athlete of Tracy Walter's and former teammate of Gerry Lindgren, but he only initially knew of him as that coach across town. Len was the head coach at North Central acting as the cross town rival with Ferris during the late 70s and early 80s. Len coached North Central to a state boys cross country title in 1977 and three other second place finishes in the 70s.

Len and Herm were coaches with distinct approaches. Herm's approach was more militaristic whereas Len's was more free spirited; their coaching style grew out of the time period they lived.

Jon had his share of individual setbacks in racing. In 1979, during Jon's sophomore year he qualified for state in cross country and finished fourth overall, leading Ferris to a fourth place team finish. The highest placing team at state from the GSL that year was North Central coached by Len Long who

Herm Caviness far left; Jon Knight holding the 4th place team trophy at state

had his team finishing second overall. Jon's sophomore year of track in 1980 was interrupted with the Mt. Saint Helens eruption. Jon's family met at Hutton Elementary to divert themselves as gray ash came falling out of the sky like snow. Jon's uncle was a teacher at Hutton. As a means of distraction, Jon, his father and uncles decided to play basketball while the city came to a standstill. In the process of getting a rebound, Jon came down and twisted his ankle. That year, due to the Mt. Saint Helens eruption, the district coaches came together to decide who would go on and represent the area. Jon's ill timed injury kept him from advancing forward. Herm's success at Ferris was attacked by other coaches; seeing Jon's injury they banded together to keep the kid coming off of an injury from competing at state.

During Jon's junior year of cross country in 1980 he again led the charge for Ferris taking second place individually as the team won the state championship. During track in 1981 he had gone through the season undefeated up until the district race when he came down with bronchitis. At districts he finished fifth and had to watch from the sidelines as others competed at state.

Jon's senior year during cross country in 1981 he ran exceptionally well and at the state meet he finished second place overall yet again. The team again won the state title, the last that they would win for over twenty years.

Jon had one more offseason to prove himself and to come to grips with the reality that his father was dying.

Jon used the time ahead of him to prepare. He could not control what would happen to his father. He could not control what would happen to his future or anyone else's, but he could control his effort on the roads and trails each day. Running was a relief, an exhaust, an escape, and a necessity.

Anger welled up in Jon and then was poured out on the pavement and trails he blazed morning and night. He had this gift and ability that he worked so hard to improve upon, and yet he had been denied the opportunity to show his potential.

Rick Riley had been a multiple state champion.

Randy James, who had also run at Ferris, had won multiple state titles before heading off to run at the University of Oregon where he became teammates with

Prefontaine and Pat Tyson. Randy had returned to teach at Ferris High School and was a very real inspiration for Jon as he sat in his science class.

The individual titles that had been so close for Jon seemed illusive.

Jon knew he had one last opportunity. It was an opportunity to wake up early and train. He tried to see through the dark early morning skies while keeping alive the bright dreams he had inside. It was an opportunity to push the pace and break away from everyone no matter the workout or race in front of him.

Jon was ready for his senior year of track, and nothing would deter him from the final goal of winning the mile and two mile.

Everything had gone according to plan, all except for a pain that appeared right after the district meet in 1982. His right foot throbbed. He knew his body well and knew it was something more than a strain.

Jon had a broken foot.

He had placed so much stress, strain, and torque on his foot that the bone inside it fractured.

With a week to prepare for his final high school races in the mile and two mile, it appeared that Jon would be denied once more the goal of winning.

The week before state was not full of much running anyway, but Jon had to stay mentally intact. Everything hurt. The pace hurt, the warm ups hurt, the workouts hurt, the cool downs hurt, the movements of that foot hurt.

Jon was still coming to grips with the reality that his father was dying; an experience that had jolted him at the district meet in cross country the previous fall. Running was where he had taken his pain, and now it seemed he could not even do that.

He had one last week to give his all. Rest would come, but before that recovery he had to put one foot painfully in front of the other. He had to use his mind and heart to overrule what he was currently feeling.

On May 28, 1982 Jon took off his warm ups and lined up in the 1,600 meter final at the Lincoln Bowl in Tacoma. He had envisioned this race previously, the only thing absent was his broken foot. The race started quickly, but not overly fast for a mile event.

The first half of the race was run in 2:11 which was 4:22 pace. But it was precisely at half a mile that the real racing started.

Jon tried to put himself into a position to win.

With a foot on fire with pain, Jon went on the outside lane to pass and move towards the front. He ran down the backstretch with shooting pain in every step, struggling to keep it all together.

Through the curve and into the homestretch he went by hearing the bell lap and the time: 3:13.

Jon had just run a 62 second lap and he still needed to run faster.

Everyone was making their final charge, their last ditch effort, trying to chase down their own individual dreams.

Jon, with his broken foot, broke away from those chasing him and kept charging down the backstretch, opening up a slight lead. Around the curve he went, hurting the whole time. He broke the field and finished first clocking 4:11.61. Second place was three seconds back.

The elation of winning was evident, but the burden Jon felt as he climbed to and from the podium came as he realized that the following night he had the two mile race still to run.

Running through that two mile race Jon knew inside that he was running through hell. He confronted the pain, fortunate that the break had occurred the previous week and not two weeks ago. He could endure difficulty, but he could not endure forever.

Once more Jon won, running 9:03.89 and again beating the second place finisher by three seconds.

Those would be the last races Jon's father would see him run.

After graduating from Ferris, Jon attended the University of Montana and ran on their cross country and track team. During the end of his freshman year, Jon's father passed away from terminal brain cancer.

Shooting Clay Tiles

After only a year and a half at the University of Montana, Jon eventually transferred to Washington State University. He continued his studies as a pre-med major, hoping to one day go on to medical school. Amidst his busy academic schedule he competed on the WSU team and helped them earn a seventh place finish at the NCAA Championships in 1984. He also ran his way to personal bests: 3:48 for 1,500 meter, 14:05 for 5k, and 29:25 for 10k. During his junior year at WSU he won all their league meet 5k's which is a tradition no longer occurring in the current PAC 12.

The shift from pre-med to high school teacher and coach was quite unexpected for Jon. At a track meet he saw a teammate take a nasty fall at a water station in the steeplechase. His first inclination was not to use his medical knowledge to help out but to actually run the other direction as he averted his eyes. He realized that was not a good sign to continue on his current academic route. Part of the reason to go into the medical field had to do with his father's death. Jon had also spent some time with Dr. Reynolds in Spokane, a pediatric oncology doctor and he came to the realization that his life would not be spent in the medical field.

Jon's next academic goal was to get a PhD in history and he went down that avenue. However, as he spent more and more time studying and preparing his dissertation he realized that the eventual road he was on led to a college somewhere in obscurity hovered behind books and away from people. He envisioned himself in some small college in South Dakota reading and preparing notes for the next classroom lecture and so he decided that future was not something he wanted to see played out. He still plans on finishing his PhD someday but he knew that he needed to do something else for the time being.

Textbooks had shown him how to analyze anatomy and the makeup of history but Jon felt he lacked control over his own destiny. He did not know what story would be written of his own life, but he knew what he did not want to do. He wanted to make a difference in the lives of young people, to stay close to his family, and to have a reliable paying job.

Finally, Jon decided to earn his teaching certificate and become a high school teacher. He returned to Spokane and had his first and only teaching job starting at North Central High School. Jon went to work envisioning himself as an educator. Never before did he think he would be a coach. However, after his first year at the school a coaching vacancy opened up and he was hired.

The school that Tracy Walters attended and started on his running odyssey had transformed since the 1940s. Spokane had grown and expanded. As the frontier of Spokane pushed farther and farther out, those with money and means continued to build newer and nicer homes further from the heart of Spokane.

Sitting nearly dead center from an aerial map of the city one sees North Central High School. The population at the school ebbed initially but lately has flowed out to other schools. The houses slated for that school are old and those able to afford them and willing to live there are kids whose parents have little money. Jon Knight sees former and younger versions of himself walking through the halls at school everyday. Jon Knight was a North Central kid who just happened to go to Ferris.

Jon's arrival at North Central and his initial coaching endeavors came in the early 1990s. He was thrown into the thick of it trying to catch up to Pat Tyson at Mead while also trying to go against Bob Barbero at University High School and Mike Hadway at Ferris. The problem Jon faced was the problem all the coaches had at the time; trying to figure out how to compete and survive amongst the best.

The solution to North Central's problem seemed counterintuitive: they should move down in classification. Instead of trying to beat themselves up by running in the 4A classification, they should acknowledge that the number of students attending their school would rightfully place them in the 3A competition. Instead of dying to try and even make it to state, North Central could make it to state in the 3A and have a chance to win. Once he could convince his athletes that

© Lori Wordell

Len Long & Jon Knight

they were winners and that the program had value, then the students would continue to show up and North Central would have established their own excellence.

The move to 3A started in 2004 when North Central made it to state and finished second to Bishop Blanchet by only six points. In the 4A division that year Ferris won and Mead took second. The following year, in 2005, North Central again took second place, but this time to Sehome and they lost by twenty-six points. The team was so close to winning. Once again, in the 4A category that year Ferris won followed by Mead.

Finally in 2006, North Central won the state meet in the 3A classification. The seven athletes on that first team title were: Andy Kimple (sophomore), Steve Hicks (junior), Leon Dean (sophomore), Adam Tyler (junior), Jeff Howard (sophomore), Mitch Maly (junior), and Adam Reid (sophomore). The team did not have a single person graduating and they had won by 14 points. In 2004 and 2005 North Central had three seniors on their squads each year. Young athletes had finally bought into what the older guys on the team had tried to accomplish and they finally helped North Central win their first title.

An outsider looking in could say that this group in 2006 was merely running against watered down competition; that their title was not as valid or meaningful as those running against the larger schools. The 2006 North Central team's average time for the state meet was 16:44 and the spread between their first and fifth runner was forty-nine seconds. By the time these sophomores on the team were seniors, only two years later, the average team time at state dropped to 15:36 and the spread from their first to their fifth athlete was only twenty three seconds.

They were as a whole more than a minute faster and closer together.

This was the future national championship team. When North Central lined up at the Nike Cross Nationals race in 2008, the only race to determine the true national championship team, they won. In the process of winning, they beat York High School's squad coached by one of the greatest high school coaches ever, Joe Newton. York won the inaugural race in 2004. The small, little 3A school from downtown Spokane was better than every other big name school in the country.

Leon Dean chronicled their season and published a book titled *Footsteps in Time*. Leon was part of that first team to win in 2006 as a sophomore. As a senior he helped North Central win the first and only Nike Cross National team title from Spokane. This one city has accounted for more podium appearances at this event than any other city in the country on the boy's race, totalling seven podium appearances.

In the first 14 years of the race, Spokane sent seventeen teams to the event. For at least four of those years they sent two teams from the same town and same league to the national title race.

The rise of North Central's distance program is nothing short of remarkable. North Central as a team had not competed at the state meet since 1987 (where they took second) and had not qualified for the state meet for seventeen years. Jon started coaching at North Central in 1992, right as Pat Tyson was getting the Davis boys to lead the way for the greatest high school team ever. Jon's first twelve years coaching brought with it frustration at having never sent a team to state. Almost the entire lifetimes of those athletes on the team represented the last time that North Central had participated in the state meet.

So what changed?

The move to 3A definitely helped North Central, but it was more than that; it was the work and wisdom of Jon Knight. He will gladly shift the balance of success towards others involved with the program: to the athletes, the parents, to his assistant Len Long, to the tradition started by Tracy (whom he refers to as Grandpa Coach). The reality is that much of that success stems from his inspiration.

Tracy Walters, far right; Len Long, 2nd from right; Jon Knight, 3rd from right; with the 2008 National Champions, North Central High School

When Jon Knight goes to a coaches clinic he is seeking out inspiration, but he will often go to unlikely sources to find it. Instead of standing around talking to other coaches about how to dice up workouts and what the proper amount of mileage to rest ratio should be, Jon will seek out throwers coaches and ask them about their craft. Perhaps there is something new to learn from an unlikely source or a connection to be made from an alternative point of view.

Jon learned that surrounding oneself with the same voice is dangerous.

Hearing the same thing over and over again eliminates innovation. Arthur Lydiard, Percy Cerutty, Bill Bowerman and Mihaly Igloi were making advances for their time because they were experimenting and challenging the traditional narrative of training.

One of the most influential trademarks of North Central's program comes not from the chocolate milk they drink after hard workouts, or the Bulgarian deadlifts in the weight room, but Eastern Philosophy.

From *Tao Te Ching* by Laozi, written around the sixth century before Christ, Jon explains to his athletes the analogy of shooting for clay tiles. Archers at the time would shoot clay tiles as a means of honing in on their craft. This particular skill was useful in wartime and it could provide financial success.

The philosophy goes that if someone shot clay tiles for nothing or merely for fun then they will do well and presumably hit nearly every shot. However, once someone starts to shoot these same clay tiles for a brass buckle (or something of value) they start to become nervous and likely start to miss their mark. Finally, if someone shoots for gold then they will either become blind or see multiple targets instead of one.

Jon points out to his athletes that the tiles these ancient warriors shot at were the same size and dimension during each shot, but it was the motivation that changed the approach. He ingrains into his athletes the idea that they simply need to go out and execute. They are to approach the state meet the same as they approached every other meet that season, with the desire and approach that they can win if they run tough. The state meet or national title are important but also meaningless.

For athletes on his team mystified by the Eastern Philosophy, Jon will borrow from Lou Holtz, the former Notre Dame college coach and paraphrase what he said regarding football. "When they run come forward and when they pass draw back. Don't complicate the game." He helps nervous young athletes navigate their emotions as they approach big races.

From *The Art of War* by Sun Tzu, written around the fifth century before Christ, Jon will explain how ancient Chinese war tactics align nicely with race strategy. In war, like in running, it is best to show up and strike when the enemy is tired. Planning out when to throw a surge to break away from a competitor can be very valuable. These racing tactics are helpful, but ultimately Jon is more concerned about what happens to the minds and hearts of his athletes when they are not out on the trails and roads of Spokane.

The Honor Code or Code of Honor

One of the unflinching rules that Jon has built his program around is what he terms the *1-30 Rule*. If his team runs thirty guys deep he will do nothing unless it helps everyone, no matter if they are number one or number thirty. If something does not benefit everyone, or it only benefits the top seven on varsity, then he will not allow that activity or idea to persist.

Consequently, Jon knew that he had to see more than time. Running and winning are nice; they are fun when coupled together. But, as a coach, there ought to be more than helping a kid on JV break six minutes in the mile, or helping a kid run on the varsity squad, or providing a way for his top athletes to win individual state titles, team titles, and even a national title.

This time of introspection corresponded with Jon's family attending the Unitarian Universalist Church of Spokane. Jon's daughter was in second grade at the time and many of her friends went to church and so Jon and his wife decided they should start to attend as well. Jon saw that running had to mean more than lowering times. Running and training should influence the way that his athletes viewed time and these lessons should stick with his athletes long after they recovered from the workouts he put them through. Jon saw that he could help these young boys become men that would eventually become husbands and fathers in their respective communities.

For over ten years the Honor Code Jon decided to implement has been a staple that each athlete of his decides to live by while they run for him at North Central. As part of that honor code the boys on the team will provide service to the local community. One project might include aiding Riverside State Park by cutting back small trees. Another ongoing project for the past four years includes sponsoring a young student in Nepal so that he can have an education. They help to pay for his books, tuition, uniform and course load, all so that he can have an opportunity to make his own strides in the world. During Thanksgiving you will find North Central athletes preparing place settings of food for over a thousand women and young children from the local shelters in need.

These moments are not trumpeted, but silently and dutifully done. There is a very real need in all of the communities across the country for people to involve themselves in serving their fellow men. Jon just helps the boys to see the opportunity to fight these very real and often tragic social wars. Whether it's running for a state title or serving up a Thanksgiving meal, the tasks are really like clay tiles. Small repetitive tasks that need to be fulfilled, which in and of themselves are fulfilling. They do it without the thought of reward at the end.

They do it for nothing because it is simply fun and good to do.

Jon sat on the receiving end of service shown to him and his family. As his father's health continued to deteriorate, his coach, Herm Caviness showed up with a pallet of canned food and plenty of split firewood for the family. Herm's church bandied together to help someone in need. Jon has seen Tracy Walters open up his house to everyone and anyone over the years. The impact of Tracy's Camp Reed allowed Jon to have his first race. The string of decisions that followed has allowed North Central to become one of the greatest programs in GSL history.

No one knows how long Jon will continue to shoot clay tiles as a coach. If he is anything like his predecessors he will not be able to stay away from the sport. Anyone showing up to the Washington State cross country meet will likely find Tracy walking around as well as Herm. Pat Tyson still shows up to recruit for Gonzaga. Bob Barbero is helping his son at University build their program. Mike Hadway in the spring of 2018 finished up his final track season and has been aided by Herm Caviness' son, Chris Caviness. Herm's grandson and granddaughter both run on Ferris' teams. Likewise, Tracy Walters has watched his grandchildren compete as his son Kelly was the head track coach at North Central High School from 1998 to 2011. He lead their teams to four state titles. Don continues to keep Bloomsday plugging and chugging along. Sylvia has not stopped volunteering. Gerry keeps running in Hawaii and Rick keeps coaching at St. Georges private school in Spokane. Tyler Byers works with his wife to raise their children. Likewise the Hawkins children are all married now and are in the process of passing the baton off to the next generation.

Like Pre, Tom, or others that have gone on, all will eventually finish their race. The questions become: What are we doing with our time? Who are we trailing and how close are we to them? What and who are we racing for?

One of the great traditions at North Central involves the end of year toasts. Following their belief and rule of 1-30, the team has their last meal together before the JV All City meet. It is the last time that the whole team is together. Everyone has the opportunity to raise their glass (full of apple juice and not champagne) to honor those on the team and to speak of what the season has meant to them. The underclassman are often short and joking in their speeches. The juniors and seniors are much more heartfelt as they express what four years of involvement in the program has meant to them. Tears are often shed as these boys search for words that act as weak substitutes for what they feel.

This is the story of the *human* race; competitive, courageous, difficult, and demanding as it should be.

Representing America

Jon biked from Spokane, Washington to Washington DC with his father and scout troop. Little did young Jon know that he would go from spanning the country to someday representing it.

Jon had the unique opportunity to represent the United States of America with the junior national team. He competed at a cross country race in Milan, Italy in 1982. Jon's father had wanted to inspire his son and those in his scout troop to greatness. Jon, like his father, also wanted to pass forward those same opportunities to his own children.

Jon's daughter Katie Knight competed with the same grit and determination of her father. After finishing as the runner up in cross country to Amy Eliose-Neale of Glacier Peak High School, for multiple years, Katie finally broke

Katie Knight, center; Representing USA in Edinburgh, Scotland 2012

through and won her own individual state cross country title in 2011. She followed up her state championship victory with another win at the prestigious BorderClash meet featuring Washington and Oregon's best prep runners. Finally she competed at the junior women's 4k race at the BUPA Great Edinburgh Cross Country International Challenge meet at Holyrood Park. The race featured teams from the USA, Great Britain, and a European select team. She finished third in the race. Katie was not the lone Spokane athlete competing and representing team USA.

Nathan Weitz of Shadle Park High School and Andrew Gardner of Mead High School would also compete in the 6k race at this International meet. Andrew Gardner finished fifth and Nathan Weitz finished eleventh. Of the boys six member international team, one third of the it was made up of runners from Spokane.

This international experience for Spokane athletes was not an isolated incident.

At the 2013 state championship North Central High School had not only the fastest team but the fastest runner: Tanner Anderson. Placing first overall

Left to right - Kai Wilmot; Tanner Anderson; John Dressel;
Comprising half the USA National Team

in 2013, Tanner improved from his sophomore season by beating cross town rival John Dressel of Mt. Spokane. John had finished second at the state meet in 2012. Tanner did so by dropping a 14:44 time for 5k which was 50 seconds faster than his time from the previous year. It's hard to show up Tanner Anderson's performance at state, but his teammate Kai Wilmot did just that at Nike Cross Nationals.

At the 2013 national race, Kai opened a lead late in the race that was insurmountable and became the national champion and new course record holder running 14:59 for 5k. Tanner finished third overall and the North Central boys team finished eighth in the country.

John Dressel was not to be outdone. He competed at the 2013 Foot Locker Nationals race where he led with only 150 meters to go before being outkicked. He finished second overall. The best male distance runners in the country were once more from one town, Spokane, and two different high schools: North Central and Mt. Spokane.

These three athletes: Kai Wilmot, Tanner Anderson, and John Dressel represented the USATF junior national team that competed in Edinburgh, Scotland in January 2014. Of the six member team, half of it was made up of athletes from Spokane.

State championships and national titles do not occur everyday. International teams are made up of few athletes. People ask, why does Spokane continue to achieve? The answer to this question has little to do with geography or training programs. It has everything to do with people giving their best and being inspired by the efforts of those around them. This starts in elementary school and continues through middle and high school. From beginning to end people need best efforts and high expectations. Work becomes a joy when effort is rewarded.

The same question could be asked of the runners from Ethiopia or Kenya. Why do they perpetually succeed? Is it some secret workout? Altitude? The answer is that they have people who see sacrifice and success. They witness it firsthand and then say to themselves, *Why not me?*

America is a country built upon the success of those willing to sacrifice. Our communities are built and sustained by sacrifice. Marriages and families are sustained by those willing to sacrifice. Teams are united by those willing to sacrifice. And those who see sacrifice as a bargain are the ones who will perpetually succeed. It is important to recognize what qualifies as success. If success only means those that run on state championship, national championship, or Olympic teams, then almost all people are failures. Success in running, as in life, comes from sustained striving towards your own personal excellence. It is for the person crossing the line first as well as the person finishing last and everyone between so long as they improve against their previous efforts and times. Most great running stories and tales are never known because we are distracted by those at the front.

Starts and Finishes

The start of the running revolution in Spokane began with Tracy Walters taking up track during the spring of his senior year of high school in 1948. This seemingly small event involving Tracy's participation in an after school program shifted the trajectory of lives untold. Years went by before his efforts would impact Gerry Lindgren; the pair of them would aid the inspiration for Herm Caviness and Rick Riley to dare and dream. People from across the state, Pat Tyson and Don Kardong, were inspired by the news of those runners coming out of Spokane. Sitting in the neighboring state of Oregon, Steve Prefontaine saw the times and knew the stories of Gerry and Rick and wanted to chase after their records. Each runner passing through ushers in another round of inspiration. Their efforts to attempt the impossible fuel the desire for others to try.

What is remarkable about running is the honesty it requires of its participants. Sustained best efforts are expected from the very beginning to the very end. Runners try to go from where they currently are to where they think they can be. This is as true of someone on a world class level as it is of anyone at the back of the pack. Time is the measuring piece. There are positions, placements, mile markers, and other statistics, but the greatest measurement of success in a runner is found in their willingness to run into the unknown.

The start of Spokane's success has been sustained by those following after the initial efforts of those highlighted in part one of this book. The running boom in Spokane continued because there were coaches not highlighted in these pages that also prepared their athletes for success. There were other families not mentioned in this book that were also bit by the running bug. There were guys and girls on junior varsity squads not mentioned here that gave everything in practices and races, and made those on varsity earn their place. Sylvia Quinn may be the captain of the volunteers in Spokane but there are many others who have served alongside of her.

The hope with running is to win. The reality is that everyone loses. There just needs to be a large enough sample of people over a long enough period of time and every champion will lose. But losses do not define success.

The running legacy of Spokane could end. The start of a legacy somewhere else in this country and around the world could begin. Another Rift Valley of distance running is just one season or race away.

All it takes are people daring to dream while continually running into the unknown.

Acknowledgments

Acknowledgments

This book has likewise been an attempt to toast the efforts of those who have made Spokane distance running hold its value. I appreciate all of these incredible people who allowed me to interview them and share their stories. I hope that others can create their own Rift Valleys across America and throughout the world. *Varsity Seven* is an ideal that each person strives to achieve as they explore their own unknown peaks and valleys, while eventually laying tracks of excellence for others to follow. To achieve such success there has to be coaches, athletes, and families that are all committed.

I have been honored to write this book. It has been one of the greatest adventures of my life. I want and need to thank everyone for allowing me to interview them and tell their stories. Tracy Walters, Herm Caviness, Gerry Lindgren and Tyler Byers, Rick Riley, Don Kardong, Pat Tyson, Mike Hadway, Dave Fuller, Jim McBride, Bob Barbero, Jon Knight, Sylvia Quinn, Hannah Ungricht and all my family. This has been a labor of love.

I must thank my wife Mary, who was and is a distance runner in her own right. She gave me the time and support to chase down this dream. She blazes a trail of greatness that I will forever follow.

Index: Stats

State Meet Team Champion Results 4A since the first Washington State Cross Country Meet in 1959:

1959 - Shadle Park 1st

1960 - Gonzaga 2nd, Shadle Park 3rd

1961 - Lewis & Clark 1st, Shadle Park 4th

1962 - Shadle Park 1st, Rogers 3rd

1963 - Rogers 1st, Shadle Park 2nd, North Central 5th

1964 - Rogers 2nd, Shadle Park 4th

1965 - Rogers 1st, Shadle Park 5th

1966 - Lewis & Clark 1st (Division 2)

1967 - Rogers 3rd, Lewis & Clark 16th

1968 - Ferris 1st, Lewis & Clark 6th

1969 - Lewis & Clark 2nd

1970 - Lewis & Clark 3rd

1971 - Ferris 2nd, North Central 3rd

1972 - North Central 2nd, Ferris 7th

1973 - Ferris 3rd, North Central 7th

1974 - Ferris 2nd, Rogers 8th

1975 - Shadle Park 5th, Mead 6th

1976 - Mead 1st, North Central 5th

1977 - North Central 1st, Mead 2nd

1978 - North Central 2nd, Ferris 4th

1979 - North Central 2nd, Ferris 4th

1980 - Ferris 1st, North Central 2nd

1981 - Ferris 1st, Shadle Park 8th

1982 - Shadle Park 1st, University 6th

1983 - Mead 2nd, University 7th

1984 - University 5th, Ferris 6th

1985 - North Central 4th, Ferris 8th

1986 - Mead 9th, Shadle Park 13th

1987 - North Central 2nd, Shadle Park 5th

1988 - Mead 1st, Ferris 2nd

1989 - Mead 1st, University 2nd

1990 - Mead 1st, University 2nd

1991 - Mead 1st, University 4th

1992 - Mead 1st, Lewis & Clark 7th

1993 - Mead 1st, Ferris 3rd

1994 - Mead 1st

1995 - Mead 1st, Ferris 2nd

1996 - Mead 1st, University 2nd

1997 - University 1st, Mead 2nd, Gonzaga Prep 3rd

1998 - University 1st, Mead 2nd, Lewis & Clark 3rd

1999 - University 1st, Mount Spokane 2nd, Mead 3rd

2000 - Mead 1st, University 2nd, Mt. Spokane 3rd, Ferris 5th

2001 - Mead 1st, Mt. Spokane 2nd, Ferris 3rd

2002 - Mead 1st, Ferris 3rd, Mt. Spokane 7th

2003 - Ferris 1st, Mead 3rd, Mt. Spokane 4th

2004 - Ferris 1st, Mead 2nd, Lewis & Clark 5th

2005 - Ferris 1st, Mead 2nd, Lewis & Clark 15th

2006 - Ferris 1st, Mead 2nd, Central Valley 3rd

2007 - Mead 1st, Central Valley 4th

2008 - Mead 1st, Ferris 3rd

2009 - Ferris 1st, Lewis & Clark 5th

2010 - Lewis & Clark 2nd, Ferris 4th

2011 - Central Valley 5th

2012 - Central Valley 1st, Lewis & Clark 4th

2013 - Central Valley 3rd

2014 - Central Valley 5th, University 7th

2015 - Ferris 4th, University 7th, Central Valley 9th

2016 - Central Valley 2nd, Ferris 4th

2017 - Lewis & Clark 1st, Central Valley 2nd

One could say that in the late 2000s the GSL has lost a step. It is important to remember that North Central moved down to the 3A category and has won state titles from 2006-2016 and have since won the high school national championship at Nike Cross Nationals in 2008. Gig Harbor and Eisenhower may not have actually been the better team that day if North Central had been in the race.

GSL State Champs for 4A: 1959 - 2017

$36/59 = 61\%$

GSL State Champs for 3A with North Central:

2006 - 2016

If state championships are but one indicator, it is important to note how many individual athletes competed at Foot Locker Nationals from Spokane since the inaugural race in 1979. The following is a list of both male and female athletes from Spokane that have competed at Foot Locker with the year they competed, the place they finished, the school they represented and the time on the course.

1979 - 13th, Mike McGlade, Northwest Christian, 15:38

1982 - 19th, Annette Hand, Central Valley, 17:58

1983 - 16th, Christine Slentz, Lewis & Clark, 18:08

1987 - 12th, Chris Lewis, Mead, 15:22

1988 - 25th, Lisa Dressel, Rogers, 18:43

1989 - 7th, Stuart Burnham, Ferris, 15:15
   16th, Greg Kuntz, Mead, 15:31
   3rd, Sarah Schwald, Mead, 17:35
   14th, Carrie Moller, Rogers, 18:14

1992 - 31st, Matt Davis, Mead, 16:51
   25th, Jessica Fry, Rogers, 18:58

1993 - 3rd, Matt Davis, Mead, 15:08
   10th, Micah Davis, Mead, 15:24

1994 - 30th, Skiy Detray, Mead, 16:08

1995 - 12th, Isaac Hawkins, Ferris, 15:33

1996 - 26th, Isaac Hawkins, Ferris, 16:29

2000 - 23rd, Michael Kiter, Shadle Park, 15:41

2001 - 10th, Jesse Fayant, Mead, 15:07

2002 - 11th, Jamie Geissler, Mead, 17:53

2003 - 15th, Evan Garber, Mead, 15:31

2005 - 36th, Taylor Nepon, Mead, 16:14

      4th, Megan O'Reilly, Mt. Spokane, 17:36

2010 - 4th, Andrew Gardner, Mead, 15:18

      31st, Nathan Weitz, Shadle Park 15:52

      36th, Kendra Weitz, Shadle Park, 18:38

2011 - 3rd, Nathan Weitz, Shadle Park, 15:21

      6th, Andrew Gardner, Mead, 15:24

2012 - 11th, Andrew Gardner, Mead, 15:34

      14th, John Dressel, Mt. Spokane, 15:37

2013 - 2nd, John Dressel, Mt. Spokane, 15:10

2014 - 6th, John, Dressel, Mt. Spokane, 15:18

2015 - 25th, Justin Janke, North Central, 15:45

2016 - 6th, Kearan Nelson, Central Valley, 17:48

      16th, Amir Ado, Ferris, 15:31

2017 - 37th, Turlan Morlan, Gonzaga Prep, 16:38

      19th, Katie Thronson, Lewis & Clark, 18:26

Out of the 38 years that Foot Locker has been run, Spokane has sent at least one male or female athlete to 24 years worth of competition; that is just over 63% of the time there has been someone representing one city, and in some years there were multiple people sent.

The final set of statistics that sets Spokane apart as a national force in distance running, would be the most recent national race, the Nike Cross Nationals. The race takes place in Portland, Oregon and Nike flies out teams of athletes from across the country to compete for the national title each year. The first race was run in 2004. Since that time, there has only been two years in which one team did not represent Spokane. The results indicate the year, the place of the team, the team name, and the school they represented.

2004 - 3rd, Tyson's Army, Mead
       13th, Southside Farm Team, Ferris
2005 - 4th, Mead XC Club, Mead
       10th, Spokane XC Club, Ferris
2006 - 3rd, Spokane XC Club, Ferris
       5th, Mead XC Club, Mead
2007 - 6th, North Central XC Club, North Central
2008 - 1st, North Central XC Club, North Central
2009 - 2nd, South Spokane XC Club, Ferris
       7th, North Spokane XC Club, North Central
2010 - 6th, North Spokane XC Club, North Central
       15th, Central Spokane XC Club, Lewis & Clark
2011 - 7th, North Spokane XC Club, North Central
2012 - 3rd, North Spokane XC Club, North Central
2013 - 8th, North Spokane XC Club, North Central
2014 - 3rd, North Spokane XC Club, North Central
2017 - 13th, Verdale, Central Valley

Of the 14 Nike Cross Nationals run, Spokane has sent at least one team 12 times, with six of those teams making the podium by being in the top three, and one of those teams winning the national title. Spokane has sent five different schools to compete at the national event: Ferris, Mead, North Central, Lewis & Clark and Central Valley. The Greater Spokane League is only made up of ten teams; half of the league has competed on the national level. The recent success is only an outgrowth of the start of Spokane's distance running.

Bibliography

Introduction: Spokane, a Rift Valley of American Distance Running
"Nairobi." *Wikipedia*, Wikimedia Foundation, 10 Jan. 2018, en.wikipedia.org/wiki/ Nairobi.
"Iten." *Wikipedia*, Wikimedia Foundation, 6 Jan. 2018, en.wikipedia.org/wiki/Iten.
"Colm O'Connell." *Wikipedia*, Wikimedia Foundation, 5 June 2017, en.wikipedia. org/ wiki/Colm_O%27Connell.
Mcloughlin, Anne. *Man On A Mission*. Motive Television Ltd, 2011, vimeo.com/33808532.
"Washington (State)." *Wikipedia*, Wikimedia Foundation, 10 Jan. 2018, en.wikipedia. org/wiki/Washington_(state).
"State Cross Country Past Results 1959-Present." *WIAA | Washington Interscholastic Activities Association*, www.wiaa.com/ardisplay.aspx?ID=1277.
"NikeCrossNationals.com - Nike Cross Nationals Official Site - NXN - Results - 2004-2017 NXN Results." *RunnerSpace.com*, nxn.runnerspace.com/eprofile. php?do=title&title_id=187&event_id=13.
"Foot Locker Cross Country History." *Foot Locker Cross Country*, www.footlockercc. com/history/history.shtml.
"High School Sports Participation Increases for 28th Straight Year, Nears 8 Million Mark." *NFHS*, 6 Sept. 2017, www.n s.org/articles/high-school-sports-participation-increases-for-28th-straight-year-nears-8-million-mark/.
Part One: The Hounds and the Hares
"Paper Chase (Game)." *Wikipedia*, Wikimedia Foundation, 25 Oct. 2017, en. wikipedia. org/wiki/Paper_Chase_(game).
Tracy Walters: From Wimpy to Tuffy
Editor, Justin Reed | Sports. "A Look at Gonzaga's Football History." *The Gonzaga Bulletin*, 28 Sept. 2016, www.gonzagabulletin.com/sports/article_94427394-8112- 11e6-94ba-1f37e0d69c58.html.
"Javier Montez Bio, Stats, and Results." *Olympics at Sports-Reference.com*, www. sports- reference.com/olympics/athletes/mo/javier-montez-1.html.
"Endicott, Washington." *Wikipedia*, Wikimedia Foundation, 2 Jan. 2018, en. wikipedia. org/wiki/Endicott,_Washington.
Lindeen, Gordon Reinhold. History of the Settlement and Development of Endicott, Washington, to 1930. A thesis submitted in partial fulfillment of the requirements for the degree of Master of Arts in History. Washington State University. Special Collections. 1960. Print
Spokesman-R, John Blanchette e. "Cougars Lose Legend; 'Tuffy' Ellingsen Dies." *Spokesman.com*, e Spokesman-Review, 28 Aug. 2011, www.spokesman. com/stories/1997/oct/28/cougars-lose-legend-tuffy-ellingsen-dies/.
"HistoryLink.org." *Shadle Park: Spokane's First "Modern" High School - HistoryLink. org*, www.historylink.org/File/8724.
"John Rankin Rogers." *Wikipedia*, Wikimedia Foundation, 28 Dec. 2017, en.wikipedia. org/wiki/John_Rankin_Rogers.
Gerry Lindgren: Hillyard's Finest
"HistoryLink.org." *Spokane Neighborhoods: Hillyard -- Thumbnail History - HistoryLink. org*, www.historylink.org/File/8406.
"Paper Chase (Game)." *Wikipedia*, Wikimedia Foundation, 25 Oct. 2017, en. wikipedia. org/wiki/Paper_Chase_(game).
Martinez, Dan. *Running_Shots_21*, www.runningentertainment.com/runningshots21. html.
"State Cross Country Past Results 1959-Present." *WIAA | Washington Interscholastic Activities Association*, www.wiaa.com/ardisplay.aspx?ID=1277.
"Mile Run World Record Progression." Wikipedia, Wikimedia Foundation, 23 Dec. 2017, en.wikipedia.org/wiki/Mile_run_world_record_progression.

Bibliography

Clarke, Ron, and Norman Harris. *The Lonely Breed*. Pelham Books, 1972. Page 87,
"it is a mistake to send a boy against our giants."

"Once Upon a Time in the Vest." *Vol. 4 No. 26 e USA Soviet Union Dual Meet 1964*,
14 Apr. 2014, onceuponatimeinthevest.blogspot.com/2014/04/vol-4-no-26-
usa-soviet-union-dual-meet.html.

Moore, Kenny. "A LIFE ON THE RUN." *SI.com*, 13 Oct. 2015, www.si.com/
vault/1987/05/18/8081709/a-life-on-the-run--once-upon-a-time-gerry-
lindgren- was-the-uss-best-distance-runner-then-he-disappeared-swapping-
the-res-ponsibilities-of-marriage-and-fatherhood-for-a-new-identity-and-a-
succession- of-odd-jobs-the-author-an-old-.

"Population of Cities in Kansas, 1900-2010." www.ipsr.ku.edu/ksdata/
ksah/ population/2pop33.pdf.

"Spokane, Washington Population History 1910 - 2016." *Spokane, Washington Population
History | 1910 - 2016*, www.biggestuscities.com/city/spokane-washington.

"Pine Ridge, South Dakota." *Wikipedia*, Wikimedia Foundation, 6 Jan. 2018, en.
wikipedia.org/wiki/Pine_Ridge,_South_Dakota.

"Once Upon a Time in the Vest." *V. 5 N. 72 1965 AAU Championships*, 7 Aug.
2015, onceuponatimeinthevest.blogspot.com/2015/08/v-5-n-72-1965-aau-
championships.html.

Herm Caviness: Spokane's First Hound

"Joel Edward Ferris (1874-1960) - Find A Grave..." *(1874-1960) - Find A Grave
Memorial*, www. ndagrave.com/cgi-bin/fg.cgi?page=gr&GRid=34688376.

"Ferris, Joel Edward, 1874-1960. @ SNAC." *Social Networks and Archival Context*,
socialarchive.iath.virginia.edu/ark:/99166/w6ms5113.

Rick Riley: Running in the Shadows

"Jack Bacheler." *Wikipedia*, Wikimedia Foundation, 10 Jan. 2018, en.wikipedia.org/
wiki/Jack_Bacheler.

Duffau, Paul. "Home." *An Itinerant Storyteller*, 29 July 2015, www.paulduffau.
com/?s=Rick%2BRiley.

"Frank Shorter." *Wikipedia*, Wikimedia Foundation, 10 Jan. 2018, en.wikipedia.
org/ wiki/Frank_Shorter.

"History of US Nationals Results: 5000 Meters - Men." *Track & Field News*, 5 July
2017, www.trackandfieldnews.com/index.php/tafn-presults?list_id=36&sex_
id=M&event_id=11.

"A History Of The NCAA Championships, 1921–2017." *Track & Field News*, 2017,
www.trackandfieldnews.com/index.php/category-lists/1028-a-history-of-the-
ncaa-championships.

"State Cross Country Past Results 1959-Present." *WIAA | Washington Interscholastic
Activities Association*, www.wiaa.com/ardisplay.aspx?ID=1277.

"Grandview, Washington." *Wikipedia*, Wikimedia Foundation, 7 Jan. 2018, en.
wikipedia.org/wiki/Grandview,_Washington.

"Bill Dellinger." *Wikipedia*, Wikimedia Foundation, 6 Jan. 2018, en.wikipedia.org/
wiki/ Bill_Dellinger.

Don Kardong and the Late Bloomers

Joan. "Washington Track Historical Data Regarding High School Track &
Field." *Washington Track*, new.washingtontrack.com/wordpress/.

"State Cross Country Past Results 1959-Present." *WIAA | Washington Interscholastic
Activities Association*, www.wiaa.com/ardisplay.aspx?ID=1277.

"Duncan MacDonald Bio, Stats, and Results." *Olympics at Sports-Reference.com*,
www. sports-reference.com/olympics/athletes/ma/duncan-macdonald-1.html.

"NCAA Cross Country ChampionshipsMen's Results." *NCAA Cross Country Championships
Men's Results*, www.trackandfieldnews.com/index.php/category-archive/445-ncaa-
cross-country-championships-mens-results.

Hymans, Richard. " The History of the United States Olympic Trials-Track & Field." 2008. Print.

Payne, Bob. "Don Kardong Not Your Everyday Teacher." *Spokesman-Review*, 24 May 1976, pp. 17–17.

Pileggi, Sarah. "SI Vault- May 31, 1976- Page 25-It Took Shorter A Little Longer." *Sports News, Scores and Highlights from Sports Illustrated*, www.si.com/vault/issue/43177/27/2.

Joyce, Gary. "Memories of a Dirty Olympic Marathon." *ESPN*, ESPN Internet Ventures, 25 Aug. 2008, 2:53 PM ET, www.espn.com/espnpage2/ story?page=joyce%2F080822.

"Lilac Bloomsday Run." *Bloomsday Run General Results from 1977-Present*, www.bloomsdayrun.org/results/results-history/general-(1977plus).

"List of Largest Running Events." *Wikipedia*, Wikimedia Foundation, 30 Dec. 2017, en.wikipedia.org/wiki/List_of_largest_running_events.

Pat Tyson: Growing Up Never Saying No

"State Cross Country Past Results 1959-Present." *WIAA | Washington Interscholastic Activities Association*, www.wiaa.com/ardisplay.aspx?ID=1277.

Foot Locker Cross Country History, www.footlockercc.com/history/history.shtml.

Joan. "Washington Track Historical Data Regarding High School Track & Field." Washington Track, new.washingtontrack.com/wordpress/.

"Tacoma, Washington." Wikipedia, Wikimedia Foundation, 10 Jan. 2018, en. wikipedia. org/wiki/Tacoma,_Washington.

"Dan Watson." WSTFCA: Washington State Track and Field Coaches Association, wstfca.com/HOF/dan-watson.

Tyson, Pat, and Doug Binder. Coaching Cross Country Successfully. Human Kinetics, 2014.

"Bill Bowerman, USTFCCCA Class of 1995." USTFCCCA, www.ustfcccca.org/ustfcccca- hall-of-fame/ustfcccca-hall-of-fame-class-of-1995/bill-bowerman-ustfcccca-class- of-1995.

"Bill Bowerman." Wikipedia, Wikimedia Foundation, 10 Jan. 2018, en.wikipedia. org/wiki/Bill_Bowerman.

Moore, Kenny. Bowerman and the Men of Oregon: the Story of Oregon's Legendary Coach and Nike's Cofounder. Rodale, 2006.

"Arthur Lydiard." Wikipedia, Wikimedia Foundation, 9 Jan. 2018, en.wikipedia. org/wiki/Arthur_Lydiard.

"Arthur Lydiard." Runner's World, 26 May 2015, www.runnersworld.com/race-training/arthur-lydiard.

"Top 10 Steve Prefontaine Quotes." e Latest FloTrack News & Videos! - FloTrack, www. otrack.org/article/39233-top-10-steve-prefontaine-quotes#. WWPlUYTyvIU.

Bob Barbero: The Record Keeper

Chen, C. Peter. "Italy in World War II." *WW2DB*, ww2db.com/country/Italy.

"Sonora Smart Dodd." *Wikipedia*, Wikimedia Foundation, 7 Jan. 2018, en.wikipedia. org/wiki/Sonora_Smart_Dodd.

"State Cross Country Past Results 1959-Present." *WIAA | Washington Interscholastic Activities Association*, www.wiaa.com/ardisplay.aspx?ID=1277.

Moore, Kenny. *Bowerman and the Men of Oregon: the Story of Oregon's Legendary Coach and Nike's Cofounder*. Rodale, 2006.

Joan. "Washington Track Historical Data Regarding High School Track & Field." *Washington Track*, new.washingtontrack.com/wordpress/.

Mike Hadway: Cut out of Wood

"State Cross Country Past Results 1959-Present." *WIAA | Washington Interscholastic Activities Association*, www.wiaa.com/ardisplay.aspx?ID=1277.

"John Rankin Rogers." *Wikipedia*, Wikimedia Foundation, 28 Dec. 2017, en.wikipedia. org/wiki/John_Rankin_Rogers.

"HistoryLink.org." *B-17 Bomber "Day's Pay" Christened at the Hanford Airport on July 23, 1944. - HistoryLink.org*, www.historylink.org/File/7491.

Bibliography

"Lockheed P-38 Lightning." *Wikipedia*, Wikimedia Foundation, 10 Jan. 2018, en. wikipedia.org/wiki/Lockheed_P-38_Lightning.

Joan. "Washington Track Historical Data Regarding High School Track & Field." *Washington Track*, new.washingtontrack.com/wordpress/.

"NWAC Hall of Fame." *Northwest Athletic Conference NWAC Volleyball Sports Banner Image. NWAC Slogan: Character, Competition, Community*, www.nwacsports.org/ hall_of_fame/HOF-member-bio.php?id=37.

Part Two: Turning for Home

Bhatt, Sanjay. "Nalley's Food Plant Closes in Tacoma, Workers Try to Move On." *The Seattle Times*, The Seattle Times Company, 7 Aug. 2011, www.seattletimes. com/business/nalleys-food-plant-closes-in-tacoma-workers-try-to-move-on/.

"Peter Vidmar." *Wikipedia*, Wikimedia Foundation, 22 Feb. 2018, en.wikipedia.org/ wiki/Peter_Vidmar.

Isaac Hawkins: The First One

Johnson, Carla K. "Ridgerunners Raise Cash In Race Against Cancer Elementary Students Team Up For Event Usually Dominated By Adults." *Spokesman.com*, e Spokesman-Review, 14 July 2011, www.spokesman.com/stories/1995/jun/03/ ridgerunners-raise-cash-in-race-against-cancer/.

Joan. "Washington Track Historical Data Regarding High School Track & Field." *Washington Track*, new.washingtontrack.com/wordpress/.

"State Cross Country Past Results 1959-Present." *WIAA | Washington Interscholastic Activities Association*, www.wiaa.com/ardisplay.aspx?ID=1277.

"Foot Locker Cross Country History." *Foot Locker Cross Country*, www.footlockercc. com/history/history.shtml.

Emily Hawkins: The Second One

"Player Bio: Jennifer Smith : Women's Cross Country." *Washington Huskies*, gohuskies. com/ sports/2013/4/18/208220676.aspx.

Joan. "Washington Track Historical Data Regarding High School Track & Field." *Washington Track*, new.washingtontrack.com/wordpress/.

"State Cross Country Past Results 1959-Present." *WIAA | Washington Interscholastic Activities Association*, www.wiaa.com/ardisplay.aspx?ID=1277.

Foot Locker Cross Country Championships West Regional Past Results, footlockercc. com/west/results/index.html.

"Eastern Washington University." *Eastern Washington University Athletics Hall of Fame-Wayne Gilman*, goeags.com/hof.aspx?hof=29&mobile=skip.

Tyler Byers: Iron Wheel

"Byers Flys in Meet on Wheels of Gold." *Spokesman-Review*, 27 July 1999.

"Cheri Blauwet Visa Commercial." *Youtube.com*, 16 Nov. 2010, www.youtube. com/ watch?v=oz5R1jq_ax4.

"Cheri Blauwet." *Wikipedia*, Wikimedia Foundation, 19 Dec. 2017, en.wikipedia. org/ wiki/Cheri_Blauwet.

Paulson, Billye Jill. "East Valley Recreation: Mesa Man Refuses to Let Disease Slow Him Down." *Eastvalleytribune.com*, 13 Sept. 2007, www.eastvalleytribune.com/ sports/ article_8f88ce73-2547-55d6-9797-651cef09c79d.html.

McCauley, Janie. "Jackets Required." *Spokesman-Review*, 1 June 2000, pp. C1–C7.

McCauley, Janie. "Leave Your Sympathy at Home." *Spokesman-Review*, 5 Feb. 1999, pp. C1–C5.

Macur, Juliet. "A Wheelchair Rivalry Takes Root in the Desert." *The New York Times*, The New York Times, 3 Nov. 2006, www.nytimes.com/2006/11/04/ sports/sportsspecial/04wheelchair.html.

Joan. "Washington Track Historical Data Regarding High School Track & Field." *Washington Track*, new.washingtontrack.com/wordpress/.

"State Cross Country Past Results 1959-Present." *WIAA | Washington Interscholastic Activities Association*, www.wiaa.com/ardisplay.aspx?ID=1277.

Ben Hawkins: A Longer Race to Run

"Peter Vidmar." *Wikipedia*, Wikimedia Foundation, 22 Feb. 2018, en.wikipedia.org/wiki/Peter_Vidmar.

Joan. "Washington Track Historical Data Regarding High School Track & Field." *Washington Track*, new.washingtontrack.com/wordpress/.

"State Cross Country Past Results 1959-Present." *WIAA | Washington Interscholastic Activities Association*, www.wiaa.com/ardisplay.aspx?ID=1277.

Crawford, J. *EASTERN WASH REGIONAL CROSS COUNTRY*, www.jcrawford.net/regionalcc.html.

Foot Locker Cross Country Championships West Regional Past Results, footlockercc. com/west/results/index.html.

Tyson, Pat, and Doug Binder. *Coaching Cross Country Successfully*. Human Kinetics, 2014.

Sylvia Quinn: Captain of the Volunteers

"Iota, Louisiana." *Wikipedia*, Wikimedia Foundation, 21 Feb. 2018, en.wikipedia.org/wiki/Iota,_Louisiana.

"Lilac Bloomsday Run." *Bloomsday - Home*, www.bloomsdayrun.org/results/all-finishers.

"Lilac Bloomsday Run Gender Stats History." *Bloomsday - Home*, www.bloomsdayrun. org/history-stats/gender-stats.

"List of Largest Running Events." *Wikipedia*, Wikimedia Foundation, 30 Dec. 2017, en. wikipedia.org/wiki/List_of_largest_running_events.

USA Track & Field - Top25AgeGradedMarathon, www.usatf.org/Resources-for---/ Masters/LDR/Rankings/2015-Masters-LDR/Top25AgeGradedMarathon.aspx

Wojcik, Jerry. "Metzmaker, Quinn Win U.S. 8k X-C." *National Masters News*, no. 230th, Oct. 1997, pp. 1–1.http://www.mastershistory.org/NMN/10_1997.pdf

"World Single Age Records- Marathon." *SA_Mara*, 17 Nov. 2017, www.arrs.net/SA_ Mara.htm.

runbikedude. "Gunhild Swanson's Epic 2015 Western States 100 Finish!!" *YouTube*, YouTube, 30 June 2015, www.youtube.com/watch?v=RM7MRNNLuLk.

Liz Hawkins: Races Worth Running

Foot Locker Cross Country Championships West Regional Past Results, footlockercc. com/west/results/index.html.

Peter Hawkins: Number 5

Joan. "Washington Track Historical Data Regarding High School Track & Field." *Washington Track*, new.washingtontrack.com/wordpress/.

"State Cross Country Past Results 1959-Present." *WIAA | Washington Interscholastic Activities Association*, www.wiaa.com/ardisplay.aspx?ID=1277.

Crawford, J. *EASTERN WASH REGIONAL CROSS COUNTRY*, www.jcrawford.net/regionalcc.html.

Foot Locker Cross Country Championships West Regional Past Results, footlockercc. com/west/results/index.html.

"NikeCrossNationals.com - Nike Cross Nationals Official Site - NXN - Results - 2004-2017 NXN Results." *RunnerSpace.com*, nxn.runnerspace.com/eprofile. php?do=title&title_id=187&event_id=13.

Paul Gordon Hawkins Jr: Yielding Seeds of Time

Joan. "Washington Track Historical Data Regarding High School Track & Field." *Washington Track*, new.washingtontrack.com/wordpress/.

"State Cross Country Past Results 1959-Present." *WIAA | Washington Interscholastic Activities Association*, www.wiaa.com/ardisplay.aspx?ID=1277.

Crawford, J. *EASTERN WASH REGIONAL CROSS COUNTRY*, www.jcrawford.net/ regionalcc.html.

Foot Locker Cross Country Championships West Regional Past Results, footlockercc. com/west/results/index.html.

"NikeCrossNationals.com - Nike Cross Nationals Official Site - NXN - Results - 2004-2017 NXN Results." *RunnerSpace.com*, nxn.runnerspace.com/eprofile. php?do=title&title_ id=187&event_id=13.

Tom Hawkins: The First Shall be Last and the Last Shall be First
"State Cross Country Past Results 1959-Present." *WIAA | Washington Interscholastic Activities Association*, www.wiaa.com/ardisplay.aspx?ID=1277.
Foot Locker Cross Country Championships West Regional Past Results, footlockercc.com/west/results/index.html.
"NikeCrossNationals.com - Nike Cross Nationals Official Site - NXN - Results - 2004-2017 NXN Results." *RunnerSpace.com*, nxn.runnerspace.com/eprofile.php?do=title&title_id=187&event_id=13.
USATF - Events - 2009 USATF Junior Olympic Cross Country Championships - Results, www.usatf.org/events/2009/USATFJuniorOlympicXCChampionships/results/national/YoungMen.asp.

Jon Knight: Coming Full Circle
Joan. "Washington Track Historical Data Regarding High School Track & Field." *Washington Track*, new.washingtontrack.com/wordpress/.
"State Cross Country Past Results 1959-Present." *WIAA | Washington Interscholastic Activities Association*, www.wiaa.com/ardisplay.aspx?ID=1277.
"NikeCrossNationals.com - Nike Cross Nationals Official Site - NXN - Results - 2004-2017 NXN Results." *RunnerSpace.com*, nxn.runnerspace.com/eprofile.php?do=title&title_id=187&event_id=13.
"Foot Locker Cross Country History." *Foot Locker Cross Country*, www.footlockercc.com/history/history.shtml.
Merca, Paul. *Spokane High Schoolers Katie Knight & Andrew Gardner Finish Fourth & Fifth in Edinburgh*, 7 Jan. 2012, paulmerca.blogspot.com/2012/01/spokane-high-schoolers-katie-knight.html.
Binder, Doug. "News - Matthew Maton, Tanner Anderson Discuss Great Edinburgh XC - 2014 DyeStat." *RunnerSpace.com*, 16 Jan. 2014, www.dyestat.com/gprofile.php?mgroup_id=44531&do=news&news_id=202117.

PETER HAWKINS is a native of Spokane, Washington. He ran on two state cross country championship teams at Ferris High School. After his high school running, Peter served a two year church service mission to Lisbon, Portugal. He then transferred to Brigham Young University where he earned a degree in English. He went on to receive a Masters in Teaching from the University of Arkansas and now teaches English at the high school level. He lives in Richland, Washington with his wife and two sons.